EDEXCEL A LEVEL

FURTHER MATHEMATICS
Decision

SERIES EDITOR
HEATHER DAVIS
CONSULTANT EDITOR
SARA PULLMAN
AUTHORS
NICK GEERE, ROB BUTLER, JAN DANGERFIELD

HODDER
EDUCATION
AN HACHETTE UK COMPANY

Orders: please contact Bookpoint Ltd, 130 Milton Park, Abingdon, Oxon OX14 4SB. Telephone: (44) 01235 827720. Fax: (44) 01235 400454. Lines are open from 9.00–5.00, Monday to Saturday, with a 24-hour message answering service. You can also order through our website www.hoddereducation.com

© Nick Geere 2018

Published by Hodder Education
An Hachette UK Company
Carmelite House, 50 Victoria Embankment, London EC4Y 0DZ

| Impression number | 5 4 3 2 1 |
| Year | 2021 2020 2019 2018 |

Cover photo © ARCHITECTEUR/Shutterstock

Illustrations by Aptara Inc.

Typeset in BemboStd 11/13 pt by Aptara Inc.

Printed in the UK

A catalogue record for this title is available from the British Library

ISBN 9781510433359

Contents

Getting the most from this book iv

Prior knowledge v

1 Algorithms and graph theory
1.1 About algorithms 1
1.2 Packing and sorting 9
1.3 Types of graphs 15
1.4 Planarity of graphs 22

2 Algorithms on graphs
2.1 The minimum connector problem 28
2.2 The route inspection problem 35
2.3 Dijkstra's algorithm 41
2.4 Floyd's algorithm 44
2.5 The travelling salesperson problem 50

3 Critical path analysis
3.1 Constructing an activity network 58
3.2 Critical paths and Gantt charts 62
3.3 Using Gantt charts 66

4 Linear programming
4.1 Solving linear programming problems 72
4.2 The Simplex algorithm 76
4.3 Advanced Simplex methods 82

5 Allocation problems
5.1 Cost matrix reduction 87
5.2 The Hungarian algorithm 90
5.3 Modifications 93
5.4 Formulation as a linear programming problem 94

6 Recurrence relations
6.1 Solving first-order recurrence relations 98
6.2 Solving second-order recurrence relations 103
6.3 Generating functions 108

7 Network flows
7.1 The language of network flows 113
7.2 Flow augmenting 117
7.3 Refinements 121

8 Game theory
8.1 Pay-off matrices 126
8.2 Dominated strategies 130
8.3 Optimal mixed strategies 131
8.4 Converting games to linear programming problems 136

9 Transportation problems
9.1 Finding initial solutions 142
9.2 Finding an improved solution 150
9.3 Formulation as a linear programming problem 157

10 Dynamic programming
10.1 Principles of dynamic programming 161
10.2 Solving problems using dynamic programming 166

11 Decision analysis
11.1 Decision analysis 177

Answers 187

Mathematics is not only a beautiful and exciting subject in its own right but also one that underpins many other branches of learning. It is consequently fundamental to our national wellbeing.

This book covers the Decision Mathematics elements in the Edexcel AS and A Level Further Mathematics specifications. Students start these courses at a variety of stages. Some embark on AS Further Mathematics in Year 12, straight after GCSE, taking it alongside AS Mathematics, and so have no prior experience of A Level Mathematics. In contrast, others only begin Further Mathematics when they have completed the full A Level Mathematics course. This book requires no prior knowledge of A level Mathematics and so can be started at any time. Both AS and A level content is included in each of the first eight chapters with the sections on the AS content generally coming first. The last three chapters are A level only. Chapters 1 to 4 cover the Decision Mathematics 1 paper and Chapters 5 to 11 cover the Decision Mathematics 2 paper. There is more detail on the split in each chapter in the section on prior knowledge.

Between 2014 and 2016 A Level Mathematics and Further Mathematics were very substantially revised, for first teaching in 2017. Changes that particularly affect Decision Mathematics include increased emphasis on

■ Problem solving

■ Mathematical rigour

■ Use of ICT

■ Modelling.

This book embraces these ideas. A large number of exercise questions involve elements of problem solving and require the application of the ideas and techniques in a wide variety of real world contexts. This develops independent thinking and builds on thorough understanding. Decision Mathematics often provides descriptions of real world situations that make them tractable to calculations, and so modelling is key to this branch of mathematics. It pervades much of the book, particularly the chapters on the use of graphs to solve real world problems.

Throughout the book the emphasis is on understanding and interpretation rather than mere routine calculations, but the various exercises do nonetheless provide plenty of scope for practising basic techniques. The exercise questions are split into three bands. Band 1 questions (indicated by a light grey) are designed to reinforce basic understanding; Band 2 questions (a darker bar) are broadly typical of what might be expected in an examination; Band 3 questions (a solid black bar) explore around the topic and some of them are rather more demanding. In addition, extensive online support, including further questions, is available by subscription to MEI's Integral website, http://integralmaths.org.

At the end of each chapter there is a list of key points covered as well as a summary of the new knowledge (learning outcomes) that readers should have gained.

Two common features of the book are Activities and Discussion points. These serve rather different purposes. The Activities are designed to help readers get into the thought processes of the new work that they are about to meet; having done an Activity, what follows will seem much easier. The Discussion points invite readers to talk about particular points with their fellow students and their teacher and so enhance their understanding.

Answers to all exercise questions are provided at the back of the book, and also online at www.hoddereducation.co.uk/EdexcelFurtherMathsDecision.

No prior knowledge of Decision Mathematics is needed for this book. It does, however, assume that the reader is reasonably fluent in basic algebra and graphs: working with formulae and expressions; solving linear simultaneous equations; graphing inequalities.

Matrices are used to store information but manipulation of them is not required.

Decision Mathematics 1

Chapter 1 Algorithms and graph theory

This chapter is accessible from GCSE and many of the ideas are developed later in the book. Section 1.4 is material for A Level only.

Chapter 2 Algorithms on graphs

The ideas from Chapter 1 are developed here with Sections 2.4 and 2.5 being material studied at A Level only.

Chapter 3 Critical path analysis

The first two sections are about going through the whole process of creating and using an activity network, up to a Gantt chart. The third section is material for A Level only, on using the results to make decisions. This builds on the ideas in graph theory in Chapter 1.

Chapter 4 Linear programming

The first section uses graphical methods. The second and third sections develop more complex methods and are examined at A Level only.

Decision Mathematics 2

Many of the topics in Decision Mathematics 2 require familiarity with the content of Decision Mathematics 1. In particular, the ideas and vocabulary of graph and network theory, linear programming and the Simplex algorithm are used.

Chapter 5 Allocation problems

The first three sections on the Hungarian method are material studied at AS and the final section on reformulating as a linear programming problem is A Level work.

Chapter 6 Recurrence relations

The first section on first-order recurrence relations is AS material. The rest of the chapter deals with second-order recurrence relations and is material for A Level only.

Chapter 7 Network flows

The first two sections are AS work and the section on refinements is material studied at A Level only. This develops work on networks in Decision 1.

Chapter 8 Game theory

The first two sections are AS work and the last two consist of material studied at A Level only. Matrices are used but not manipulated. Linear graphs, and solving simultaneous equations to find their intersection, are needed.

Chapter 9 Transportation problems

This chapter is all A Level only. Matrices are used but not manipulated.

Chapter 10 Dynamic programming

The work in this chapter is A Level only.

Chapter 11 Decision analysis

This chapter is A Level only. Familiarity with tree diagrams from GCSE is helpful.

1

An algorithm must be seen to be believed.
Donald Knuth (1938–)

Algorithms and graph theory

➡   Use long division to work out $98\,606 \div 47$.

1 About algorithms

An **algorithm** is a finite sequence of operations for carrying out a procedure or solving a problem. Cooking recipes, knitting patterns and instructions for making flat pack furniture are algorithms, but obviously these are not mathematical algorithms.

Do you know on which day of the week you were born? Zeller's algorithm can be used to work it out. Try the algorithm using your date of birth.

ACTIVITY 1.1

Zeller's algorithm	Example: 29th Feb 2000
Let day number = D Let month number = M Let year number = Y	$D = 29$ $M = 2$ $Y = 2000$
If $M = 1$ or 2, add 12 to M and subtract 1 from Y	$M = 14$ $Y = 1999$
Let C be the first two digits of Y and X be the last two digits of Y	$C = 19$ $X = 99$
Calculate $\text{INT}(2.6M - 5.4) + \text{INT}(X \div 4) + \text{INT}(C \div 4) + D + X - 2C$	$31 + 24 + 4 + 29 + 99 - 38 = 149$
Find the remainder when this is divided by 7	2
If the remainder is 0 the day was Sunday, if it is 1 the day was Monday, and so on	Tuesday

Table 1.1

This uses the current (new) value of Y.

$\text{INT}(N)$ is the integer part of N. This is the largest integer that is less than or equal to N. For example, $\text{INT}(2.3) = 2$, $\text{INT}(6.7) = 6$, $\text{INT}(4) = 4$ and $\text{INT}(0) = 0$. The integer part of a negative number N is the negative of $\text{INT}(-N)$, for example, $\text{INT}(-1.7) = -1$.

The remainder when N is divided by 7 is the same as $N - 7 \times \text{INT}(N \div 7)$.

In mathematics an algorithm has an initial state and involves inputs, outputs and variables. The initial state is the 'factory setting' values of any variables that are not defined within the algorithm. Usually this means that all variables have the value 0 until they are updated.

For Zeller's algorithm as given above, the inputs are the initial values of D, M and Y, the output is the day and the variables are C, D, M, X and Y.

The output may be printed or displayed.

Communicating an algorithm

How do you communicate an algorithm? The form of communication depends on who (for example a seven-year-old) or what (for example a computer) will be using the algorithm.

Whatever method is used to communicate the steps of an algorithm it must be:

- **unambiguous**, so the person or machine running the algorithm does not have to make any choices
- **deterministic**, so there is no chance or randomness involved
- **finite**, so that the algorithm stops.

This means that each time the algorithm is used with a certain input, it gives the same output, and that it does this in a finite number of steps.

An algorithm may be communicated in ordinary language, in a **flowchart** or in **pseudocode**.

Zeller's algorithm could be written in pseudocode as:

Step 1   Let D be day number
            Let M be month number
            Let Y be year number

> $M = M + 12$ means that the value of (old) $M + 12$ becomes the value of (new) M.

Step 2   If $M < 3$ then $M = M + 12$ and $Y = Y - 1$
Step 3   Let $C = \text{INT}(Y \div 100)$
            Let $X = Y - (100 \times C)$
Step 4   Let $S = \text{INT}(2.6M - 5.4) + \text{INT}(X \div 4) + \text{INT}(C \div 4) + D + X - 2C$
Step 5   Let $A = S - (7 \times \text{INT}(S \div 7))$ and display the value of A

Note that the output is the day number and not the name of the day.

Algorithms for mathematical processes can usually be broken up into a number of sequential steps. Sometimes an algorithm will involve decisions ('if … then …') and may loop back to an earlier step ('go to Step …').

> Completing a pass means that you have worked through the instructions once, as far as either terminating or looping back to an earlier step.

Algorithms may involve iterative processes. This means that after completing one **pass** through the instructions a solution has been obtained that may only be part way to the answer to the problem. By going back and carrying out further passes the solution can be improved.

For example, an algorithm for finding square roots is given below:

Step 1   Input a positive number N
Step 2   Let $A = \frac{1}{2}N$
Step 3   Let $B = \frac{1}{2}\left(A + \frac{N}{A}\right)$

Step 4   If $(A - B)^2 < 0.001$ then go to Step 6
Step 5   Let $A = B$ and then go to Step 3
Step 6   Display the value of B and STOP

ACTIVITY 1.2

Work through this algorithm with $N = 2$. The algorithm loops back to Step 3; a pass occurs each time that Step 3 is used. How many passes are carried out?

Example 1.1

The real roots of a quadratic equation

$$ax^2 + bx + c = 0 \ (a \neq 0)$$

can be found using the quadratic formula

$$x = \frac{-b \pm \sqrt{b^2 - 4ac}}{2a}$$

(i)   Use a flowchart to represent an algorithm for solving a quadratic equation.

(ii) Write the algorithm in pseudocode.

> This is one possible solution.

Solution

(i)

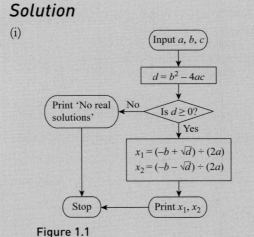

Figure 1.1

(ii) Step 1   Let $d = b^2 - 4ac$

Step 2   If $d < 0$ print 'No real solutions' and go to Step 5

Step 3   Let $x_1 = \dfrac{-b + \sqrt{b^2 - 4ac}}{2a}$

Let $x_2 = \dfrac{-b - \sqrt{b^2 - 4ac}}{2a}$

Step 4   Print x_1 and x_2

Step 5   STOP

> **Note**
>
> The word 'algorithm' has become more commonplace since the development of the computer. A computer program is simply an algorithm written in such a way that a machine can carry it out.

An algorithm gives the logical structure that underlies a computer program for solving a problem. Modelling with algorithms has obvious connections with computer science but does not require programming skills or knowledge of any specific computing language.

ACTIVITY 1.3

Below are two algorithms, one expressed in pseudocode and the other as a flowchart.

Russian algorithm for multiplying two integers

Euclid's method for finding the highest common factor of two positive integers x and y

Step 1	Write the two numbers side by side
Step 2	Beneath the left number write double that number
	Beneath the right number write the integer part of half that number
Step 3	Repeat Step 2 until the right number is 1
Step 4	Delete those rows where the number in the right column is even
Step 5	Add up the remaining numbers in the left column. This is the result of multiplying the original numbers

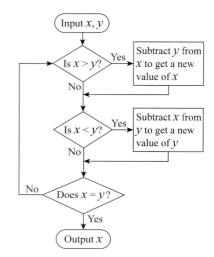

Figure 1.2

Work through the Russian algorithm with left number 13 and right number 37.

Work through the Euclidean algorithm with $x = 6$ and $y = 15$.

How could you represent these algorithms differently?

What different type of user might each representation be suitable for?

Note

Using a table is helpful for keeping track of the values.

Working through an algorithm 'by hand' is referred to as **tracing** it. For Euclid's algorithm, with inputs 120 and 75, this may look like:

x	y
120	75
45	75
45	30
15	30
15	15

$x > y$ so new $x = 120 - 75 = 45$

$x < y$ so new $y = 75 - 45 = 30$

$x > y$ so new $x = 45 - 30 = 15$

$x < y$ so new $y = 30 - 15 = 15$

$x = y$ so output 15

Table 1.2

Discussion point
➜ What are the benefits of tracing an algorithm?

Algorithmic complexity

Most problems can be solved using a variety of algorithms, some of which might be more efficient than others. 'Efficient' usually means using fewer operations (which, in turn, means running more quickly and so taking less time). There might be other considerations too, such as the amount of storage capacity needed if the algorithm is to be run on a computer.

As a simple example of improving efficiency, look back at Example 1.1, where you saw an algorithm to find the real roots of a quadratic equation. It is a good idea to calculate the value of $b^2 - 4ac$ as a first step, because the sign of that value has to be checked to see whether it is worth continuing with the calculation.

If an algorithm requires the evaluation of a quadratic expression, the way in which the expression is written can make a difference to the efficiency.

For example, $3x^2 + 2x + 9$ can be written as $(3x + 2)x + 9$. This bracketed form is called a nested form.

When $x = 5$, the evaluation with a calculator requires the following key presses:

$3x^2 + 2x + 9$: $\boxed{3}\;\boxed{\times}\;\boxed{5}\;\boxed{\times}\;\boxed{5}\;\boxed{+}\;\boxed{2}\;\boxed{\times}\;\boxed{5}\;\boxed{+}\;\boxed{9}\;\boxed{=}$

3 multiplications and 2 additions

$(3x + 2)x + 9$: $\boxed{(}\;\boxed{3}\;\boxed{\times}\;\boxed{5}\;\boxed{+}\;\boxed{2}\;\boxed{)}\;\boxed{\times}\;\boxed{5}\;\boxed{+}\;\boxed{9}\;\boxed{=}$

2 multiplications and 2 additions.

The nested form uses fewer operations (multiplications and additions) so it should be quicker (albeit by the tiniest amount of time).

Comparing the number of operations for a general polynomial of degree n gives:

$a_n x^n + a_{n-1} x^{n-1} + \ldots + a_2 x^2 + a_1 x + a_0$ $\qquad \frac{1}{2} n(n + 1) \times$ and $n +$

$\left(\left(\ldots \left((a_n x + a_{n-1})x + a_{n-2} \right) x + \ldots \right) + a_1 \right) x + a_0$ $\qquad n \times$ and $n +$

The nested method has **linear order complexity** (or order n or O(n)) because the time taken to run the calculation involves n^1 as the highest power of n. The expanded form has **quadratic order complexity** (or order n^2 or O(n^2)) because the time taken to run the calculation will involve n^2 as the highest power of n.

The nested method is more efficient than the expanded form because O(n) is a lower order complexity than O(n^2). Irrespective of what the actual linear and quadratic functions are that represent the run-times for the two methods for a polynomial of degree n, a linear function will give lower values (smaller run-times) than a quadratic function for realistic sized (huge) problems.

For example, if it takes M microseconds for a computer to multiply two numbers and A microseconds for it to add two numbers, then (once the programs have been written) inputting the coefficients is the same for both methods and the run-time is $\frac{1}{2} n(n + 1)M + nA$ for the expanded form and $nM + nA$ for the nested form.

Now, in this case, $\frac{1}{2} n(n + 1)M + nA$ is always bigger than $nM + nA$, but the details, such as the $\frac{1}{2}$ and the $(n + 1)$ are irrelevant: if n is huge, all that matters is that n^2 is much bigger than n.

Note

If any of the coefficients happened to be 0 then some work would be saved. It is usual to focus on the worst-case situation (rather than the best case or an average case). This is partly because then any predictions about run-times will be 'worst-case scenarios', but mainly because the worst case is usually the easiest to consider.

$O(n^2)$ is always less efficient than $O(n)$ once n becomes large. Similarly, $O(n^3)$ is less efficient than $O(n^2)$ and so on.

■ If an algorithm has $O(n)$ complexity then doubling the size of the problem will roughly double the run-time, or tripling the size of the problem will roughly triple the run-time. If the actual run-time is $an + b$ then scaling the problem size by a factor of k gives a run-time of $akn + b$. For large values of n, the run-time akn $(+ b)$ is roughly k times the original run-time an $(+ b)$.

■ If an algorithm has $O(n^2)$ complexity then doubling the size of the problem will roughly quadruple the run-time, or tripling the size of the problem will scale the run-time by a factor of about 9. If the actual run-time is $an^2 + bn + c$ then scaling the problem size by a factor of k gives a run-time of $ak^2n^2 + bkn + c$. For large values of n, the run-time ak^2n^2 $(+ bkn + c)$ is roughly k^2 times the run-time an^2 $(+ bn + c)$.

■ Similarly, if an algorithm has $O(n^r)$ complexity, then scaling the problem size by a factor k will scale the run-time by a factor of (approximately) k^r.

Example 1.2

An algorithm has quadratic, $O(n^2)$, complexity. A problem, using this algorithm, has run-time, $T(n)$, of 0.02 seconds when $n = 40$. Estimate its run-time when $n = 200$.

Solution

The algorithm has complexity of $O(n^2)$, so the scale factor for the run-time is the square of the scale factor for the size of the problem.

The scale factor for the size is $\frac{200}{40} = 5$

$\Rightarrow$ scale factor for the run-time is $5^2 = 25$

So the new run-time $\approx 25 \times 0.02 = 0.5$ seconds.

Note

Make sure you know the difference between run-time and the order of an algorithm.

Exercise 1.1

① Construct a flowchart that can be used to check if a number N is prime, where N is a positive integer and $N > 2$.

② The following six steps define an algorithm:

Step 1 Think of a positive whole number and call it X

Step 2 Write X in words (using letters)

Step 3 Let Y be the number of letters used

Step 4 If $Y = X$ then stop

Step 5 Replace X by Y

Step 6 Go to Step 2

(i) Apply the algorithm with $X = 62$.

(ii) Show that for all values of X between 1 and 99 the algorithm produces the same answer.

You may use the fact that, when written out, numbers between 1 and 99 all have twelve or fewer letters.   [MEI]

③ (i) An algorithm has linear order. It takes 4 milliseconds for it to solve a problem of size $n = 20$. Estimate how long it takes to solve a similar problem with size $n = 600$.

(ii) An algorithm has order $O(n^4)$. A problem with size 30 takes it 0.004 seconds to solve. Estimate the run-time for a similar problem with size 900.

(iii) The order of an algorithm is $O(n^3)$. A problem with $n = 6000$ takes it 2 seconds to solve. Estimate how long it takes to solve a similar problem of size $n = 6$.

④ The following flowchart defines an algorithm which operates on two inputs, x and y.

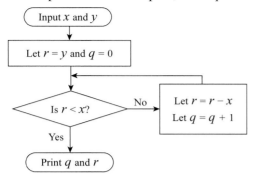

Figure 1.3

(i)   Run the algorithm with inputs of $x = 3$ and $y = 41$. Keep a record of the values of r and q each time they are updated.

(ii)   Say what the algorithm achieves.

The flowchart in Figure 1.4 defines an algorithm with three inputs, x, y_1 and y_2.

(iii)   Trace the algorithm with $x = 3$, $y_1 = 4$ and $y_2 = 1$.

The two algorithms achieve the same result.

(iv)   Suggest the advantages and disadvantages of each algorithm.   [MEI adapted]

⑤ Table 1.3 can be used to convert a number from Roman numerals into ordinary base 10 numbers.

To illustrate how this works, take the Roman numeral CIX as an example.

Always start by looking at row 1. Look at the row 1 entry in the column headed C (the first symbol in the Roman numeral) to find 100 9. Add 100 to the running total (which was 0 originally) and move to row 9.

Now look at row 9 in the column headed I (the second symbol in the Roman numeral) to find 1 11. Add 1 to the running total and move to row 11.

Finally look at row 11 in the column headed X (the third symbol in the Roman numeral) to find 8 0. Add 8 to the running total. Since this was the last symbol in the Roman numeral the algorithm now stops.

CIX = 100 + 1 + 8 = 109

(i)   Write this algorithm as a set of steps.

(ii)   What are the limitations of the algorithm?

(iii)   Write pseudocode instructions for converting ordinary base 10 numbers into Roman numerals.   [MEI adapted]

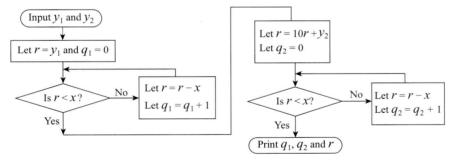

Figure 1.4

Row	M		D		C		L		X		V		I	
1	1000	2	500	3	100	9	50	5	10	10	5	7	1	11
2	1000	2	500	3	100	9	50	5	10	10	5	7	1	11
3					100	9	50	5	10	10	5	7	1	11
4					100	4	50	5	10	10	5	7	1	11
5							50	6	10	10	5	7	1	11
6									10	6	5	7	1	11
7											5	8	1	11
8													1	8
9	800	5	300	5	100	4	50	6	10	10	5	8	1	11
10					80	7	30	7	10	6	5	8	1	11
11									8	0	3	0	1	8

Table 1.3

⑥ Programmable calculators use a version of the Basic programming language that, amongst other things, can perform repetitions using 'for … next'.

To show how this works look at the following programs and their printouts.

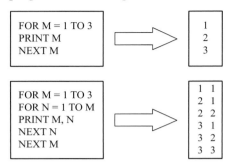

Figure 1.5

In a certain town the bus tickets are numbered 0000 to 9999.

Some children are collecting the tickets whose digits add up to 21.

(i) How many such tickets will there be in the tickets numbered from 0000 to 9999?

Two algorithms for finding the number of tickets whose digits add up to 21 are given as calculator programs below (A and B). You do NOT need to put these programs into your calculator to answer this question.

(ii) Show that each algorithm achieves the correct result.

(iii) Compare the efficiency of the two algorithms by counting the number of additions/subtractions and the number of comparisons used.

A

```
T = 0
FOR J = 0 TO 9
FOR K = 0 TO 9
FOR L = 0 TO 9
FOR M = 0 TO 9
S = J + K + L + M
IF S = 21 THEN T = T + 1
NEXT M
NEXT L
NEXT K
NEXT J
PRINT T
```

B

```
T = 0 : S = 0
FOR J = 0 TO 9
FOR K = 0 TO 9
FOR L = 0 TO 9
FOR M = 0 TO 9
IF S = 21 THEN T = T + 1
S = S + 1
NEXT M
S = S − 9
NEXT L
S = S − 9
NEXT K
S = S − 9
NEXT J
PRINT T
```

⑦ A particular algorithm has a run-time of 0.04 seconds when solving a problem of size $n = 25$. It has a run-time of 0.64 seconds when solving a similar problem of size $n = 100$. What do you think is the order of the algorithm?

⑧ The following algorithm finds the highest common factor (HCF) of two positive integers.

1 Let A be the first integer and B be the second integer

2 Let $Q = \text{INT}(B \div A)$

3 Let $R = B − (Q \times A)$

4 If $R = 0$ go to Step 8

5 Let the new value of B be A

6 Let the new value of A be R

7 Go to Step 2

8 Record the HCF as the value of A

9 STOP

(i) Work through the algorithm with $A = 2520$ and $B = 5940$.

(ii) What happens if the order of the input is reversed, so $A = 5940$ and $B = 2520$?

It has been claimed that the number of iterations of this algorithm is approximately

$$\frac{\log(M \div 1.17)}{\log\left(\frac{1+\sqrt{5}}{2}\right)}$$

where M is the larger of A and B.

(iii) Count the number of iterations of the loop in the algorithm when $A = 233$ and $B = 377$. Compare this with the number claimed by the formula above.

2 Packing and sorting

Packing

One of the situations where an algorithmic approach is useful is for one-dimensional bin-packing problems. Imagine having to send a number of files as attachments to the same email address, but there is a limit on the total size of the files attached to one email. How should the files be put together so that the number of emails needed is as small as possible?

The classic bin-packing problem packs 'boxes' of given sizes into a number of (equal sized) 'bins'.

Here are three methods that could be used:

1   **First–fit algorithm**
    Take the boxes in the order listed and pack each box in the first bin that has enough space for it (starting each time with the first bin).
2   **First–fit decreasing algorithm**
    Reorder the boxes from the largest to the smallest, then apply the first-fit method to this list.
3   **Full–bin strategy**
    Look for combinations of boxes that will fill bins. Pack these boxes. Put the rest together in combinations that result in bins that are as nearly full as possible.

Example 1.3

The boxes A to K with masses in kilograms as shown in Table 1.4 are to be packed into bins that can each hold a maximum of 15 kg. Apply each of the three bin-packing methods to this problem.

A	B	C	D	E	F	G	H	I	J	K
8	7	4	9	6	9	5	5	6	7	3

Table 1.4

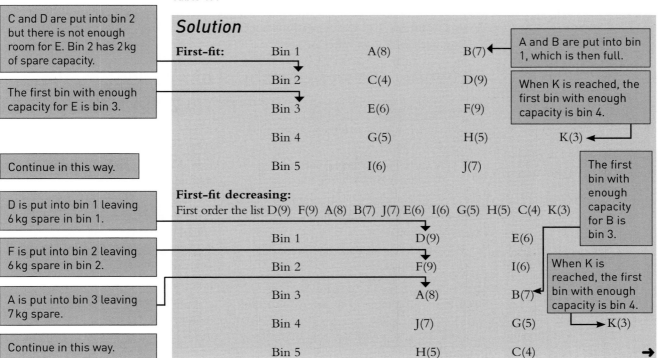

Solution

First-fit:

Bin 1	A(8)	B(7)
Bin 2	C(4)	D(9)
Bin 3	E(6)	F(9)
Bin 4	G(5)	H(5)	K(3)
Bin 5	I(6)	J(7)

A and B are put into bin 1, which is then full.

C and D are put into bin 2 but there is not enough room for E. Bin 2 has 2 kg of spare capacity.

The first bin with enough capacity for E is bin 3.

When K is reached, the first bin with enough capacity is bin 4.

Continue in this way.

First-fit decreasing:

First order the list D(9) F(9) A(8) B(7) J(7) E(6) I(6) G(5) H(5) C(4) K(3)

Bin 1	D(9)	E(6)
Bin 2	F(9)	I(6)
Bin 3	A(8)	B(7)
Bin 4	J(7)	G(5)	K(3)
Bin 5	H(5)	C(4)

D is put into bin 1 leaving 6 kg spare in bin 1.

F is put into bin 2 leaving 6 kg spare in bin 2.

A is put into bin 3 leaving 7 kg spare.

The first bin with enough capacity for B is bin 3.

When K is reached, the first bin with enough capacity is bin 4.

Continue in this way.

This is just one way to make full bins (for bins 1 to 4).

Discussion points

→ What does optimal mean in this sense?

→ Why might some other criterion be more appropriate?

→ What are the problems with using a complete enumeration?

Full-bin strategy:
For example

Bin 1	A(8)	B(7)	
Bin 2	C(4)	E(6)	G(5)
Bin 3	D(9)	I(6)	
Bin 4	J(7)	H(5)	K(3)
Bin 5	F(9)		

The full-bin strategy is not an algorithm because there is no set way to make the full bins. It is probably evident that using the items with the largest weights to make full bins is usually better than filling a bin with lots of smaller-weight items.

The only known algorithm that will always find the optimal packing is to use a complete enumeration (that is, try every possibility).

An algorithm that will usually find a good solution, although not necessarily an optimal (best) solution to a problem is called a **heuristic** (or a heuristic algorithm). A heuristic is a method that finds a solution efficiently, but with no guarantee that the solution is optimal.

The consistency with which an algorithm gives a good solution is another factor in its efficiency. Heuristics are important when classical methods fail, for example when the only way to guarantee finding the optimal solution is a complete enumeration.

The efficiency of different packing strategies could be compared by counting the number of comparisons needed in the worst case for a list of n items. In the worst possible case, both first-fit and first-fit decreasing algorithms use $1 + 2 + \ldots + (n - 1) = \frac{1}{2}(n - 1)n$ comparisons. Using this measure of complexity, both first-fit and first-fit decreasing are quadratic order algorithms, $O(n^2)$.

The ad-hoc method of the full-bin strategy is, in fact, more likely to result in an optimal solution than the algorithms but becomes very time consuming when dealing with a large number of boxes.

Note

A solution can be checked to see how close it is to an optimal solution.

In Example 1.3 the bins can contain 15 kg and the sum of the masses of the boxes to be packed is 69 kg. Dividing 69 kg by 15 kg gives 4.6, so a minimum of five bins is required. Five is a lower bound for the optimal solution.

Strengths and weaknesses of bin-packing methods

Method	Strengths	Weaknesses
First-fit	It is an algorithm so a computer can do it It does not need all of the information at the start It is a heuristic algorithm so is efficient	It has quadratic complexity so is time-consuming for large problems It is unlikely to yield an optimal solution
First-fit decreasing	It is an algorithm so a computer can do it It is a heuristic algorithm so is efficient	It has quadratic complexity so is time-consuming for large problems There is an additional step of sorting required at the start It needs all of the information at the start
Full-bin	It is more likely to give an optimal solution It may give more than one solution	It is not an algorithm so a computer cannot do it It is time-consuming for large problems

Table 1.5

Sorting

The first step in the first-fit decreasing algorithm, considered above, involves sorting the list of weights into decreasing order (largest to smallest). Sorting is used to put a list of names into alphabetical order or to rank a list of universities on their 'student satisfaction' scores. Usually such tasks are done using a computer, but how does a computer sort a list?

Sorting is an everyday activity in which the efficiency of the algorithm used is important. There are many popular algorithms for sorting a list of numbers into ascending or descending order.

The sorting algorithms that will be used here are the **bubble sort** and the **quick sort**.

These algorithms are designed for use by a computer and their efficiency depends on the length of the list and how muddled the numbers are. A human may well sort a relatively short list more quickly.

Bubble sort algorithm

The bubble sort is so named because numbers which are below their correct positions tend to move up to their proper places, like bubbles in a glass of champagne. On the first pass, the first number in the list is compared with the second and whichever is smaller assumes the first position. The second number is then compared with the third and the smaller is placed in the second position, and so on through the list. At the end of the first pass the largest number will have been left behind in the bottom position.

For the second pass, the process is repeated but excluding the last number, and on the third pass the last two numbers are excluded. The list is repeatedly processed in this way until no swaps take place in a pass. The list is then sorted.

Example 1.4

Using the bubble sort, perform the first pass to sort the list 7, 5, 2, 4, 10, 1, 6, 3 into ascending order, starting at the left-hand end.

Solution

On the first pass compare 7 and 5, and swap them; then 7 and 2, and swap them; then 7 and 4, and swap them; then 7 and 10, and do not swap them; then 10 and 1, and swap them; then 10 and 6 and swap them; then finally 10 and 3 and swap them. This pass is shown in detail in Figure 1.6. Note that the last number is now in its correct position.

→

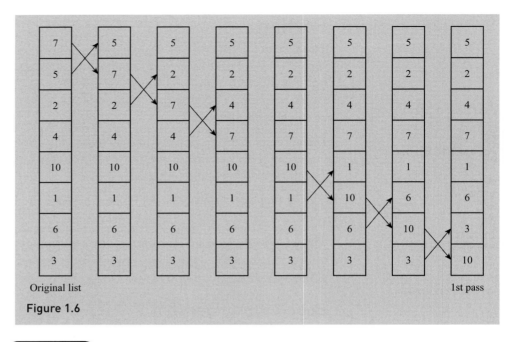

Figure 1.6

ACTIVITY 1.4

The results after making the 2nd and subsequent passes are shown in Figure 1.7. Work through the process to check that you get these results.

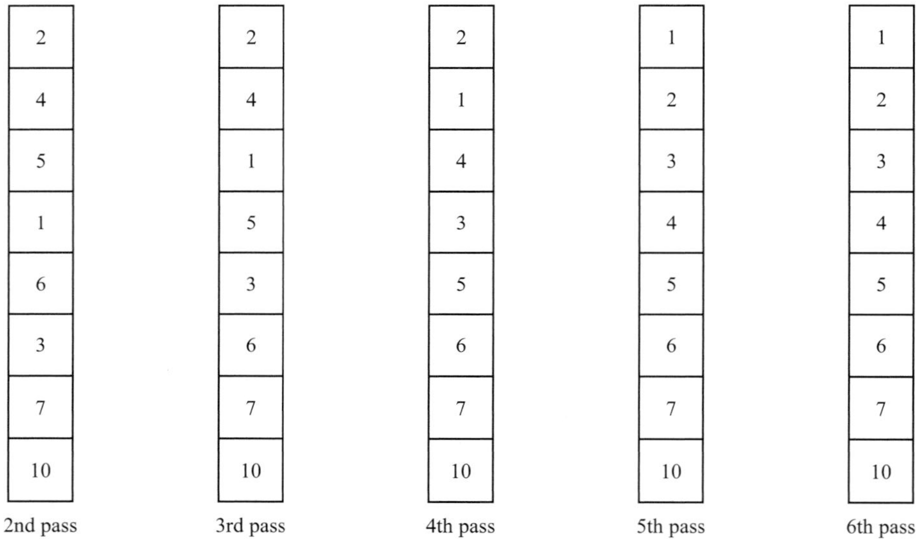

2nd pass	3rd pass	4th pass	5th pass	6th pass
2	2	2	1	1
4	4	1	2	2
5	1	4	3	3
1	5	3	4	4
6	3	5	5	5
3	6	6	6	6
7	7	7	7	7
10	10	10	10	10

Figure 1.7

The algorithm for the bubble sort for a list of length 8 can be written in computer pseudocode like this:

repeat with $i = 1$ to 7

    [repeat with $j = 1$ to $(8 - i)$

    if $L(j) > L(j + 1)$ swap $L(j)$ and $L(j + 1)$]

    if no swaps end repeat

The number of comparisons made in a bubble sort for a list of length 8 will be 7 on the first pass, 6 on the second pass, etc. If the maximum number of passes is needed, the total number of comparisons will be $7 + 6 + 5 + 4 + 3 + 2 + 1 = 28$. The number of swaps on the first pass will be anything up to 7; on the second, up to 6, etc. So the maximum possible number of swaps will also be $7 + 6 + 5 + 4 + 3 + 2 + 1 = 28$.

Generalising to a list of size n you can see that the formula will become $(n - 1) + (n - 2) + \cdots + 3 + 2 + 1 = \frac{1}{2}n(n - 1)$, showing that the bubble sort algorithm has quadratic order, depending on the length of the list.

Quick sort algorithm

To sort a list of numbers into ascending (increasing) order:

1 The middle value in the list is the pivot. For two middle values use the right-most one. Excluding the pivot, pass along the list and write down each value that is less than or equal to the pivot value. Write the pivot value and then write down the values that are greater than the pivot. This concludes the first pass.

2 Repeat Step 1 on each sublist. If a sublist contains just one value, then this becomes a pivot and is marked as being in its correct position in the final list. This concludes the next pass.

3 Continue in this way until every value is marked as being in its correct position in the final list.

> At this stage, the pivot is guaranteed to be in its correct position in the final list and can be marked in some way to indicate this. The pivot splits the list into two sublists: one containing the values that are less than or equal to the pivot (excluding the pivot itself) and the other containing the values that are greater than the pivot. It is possible that one of these sublists may be empty.

Example 1.5

Use quick sort to sort this list into ascending order:

7   5   2   4   10   1   6   3

> **Note**
> Active pivots are boxed and used pivots are underlined.

Solution

Original list	7	5	2	4	[10]	1	6	3
After 1st pass	7	5	2	[4]	1	6	3	<u>10</u>
After 2nd pass	2	[1]	3	<u>4</u>	7	[5]	6	<u>10</u>
After 3rd pass	<u>1</u>	2	[3]	<u>4</u>	<u>5</u>	7	[6]	<u>10</u>
After 4th pass	<u>1</u>	2	<u>3</u>	<u>4</u>	<u>5</u>	<u>6</u>	7	<u>10</u>
Sorted list	1	2	3	4	5	6	7	10

For a small example like this, writing down the sorted list is easy. The example is used to illustrate how quick sort works when it is applied to a much longer list.

> **Discussion point**
> → How would you adapt quick sort so that the pivot is still the middle value in the list (or sublist) but the sort is into descending (decreasing) order?

> **Note**
> Sometimes the list to be sorted is written vertically. In this case, the two sublists will be above and below the pivot instead of to the left and to the right of the pivot.

You may be asked to count the number of comparisons (or comparisons and swaps) to compare the efficiency of two algorithms being used to sort a particular list.

The worst case for quick sort, in terms of comparisons, is when the pivot at each pass is the smallest or largest value in the sublist (so one of the new sublists is empty). This would be the case when the original list is already sorted (or sorted but in reverse). In the worst case, quick sort has quadratic complexity, $O(n^2)$.

Exercise 1.2

① Sam wants to download the following programs onto four 16 GB USB sticks. Can this be done?

Program	A	B	C	D	E	F	G	H	I
Size (GB)	4	3.2	2.4	2.6	4.4	1	2	2.4	3.6
Program	J	K	L	M	N	O	P	Q	R
Size (GB)	5.6	3	4.8	3	4	2.8	8	4.8	1.6

Table 1.6

② A small car ferry has a number of lanes, each 20 m long. The following vehicles are waiting to be loaded.

Petrol tanker	14 m	Car	4 m	Range Rover	5 m	Car	4 m
Car	3 m	Van	4 m	Car and trailer	8 m	Car	3 m
Coach	12 m	Lorry	11 m	Car	4 m	Lorry	10 m

Table 1.7

How many lanes are needed to fit all the vehicles on the ferry at the same time?

③ Sort the list 6 5 9 4 5 2 using

(i)   the bubble sort algorithm

(ii) the quick sort algorithm.

④ (i) Sort the list red, pink, yellow, green, purple, blue, orange into alphabetical order using a quick sort.

(ii) How many comparisons are made?

⑤ A plumber is using pipes that are 6 m long and needs to cut the following lengths.

Length (m)	0.5	1	1.5	2	2.5	3	3.5
Number	0	2	4	3	0	1	2

Table 1.8

Use the first-fit decreasing algorithm to find a way to cut the lengths.

⑥ Six items with the masses given in Table 1.9 are packed into bags, each of which has a capacity of 10 kg.

Item	A	B	C	D	E	F
Weight	2	1	6	3	3	5

Table 1.9

(i) Use the first-fit algorithm to pack these items into bags, saying how many bags are needed.

(ii) Give an optimal solution.   [MEI]

⑦ A list of 10 items takes 0.02 seconds to sort using the bubble sort algorithm. Estimate how long it takes to sort a list of 30 items using the bubble sort algorithm.

⑧ (i) Determine the number of potential swaps when using the bubble sort for a list of length

(a) 6

(b) 7

(c) n.

(ii) Explain why the bubble sort has quadratic order.

⑨ (i) The coach of a netball team has to arrange three pre-season training sessions, each of length 90 minutes. She wants to schedule the activities that are listed below. Some are to be scheduled more than once.

Activity	Duration (mins)	Number of times activity is to be scheduled
A shooting practice	10	3
B passing practice	15	3
C blocking practice	12	3
D sprinting	5	3
E intermediate distance running	14	2
F long distance running	20	1
G team games	12	3
H 4-a-side practice game	20	2
I full-scale practice game	20	1

Table 1.10

(a) Use the first-fit decreasing algorithm to allocate activities to each of the three training sessions.

(b) The solution given by the first-fit decreasing algorithm is not satisfactory since it leads to repeated activities in the same session. The first-fit decreasing algorithm is modified so that the next activity is placed in the first available session only if it will fit and if the same activity has not already been placed in that session. Apply this modified algorithm until it fails.

(c) Prove that it is not possible to fit the activities into the three sessions so that no session contains a repeated activity.

(ii) At the end of pre-season training the coach has allocated points to ten players. She will choose the seven highest scoring players for her team for the first match.

Player	A	B	C	D	E	F	G	H	I	J
Points	81	92	76	43	82	45	51	93	71	62

Table 1.11

(a) Count the number of comparisons she would have to make if she were to

1 check along the points table from left to right, comparing the first number with the second, then the larger with the third, and so on to find the player with the highest score

2 choose that player for the team and delete the entry from the points table

3 repeat the process on the reduced points table until the team is chosen.

(b) Instead she executes a bubble sort on the numbers in the list, starting from the left and with smaller numbers moving to the right. She does this only until she can be sure that the three lowest scores are in the three right-most positions. Show the steps of this sort, and state the number of comparisons that are made. [MEI]

3 Types of graphs

The types of graph that are considered here are different from the graphs of functions that you will be familiar with. For example, the graph in Figure 1.8 shows connections between pairs of members of a discrete set (of towns and cities in south-west England). The connections could, for example, represent the existence of a direct bus route.

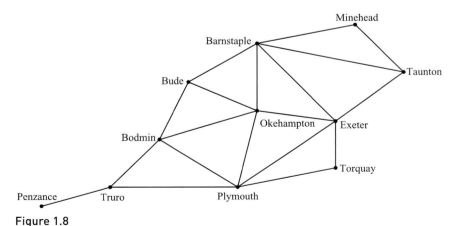

Figure 1.8

This section introduces the main terminology that is used in graph theory. It will be needed in subsequent chapters, where some of the applications of the theory are explored.

In Figure 1.8, the towns (and cities) are referred to as **vertices** (or **nodes**), whilst the connections between them are described as **edges** (or **arcs**). An edge must have a vertex at each end.

In Chapter 2 you will meet **networks**. These are graphs with numbers associated with the edges, called weights (e.g. distances, travel times, costs).

In Chapter 7 (Network flows), you will work with **directed graphs** (or digraphs), where an edge may have a direction associated with it.

Another example of a graph is shown in Figure 1.9. It represents the relationship 'share a common factor other than 1'.

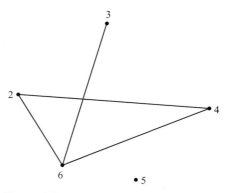

Figure 1.9

■ Within a particular graph, a **walk** is a finite sequence of edges in which the end of one edge is the start of the next (except for the last edge).

■ A **path** is a walk in which no vertex is repeated.

■ A closed path is called a **cycle**.

Example 1.6

Look at Figure 1.8. What description would you give to the following routes?

(i) Okehampton–Exeter–Barnstaple–Okehampton–Plymouth–Bodmin–Okehampton

(ii) Okehampton–Bodmin–Truro–Plymouth–Torquay

Solution

(i) It is at least a walk, as each edge follows the previous one.
It is not a path, as the vertex Okehampton is repeated.
So it is a walk.

(ii) It is at least a walk, as each edge follows the previous one.
It is not closed, as it does not return to its starting point at Okehampton.
It is at least a path, as no vertex is repeated.
So it is a path.

■ A graph is said to be **connected** if there exists a path between every pair of vertices, i.e. if no vertices are isolated. This means that the graph in Figure 1.9 is not connected.

- It is possible for two vertices to be connected by **multiple edges**, or for a vertex to be connected to itself (forming a **loop**). These situations are shown in Figure 1.10.

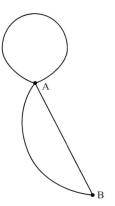

Figure 1.10

- A graph that has no multiple edges or loops is referred to as a **simple graph**.
- A **tree** is a simple connected graph with no cycles. Figure 1.11 shows an example.

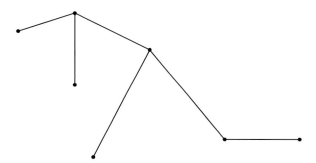

Figure 1.11

Discussion point
→ What is the smallest number of edges that a simple connected graph with n vertices can have?

- A **subgraph** is a graph that is formed from some of the vertices and edges of another graph. Note that whilst this may result in an isolated vertex, any edge has to have a vertex at each end.
- A subgraph H, of a connected graph G, is said to be a **spanning tree** of G if H is a tree and it contains all the vertices of G. One particular spanning tree for the graph in Figure 1.8 is shown in Figure 1.12. In general, there may be many possible spanning trees.

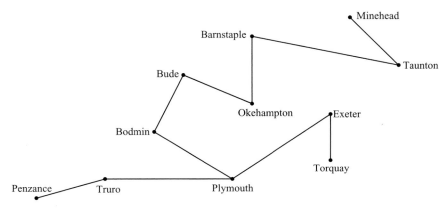

Figure 1.12

Chapter 1 Algorithms and graph theory

This concept will be of use in Chapter 2, where you will consider the minimum connector problem.

■ The **degree** (or sometimes **valency** or **order**) of a vertex is the number of edges that join it. (A loop contributes 2 to the degree of its vertex.) A vertex that has an odd degree, for example, can be referred to as an odd vertex.

ACTIVITY 1.5

Prove that, in a graph, the number of odd vertices is always even.

Eulerian graphs

An interesting problem is whether it is possible to travel round a graph without repeating any edges, so that all the edges in the graph are covered.

If such a trail ends at its starting point, it is called **Eulerian**. If it ends somewhere else, it is called **semi-Eulerian**.

Historical note

Leonhard Euler (1707–1783) was a very distinguished and versatile Swiss mathematician. His name is pronounced 'oiler'.

A graph that possesses an Eulerian or semi-Eulerian trail is called an Eulerian or semi-Eulerian graph, as appropriate.

A practical example of this would be a gritting lorry that needs to travel down all the roads in a particular area, without repeating any roads if it can. (It is assumed that the roads are narrow, so the lorry need travel in one direction only.) In the case of an Eulerian graph, the lorry would be able to return to its depot, whereas in the case of a semi-Eulerian graph it would not. This is an example of the 'route inspection problem' that you will meet in Chapter 2.

If a graph has no odd vertices, then it can be shown to be Eulerian.

You saw in Activity 1.5 that the number of odd vertices of a graph is always even.

For every edge leading into a vertex, there will be another edge leading out, and it will be possible to move round the graph, covering each edge exactly once, without getting stranded at any vertex.

Note

Euler's handshake lemma states that 'The sum of the degrees of all of the vertices is twice the number of the edges.' If the edges are considered as handshakes, and the hands are each exit from a vertex it can be seen that this must be true since any handshake requires two hands.

If just two of the vertices are odd, then the graph can be shown to be semi-Eulerian.

You can start at one of these odd vertices, cover all of the edges exactly once, and end up at the other odd vertex.

Note

For the start vertex, the number of outgoing edges is one greater than the number of incoming edges (and the other way round for the end vertex).

Planar graphs

A graph is said to be **planar** if it can be distorted in such a way that its edges do not cross. Figure 1.13 is planar, because it can be redrawn as Figure 1.14.

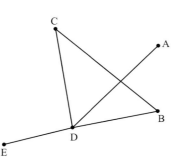

Figure 1.13

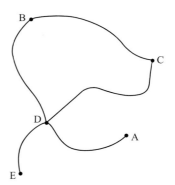

Figure 1.14

A **complete** graph is one where every two vertices share exactly one edge (and where there are no loops). A complete graph with n vertices is denoted by K_n. One representation of the K_4 graph is shown in Figure 1.15.

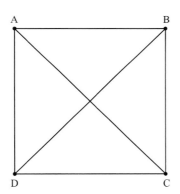

Figure 1.15

Example 1.7

How many edges does K_n have?

Solution

Labelling the vertices 1 to n, there are $n - 1$ vertices joined by an edge to vertex 1. Excluding vertex 1, there are $n - 2$ vertices joined by an edge to vertex 2, and so on until you reach vertex $n - 1$, which has one edge joined to the remaining vertex.

So the total number of edges is $(n - 1) + (n - 2) + \cdots + 1 = \frac{1}{2}(n - 1)n$.

Isomorphisms

Two graphs are said to be **isomorphic** if one can be distorted in some way to produce the other (from the Greek: same form). Isomorphic graphs must have the same number of vertices, each of the same degree, and their vertices must be connected in the same way.

You have already seen how isomorphisms can be used to demonstrate that a graph is planar. The graphs in Figures 1.13 and 1.14 were isomorphic, as they were alternative representations of a planar graph.

Figure 1.13 is repeated as Figure 1.16. The vertices of Figure 1.17 cannot be put into a one-to-one correspondence with those of Figure 1.16 (for example, there is no vertex of degree 4 in Figure 1.17 that could correspond with vertex D of Figure 1.16). Therefore these graphs are not isomorphic.

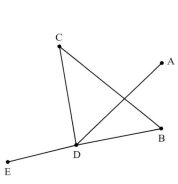

Figure 1.16   Figure 1.17

Example 1.8

Are the graphs shown in Figures 1.18 and 1.19 isomorphic?

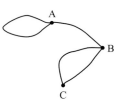 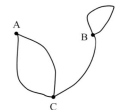

Figure 1.18   Figure 1.19

Solution

By comparing the number of edges joining each pair of vertices, it can be seen that the graphs are isomorphic. The vertices have simply been relabelled.

◤ Note

Any two complete graphs with n vertices are isomorphic.

Exercise 1.3

① (i) List all the cycles in the graph below that can start and finish at A. Note that, for example, ABCA and ACBA represent the same cycle.

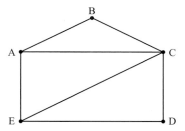

Figure 1.20

(ii) Why is ABCEDCA not a cycle?

(iii) What could ABCEDCA best be described as?

② Determine whether the graphs below are

(i) Eulerian

(ii) semi-Eulerian

(iii) neither.

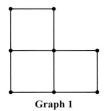 

Graph 1   **Graph 2**

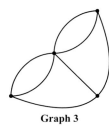 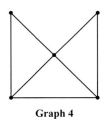

Graph 3   **Graph 4**

Figure 1.21

③ Show that the graph in Figure 1.22 is planar.

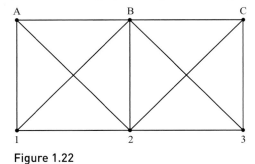

Figure 1.22

④ Which of the following graphs are isomorphic?

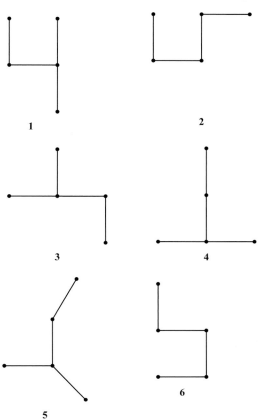

Figure 1.23

⑤ Draw three different trees, each containing five vertices and four edges. [MEI]

⑥ When is a complete graph Eulerian or semi-Eulerian?

⑦ (i) Show that the following graphs are isomorphic.

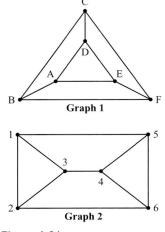

Graph 1

Graph 2

Figure 1.24

(ii) Draw a simple connected graph on six vertices, each of degree 3, which is not isomorphic to Graph 1/Graph 2.

⑧ Donald claims that the following graphs are isomorphic.

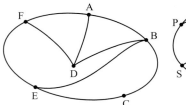

Figure 1.25

Explain why Donald is mistaken.

⑨ Vertices of the graph shown in Figure 1.26 represent objects. Some edges have been drawn to connect vertices representing objects which are the same colour.

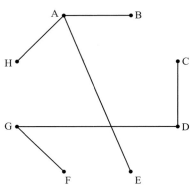

Figure 1.26

(i) Copy the diagram and draw in whichever edges you can be sure should be added.

(ii) How many edges would be needed in total if you were also told that the objects represented by B and F were the same colour?　　[MEI]

⑩ (i) A, B, C and D are the vertices of the complete graph, K_4. List all the paths from A to B.

(ii) Show that there are 16 paths from A to B in the complete graph on the vertices {A, B, C, D, E}.

4 Planarity of graphs

Hamiltonian graphs

Another interesting problem is finding a route around a graph that visits all of the vertices exactly once. Note that edges cannot be repeated, as this would mean the repetition of a vertex (however, not all edges need to be traversed). You also need to be able to return to the starting point. If such a route exists, then it is called a **Hamiltonian cycle** (also known as a **tour**), and a graph that possesses a Hamiltonian cycle is called a Hamiltonian graph. This idea is employed in the 'Travelling salesperson' problem that you will meet in Chapter 2.

ACTIVITY 1.6

Look back at Figure 1.8 again. Which town or city should be removed, in order to make the graph Hamiltonian?

Example 1.9

(i) Find a Hamiltonian cycle for the graph below.

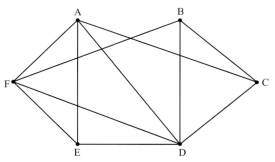

Figure 1.27

(ii) Starting with your cycle, add in edges to show that the original graph is planar.

Solution

(i) A Hamiltonian cycle is shown in Figure 1.28.

(ii) For example, you can start with the cycle shown in Figure 1.28, and manoeuvre vertices B and C, in order to remove crossing edges (giving Figure 1.29). You then add in the necessary (non-crossing) edges to give Figure 1.30, which is a distorted version of the original graph, showing that the original graph is planar.

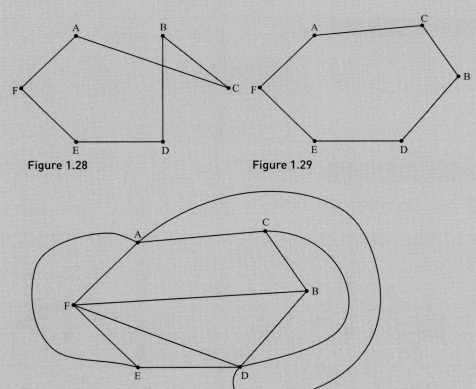

Figure 1.28

Figure 1.29

Figure 1.30

In Example 1.9 a Hamiltonian cycle was used to determine whether a graph was planar. This method is the **planarity algorithm** for determining whether a graph is planar.

■ First find a Hamiltonian cycle.

■ Manoeuvre the nodes so that no edges cross.

■ Add in the remaining edges of the original graph, avoiding crossing edges.

This gives a graph that is isomorphic to the original one and so, if it can be found, then the original graph is planar. Otherwise it is not.

The need for a Hamiltonian cycle prompts the question 'How do you know if a graph has a Hamiltonian cycle?'. There is no theorem to say whether one exists but there are a number of properties that can help you decide whether it is worth looking for one.

■ Activity 1.6 implies that a graph with a node of degree 1 cannot have a Hamiltonian cycle.

■ A graph that is not connected cannot have a Hamiltonian cycle.

■ Any complete graph, K_n, has at least one Hamiltonian cycle.

■ A graph with 'sufficiently many' edges must contain a Hamiltonian cycle.

Of course, 'sufficiently many' is not a precise statement but it serves to give you a feel for whether there is a Hamiltonian cycle in a given graph. In most cases it is necessary to actually find one to prove its existence or find a convincing argument as to why there cannot be one.

> ◤ **Note**
> - - - - - - - - - - - -
> Dirac, in 1952, found that 'A simple graph with n vertices ($n \geqslant 3$) is Hamiltonian (has a Hamiltonian cycle) if every vertex has degree $\frac{n}{2}$ or greater.'

Example 1.10

How many different Hamiltonian cycles does K_n have?

> ### Solution
> There will be $\frac{1}{2}(n-1)!$ possible Hamiltonian cycles: you can choose to start at any vertex, and there will be $n-1$ ways of choosing the next vertex to proceed to (and so on). You divide by 2 because reversing the order gives the same cycle.

Exercise 1.4

① Determine whether the graphs in Exercise 1.3 question 2 are Hamiltonian.

② Decide whether the following graphs are planar.

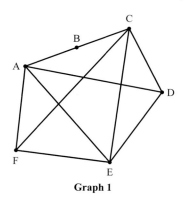

Graph 1

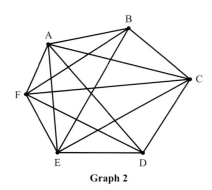

Graph 2

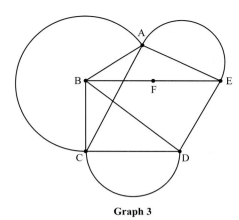

Graph 3

Figure 1.31

③ (i) Find a Hamiltonian cycle for this graph.

(ii) Hence show that the graph is planar.

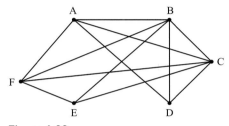

Figure 1.32

④ Referring to Figure 1.33

(i) identify a Hamiltonian cycle in the graph

(ii) use the Hamiltonian cycle identified in (i) and the planarity algorithm to show that the graph is planar.

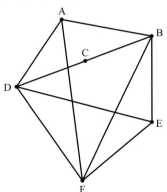

Figure 1.33

⑤ (i) Find a Hamiltonian cycle in the graph in Figure 1.34.

(ii) Use the planarity algorithm to show that the graph in Figure 1.34 is planar.

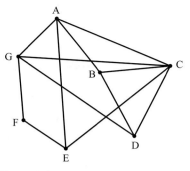

Figure 1.34

⑥ In the 18th century, the inhabitants of Königsberg (now Kaliningrad) enjoyed promenading across the town's seven bridges – shown in the diagram below. It was known not to be possible to cross each bridge once and once only.

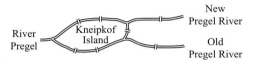

Figure 1.35

(i) Create a graph to model this situation.

(ii) How is it possible to tell that the bridges could not be crossed once and once only?

⑦ Regarding ABCDEA as different from AEDCBA, how many different Hamiltonian cycles are there in the graph in Figure 1.36?

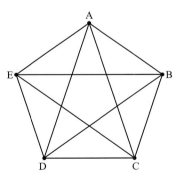

Figure 1.36

LEARNING OUTCOMES

Now you have finished this chapter, you should be able to

➤ understand what an algorithm is

➤ trace an algorithm in the form of a flowchart or as instructions written in text

➤ determine the output of an algorithm and how it links to the input

➤ solve bin-packing problems using full-bin, first-fit, and first-fit decreasing algorithms, and understand their strengths and weaknesses

➤ apply a bubble sort algorithm to a list of numbers or words

➤ apply the quick sort algorithm to a list of numbers or words, clearly identifying the pivots used for each pass

➤ identify the number of comparisons and swaps used in a given pass

➤ identify size, efficiency and order of an algorithm and use them to make predictions

➤ understand and use the vocabulary used in graph theory, e.g. degree of a vertex, isomorphic graphs, walks, paths and cycles

➤ understand and use different types of graph, e.g. complete, planar, isomorphic, simple and connected

➤ understand and use K_n notation

➤ understand and use the definition of a tree

➤ determine whether a graph is Eulerian, semi-Eulerian or neither, and find Eulerian trails

➤ apply the planarity algorithm for planar graphs

➤ determine whether a graph contains a Hamiltonian cycle.

KEY POINTS

1 An algorithm is a finite sequence of operations for carrying out a procedure or solving a problem.

2 An algorithm may be communicated in ordinary language or in a flowchart.

3 If an algorithm has $O(n^r)$ complexity, then scaling the problem size by a factor k will scale the run-time by a factor of (approximately) k^r.

4 **First-fit algorithm**

Take the boxes in the order listed and pack each box in the first bin that has enough space for it (each time starting with the first bin).

First-fit decreasing algorithm

Reorder the boxes from the largest to the smallest, and then apply the first-fit method to this list.

Full-bin strategy

Look for combinations of boxes to fill bins. Pack these boxes. Put the remaining boxes together in combinations that result in bins that are as nearly full as possible.

5 The efficiency of different packing strategies could be compared by counting the number of comparisons needed in the worst case for a list of n items. In the worst case, first-fit and first-fit decreasing both have quadratic complexity, $O(n^2)$.

6 **Bubble sort**

On the first pass, the first number in the list is compared with the second, and the smaller assumes the first position. The second and third numbers are then compared, with the smaller assuming the second position, and so on to the end of the list. The largest number is now at the end of the list.

Repeat with all but the last number. Continue until there are no swaps in a complete pass.

Quick sort

The middle value in the list is the pivot. If there is an even number of items in a list, the right-hand middle value is used. Excluding the pivot, pass along the list and write down each value that is less than or equal to the pivot value. Write the pivot value and then write down the values that are greater than the pivot. The pivot splits the list into two sublists.

Repeat the process on each sublist and continue in this way until every value has been placed.

7 Bubble sort and, in the worst case, quick sort have quadratic complexity, $O(n^2)$.

8 A graph consists of vertices and edges.

9 A path is a finite sequence of edges in which the end of one edge is the start of the next and no vertex is repeated.

10 A cycle (or circuit) is a closed path.

11 A graph is connected if there exists a path between every pair of vertices.

12 A simple graph is one that has no multiple edges or loops.

13 A tree is a simple connected graph with no cycles.

14 The degree (or valency or order) of a vertex is the number of edges that join it.

15 A graph is Eulerian if every vertex is of even degree. An Eulerian trail is a trail that includes every edge of a graph exactly once. A graph is semi-Eulerian if it has exactly two vertices of odd degree.

16 A Hamiltonian cycle is a cycle that passes through every vertex exactly once and returns to its start vertex.

17 A graph is planar if it can be distorted in such a way that its edges do not cross.

18 A complete graph is one where every two vertices share exactly one edge (and where there are no loops). K_n is the complete graph with n vertices.

19 Two graphs are isomorphic if one can be distorted in some way to produce the other.

20 The planarity algorithm starts with a Hamiltonian cycle and adds in edges to determine whether a graph is planar.

2

Algorithms on graphs

→ What is the shortest route that visits A, B, C and D in the network below and returns to its starting point?

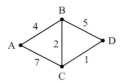

1 The minimum connector problem

The language of networks

In this chapter you will use the terms **nodes** and **arcs** (rather than vertices and edges).

A network is a **weighted** graph – i.e. a graph for which there is a number (**weight**) associated with each arc.

Figure 2.1 shows a graph from Chapter 1 with weights attached.

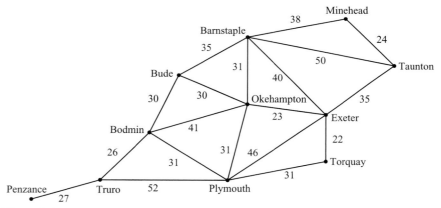

Figure 2.1

In this case, the weights are the distances in miles between the various towns and cities. In other situations the weights could be times or costs, for example.

A **table of weights** (or distance matrix, if applicable) can be used to represent the network in a form that is convenient for a computer. The network in Figure 2.1, which has no loops, multiple arcs or directed arcs, can be represented by Table 2.1.

	Pen	Tru	Ply	Tor	Exe	Tau	Min	Bar	Oke	Bud	Bod
Pen	–	27	–	–	–	–	–	–	–	–	–
Tru	27	–	52	–	–	–	–	–	–	–	26
Ply	–	52	–	31	46	–	–	–	31	–	31
Tor	–	–	31	–	22	–	–	–	–	–	–
Exe	–	–	46	22	–	35	–	40	23	–	–
Tau	–	–	–	–	35	–	24	50	–	–	–
Min	–	–	–	–	–	24	–	38	–	–	–
Bar	–	–	–	–	40	50	38	–	31	35	–
Oke	–	–	31	–	23	–	–	31	–	30	41
Bud	–	–	–	–	–	–	–	35	30	–	30
Bod	–	26	31	–	–	–	–	–	41	30	–

Table 2.1

Suppose that a cable company wishes to join up the towns and cities in Figure 2.1, using the shortest possible length of cable. This can be done by creating a spanning tree with the minimum weight.

There are several ways of doing this. One method is simply to remove arcs in order of decreasing weight, ensuring that the network remains connected.

Example 2.1

Find a minimum spanning tree for the network in Figure 2.1.

Solution

The arcs can be removed in the following order (arcs of the same weight may be chosen arbitrarily):

Tru–Ply 52

Bar–Tau 50

Ply–Exe 46

Bod–Oke 41

Bar–Exe 40

Bar–Min 38

Bud–Bar 35

(Exe–Tau 35 can't be removed, as the network would no longer be connected)

Ply–Tor 31

Bod–Ply 31

(Ply–Oke 31 can't be removed)

➜

The resulting spanning tree is shown in Figure 2.2. It has a total weight of 279.

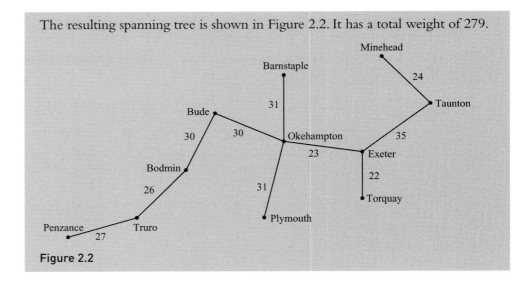

Figure 2.2

Some methods may be easier for a computer to apply. One such method is **Prim's algorithm**.

(i)   Start with any node.

(ii) Add the arc leading to the nearest node.

(iii) Add the arc leading (from any of the nodes collected so far) to the nearest new node, and repeat.

(iv) Stop once all nodes have been collected.

If two nodes are the same distance from the nodes collected so far, either node may be chosen.

Example 2.2

Use Prim's algorithm to find a minimum spanning tree for the network in Figure 2.1, starting from Okehampton. Make clear the order in which the arcs are selected.

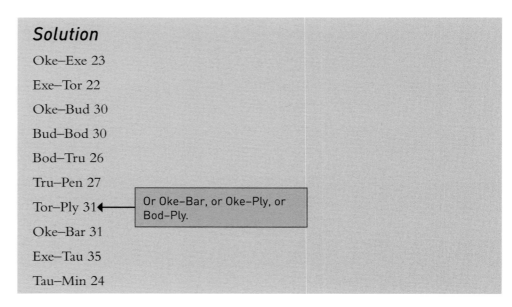

Solution

Oke–Exe 23

Exe–Tor 22

Oke–Bud 30

Bud–Bod 30

Bod–Tru 26

Tru–Pen 27

Tor–Ply 31 ◄——— Or Oke–Bar, or Oke–Ply, or Bod–Ply.

Oke–Bar 31

Exe–Tau 35

Tau–Min 24

The resulting spanning tree is shown in Figure 2.3.

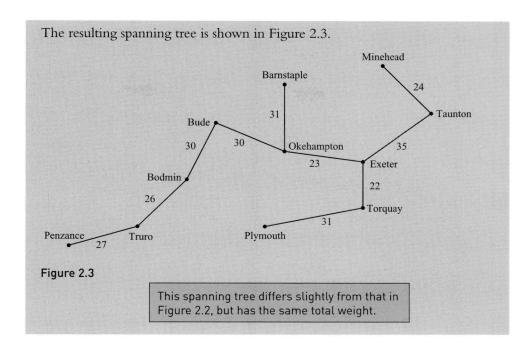

Figure 2.3

> This spanning tree differs slightly from that in Figure 2.2, but has the same total weight.

Another well-known method is **Kruskal's algorithm**:

(i)   Start with the shortest arc.

(ii) Choose the next shortest arc, provided it doesn't create a cycle, and repeat.
      (If two arcs are of equal length, then either may be chosen.)

The order in which arcs are added should be made clear.

| **Example 2.3** | Use Kruskal's algorithm to find a minimum spanning tree for the network in Figure 2.1, starting from Okehampton. Make clear the order in which the arcs are selected. |

Solution

Tor–Exe 22

Exe–Oke 23

Tau–Min 24

Bod–Tru 26

Tru–Pen 27

Bod–Bud 30   ← Or Bud–Oke.

Bud–Oke 30

Bod–Ply 31   ← Or Oke–Bar, or Oke–Ply, or Ply–Tor.

Oke–Bar 31   ← Not Ply–Oke or Ply–Tor, as these would create a cycle.

Exe–Tau 35   ← Not Bud–Bar.

→

The resulting spanning tree, with a total weight of 279, is shown in Figure 2.4.

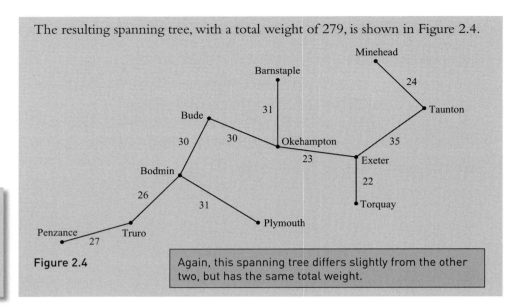

Figure 2.4

Again, this spanning tree differs slightly from the other two, but has the same total weight.

As you have seen, if some of the arcs have the same weight then there may be more than one solution. However, the total weight will always be the same.

Matrix representation for Prim's algorithm

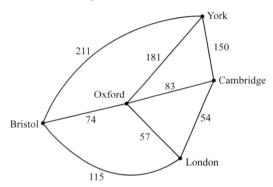

Figure 2.5

	B	**C**	**L**	**O**	**Y**
B	–	–	115	74	211
C	–	–	54	83	150
L	115	54	–	57	–
O	74	83	57	–	181
Y	211	150	–	181	–

Table 2.2

Prim's algorithm can be applied to the table of weights for a network. Referring to the network in Figure 2.5, and its table of weights in Table 2.2, the procedure is as follows.

Choosing B (for example) as the initial node, you can write (1) above B's column and shade in (or cross out) the row for B (to indicate that you no longer need to select B). See Table 2.3.

	(1)				
	B	**C**	**L**	**O**	**Y**
B	–	–	115	74	211
C	–	–	54	83	150
L	115	54	–	57	–
O	74	83	57	–	181
Y	211	150	–	181	–

Table 2.3

You then find the smallest weight in column B: 74 for O (indicating that O is the nearest node to B). You then write (2) above O's column, and place a bracket (or circle) around the 74, for future reference, as well as shading in the row for O. See Table 2.4.

	(1)			(2)	
	B	**C**	**L**	**O**	**Y**
B	–	–	115	74	211
C	–	–	54	83	150
L	115	54	–	57	–
O	[74]	83	57	–	181
Y	211	150	–	181	–

Table 2.4

You have now created the arc BO. You then find the smallest weight in either of columns B and O (i.e. you are looking for the node that is nearest to one of the nodes selected so far). This is 57 for L in column O. You then record this in the same way as before. See Table 2.5.

	(1)		(3)	(2)	
	B	**C**	**L**	**O**	**Y**
B	–	–	115	74	211
C	–	–	54	83	150
L	115	54	–	[57]	–
O	[74]	83	57	–	181
Y	211	150	–	181	–

Table 2.5

You have now created the tree BOL. The process then continues until all of the nodes have been included.

Note

Prim's and Kriskal's are both examples of **greedy** algorithms. They don't look ahead, choosing the optimal arc at each stage. They do, however, yield an optimal solution (which is not the case for many greedy algorithms).

Exercise 2.1

① Apply Prim's algorithm to the network in Figure 2.1, starting at Bodmin.

② Create a table of weights to represent the network in Figure 2.6.

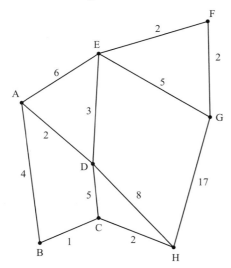

Figure 2.6

③ Draw the network with the table of weights in Table 2.6.

	A	B	C	D	E	F
A	–	10	20	–	16	12
B	10	–	15	–	–	–
C	20	15	–	11	8	–
D	–	–	11	–	7	22
E	16	–	8	7	–	14
F	12	–	–	22	14	–

Table 2.6

④ Apply Prim's algorithm to the network in question 3, starting at A. Show the order in which the steps are carried out, and give the total weight of the minimum spanning tree.

⑤ Apply Kruskal's algorithm to the network in question 3. Show the order in which the steps are carried out.

⑥ Find the minimum spanning tree for the following network which is given in tabular form.

	Malvern	Worcester	Hereford	Evesham	Ross	Tewkesbury	Gloucester	Cheltenham
Malvern	–	8	19	–	19	13	20	–
Worcester	8	–	25	16	–	15	–	–
Hereford	19	25	–	–	14	–	28	–
Evesham	–	16	–	–	–	13	–	16
Ross	19	–	14	–	–	24	16	–
Tewkesbury	13	15	–	13	24	–	10	9
Gloucester	20	–	28	–	16	10	–	9
Cheltenham	–	–	–	16	–	9	9	–

Table 2.7

⑦ Find the minimum spanning tree for this network.

	Dorchester	Puddletown	Blandford	Wimborne	Bere Regis	Lytchett Minster	Weymouth	Warnwell	Wareham	Swanage	Poole
Dorchester	–	5	–	–	–	–	8	5	–	–	–
Puddletown	5	–	12	–	6	–	–	9	14	–	–
Blandford	–	12	–	7	9	11	–	–	16	–	–
Wimborne	–	–	7	–	8	7	–	–	–	–	7
Bere Regis	–	6	9	8	–	8	19	11	8	–	–
Lytchett Minster	–	–	11	7	8	–	25	–	5	–	6
Weymouth	8	–	–	–	19	25	–	7	–	–	–
Warnwell	5	9	–	–	11	–	7	–	13	–	–
Wareham	–	14	16	–	8	5	–	13	–	10	–
Swanage	–	–	–	–	–	–	–	–	10	–	–
Poole	–	–	–	7	–	6	–	–	–	–	–

Table 2.8

2 The route inspection problem

This is also known as the Chinese postman problem.

In Chapter 1, you met the example of the gritting lorry that needs to pass along all the arcs exactly once. An Eulerian graph was defined as one where this was possible, and in such a way that the lorry would be able to return to its starting point. A semi-Eulerian graph was defined as one where the lorry could pass along all of the arcs exactly once, but would not be able to return to its starting point.

The route inspection problem involves first of all establishing whether the graph (i.e. the network without its weights) is Eulerian, semi-Eulerian or neither. Depending on the type of graph identified, you may then need to make some compromise in order to find the shortest route that covers all of the arcs at least once – returning to the starting point, if required.

You saw in Chapter 1 that the number of odd nodes in a graph has to be even, and that graphs can be divided into the following three categories.

A Those with no odd nodes, which are therefore Eulerian.

B Those with two odd nodes, which are therefore semi-Eulerian.

C Those with four or more odd nodes, which are neither Eulerian nor semi-Eulerian.

Note

An Eulerian graph is said to be **traversable**.

In the case of category **A** no compromise has to be made: each of the arcs is covered exactly once, and you end up back at the starting point. The length of the shortest route is just the total of the weights of the network.

Although the existence of such a route is guaranteed, you still need to find it. However, there is usually more than one solution, and it normally isn't difficult to find an example.

In the case of category **B** if it is permissible for the start and end nodes to be different, then no compromise is necessary. However, if you wish to end up where you started, then you have to convert the network into one that has no odd nodes.

This is done by finding the shortest possible path between the two odd nodes, and duplicating that path (so that there are multiple arcs between some pairs of nodes). In this way, the two odd nodes are made even, and any nodes along the duplicated path have their degree increased by 2 (and so will still be even).

Example 2.4

For the network shown in Figure 2.7, find the shortest route such that all arcs are covered at least once and which returns to the starting point.

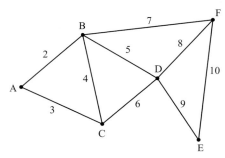

Figure 2.7

It is not necessary for BF to follow CB in the shortest route: it is sufficient that the arcs CB and BF are repeated at some point.

Solution

Here there are two odd nodes: C and F.

As the shortest route between them is CBF (of weight $4 + 7 = 11$), this path is repeated in the network, as shown in Figure 2.8.

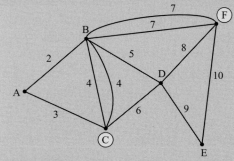

Figure 2.8

The total length of the original arcs is 54, and the effect of adding on the repeated arcs is to give a value of $54 + 4 + 7 = 65$ for the shortest route such that all arcs are covered at least once and which returns to the starting point.

ACTIVITY 2.1

For the network given in Figure 2.7, find a route that starts and ends at A.

In the case of category **C** where there are more than two odd nodes, there are several possibilities.

(i) You must return to the starting point.

(ii) You can start and finish where you like.

(iii) You must start or finish at a specified node.

For (i), the approach is similar to that for category **B**: you decide how to pair up the odd nodes in such a way that the total of the shortest distances between the paired nodes is minimised.

To do this, you first find the shortest path between each possible pair of odd nodes (AB, AC, AD, BC, BD, CD – where the four odd nodes are A, B, C and D).

Then you establish all the possible ways of pairing up the odd nodes (in the case of four nodes, there will be three possibilities: AB & CD, AC & BD and AD & BC).

You then choose the combination of pairings that gives the shortest total path (e.g. AC & BD, if AC + BD is the smallest possible total).

This total is the additional distance that has to be added to the original total of all the arcs, to give the length of the shortest route.

Example 2.5

For the network given in Figure 2.9, find the shortest route that allows all arcs to be covered at least once and which returns to the starting point.

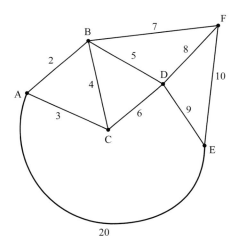

Figure 2.9

ACTIVITY 2.2

For the network given in Figure 2.9, find a route that starts and ends at A.

Solution

There are now four odd nodes: A, C, E and F.

The possible pairings, together with the shortest distances associated with them, are (by inspection) as follows.

AC 3

AE 16 (ABDE)

AF 9 (ABF)

→

ACTIVITY 2.3

For Figure 2.9, what would be the best strategy if you had to start at A and finish at B (an example of category **C**(iii))?

ACTIVITY 2.4

Find the shortest route if you have to start at A and finish at B.

CE 15 (CDE)

CF 11 (CBF)

EF 10

The possible ways of pairing up these nodes, together with the total distances in each case, are

(AC) (EF)   3 + 10 = 13

(AE) (CF)   16 + 11 = 27

(AF) (CE)   9 + 15 = 24.

The combination that gives the shortest total distance is thus (AC) (EF).

Since the total of the original arcs is 74, the effect of adding the repeated arcs is to give a value of 74 + 13 = 87 for the shortest route that allows all arcs to be covered at least once and returns to the starting point.

Discussion point

→ In the case of Figure 2.9, what would be the best strategy for category **C**(ii), where you can choose the start and end nodes?

Example 2.6

Arnold, who is a railway enthusiast, wishes to travel along each stretch of railway linking the cities A–H of a particular country, as shown in Figure 2.10, with the times (in hours) for each stretch. The total time for all the stretches is 57 hours.

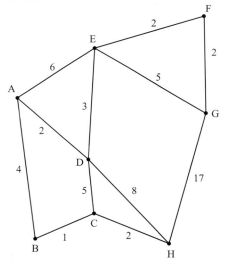

Figure 2.10

(i)   Initially he plans to set out from A and return to A. Find a route that covers each stretch of railway at least once, in the shortest possible time, and find the time taken.

(ii) There is a change of plan, and now Arnold wishes to start at A and finish at H (still covering each stretch at least once). Find the new time taken for the quickest route.

(iii) Arnold's wife wants the time reduced. If he has a free choice as to the starting and finishing cities, which should he choose, and what will the new time be?

Solution

(i) First of all, the degrees of each node are established.

A 3 B 2 C 3 D 4 E 4 F 2 G 3 H 3

Thus there are four nodes of odd degree: A, C, G and H.

In order to create an Eulerian graph (one where you can return to the starting position, having travelled along each arc exactly once), the nodes of odd degree need to be converted to even degree, by adding in extra arcs (which will be repeats of some of the existing arcs).

For example, you might join up A and C, and then G and H.

The other possibilities are AG and CH, and AH and CG.

In joining up these nodes, you need to use paths between them that have the smallest total weight.

These total weights are as follows.

AC and GH: 5[ABC] + 14[GFEDCH] = 19

AG and CH: 9[ADEFG] + 2[CH] = 11

AH and CG: 7[ABCH] + 12[CDEFG] = 19

So the best option is AG and CH, which involves repeating the arcs AD, DE, EF, FG and CH (as shown in Figure 2.11).

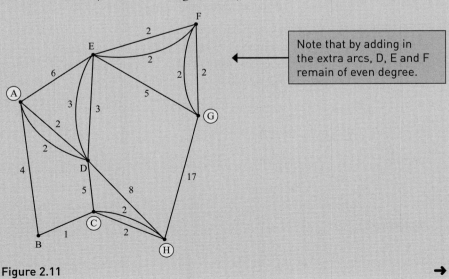

Note that by adding in the extra arcs, D, E and F remain of even degree.

Figure 2.11

One possibility is ABCDADEDHCHGEFGFEA

The time taken is then 57 + 11 = 68 hours.

(ii) Starting at A and finishing at H means that nodes A and H can remain of odd degree, so that only C and G need to be joined up.
This gives rise to an additional 12 hours (adding CDEFG), and hence the total time is now 57 + 12 = 69 hours.

(iii) Of the available options for joining up nodes of odd degree, CH has the smallest weight (of 2). Hence the best option is to start at A and finish at G, or vice versa, so that CH is travelled along twice.
This gives a total time of 57 + 2 = 59 hours.

Exercise 2.2

① (i) Use the route inspection method to find a shortest route that covers all of the arcs in Figure 2.12 at least once, starting and finishing at node 1.

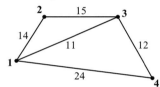

Figure 2.12

(ii) Find a shortest route that covers all of the arcs in Figure 2.12 at least once, starting and finishing at any suitable nodes.

[MEI adapted]

② Find a shortest route that covers all of the arcs in Figure 2.13 at least once, starting at Oxford and returning there. Distances are in miles.

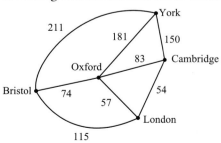

Figure 2.13

③ Find a shortest route that covers all of the arcs in Figure 2.13 at least once, starting at Oxford and ending at a different city.

④ Find a shortest route that covers all of the arcs in Figure 2.13 at least once, starting at one city and ending at a different one.

⑤ Find a shortest route that covers all of the arcs in Figure 2.14 at least once, starting at Okehampton and returning there.

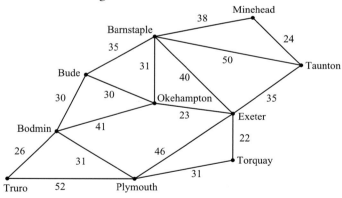

Figure 2.14

⑥ Find a shortest route that covers all of the arcs in Figure 2.14 at least once (you may start and finish at any town or city).

⑦ A highways maintenance depot must inspect all the manhole covers within its area. The road network is given in Figure 2.15. In order to make the inspection an engineer must leave the depot, D, drive along each of the roads in the network at least once and return to the depot.

(i) What is the minimum distance that she must drive?

(ii) What route enables her to drive the distance in (i)?

(iii) How many times is node F visited during this route?

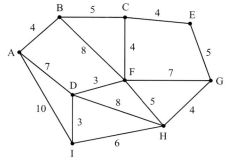

Figure 2.15

3 Dijkstra's algorithm

Dijkstra's algorithm provides a procedure for determining the shortest path between two particular nodes of a network.

Consider the network in Figure 2.16.

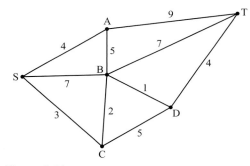

Figure 2.16

You start by recording provisional shortest distances from S to each of A, B and C. These are just the lengths of the arcs SA, SB and SC, and you say that A, B and C have been given **temporary labels** of 4, 7 and 3 respectively.

In the case of B, you see that the distance of 7 can be improved on by following the path SCB, and this will be taken into account later on.

For the moment, all you can be sure about is that the shortest distance from S to C is 3, as any other route from S to C would involve passing through A or B, and the distances SA and SB are both greater than the distance SC. So a **permanent label** of 3 is assigned to C.

Figure 2.17 shows one way of carrying out the labelling.

Note

Do not cross out working values when they are updated.

Figure 2.17

For completeness, S can also be given a permanent label of 0.

In the same way that the immediate neighbours of S were given temporary labels, you now give a temporary label to the immediate neighbours of C, based on the direct path from C. For D, this is $3 + 5 = 8$. You can also improve on B's temporary label: going via C, B can be reached in a distance of $3 + 2 = 5$.

The current position is shown in Figure 2.18.

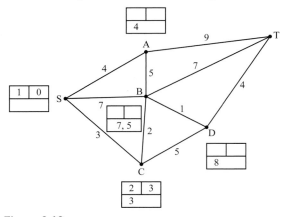

Figure 2.18

You now claim that the shortest distance from S to A must be 4, being the smallest of the temporary labels of A, B and D, and so A's label is made permanent.

> **Note**
>
> A proof of this (which may be omitted on a first reading) is as follows.
>
> Suppose that the last arc on the shortest route from S to A is not SA. More generally, suppose that the last arc leading into A does not come from a permanently labelled node. Any node that it does come from must be reached via one of the existing permanently labelled nodes (including S itself). This means that the shortest path must have passed along one of the arcs leading from a permanently labelled node to a temporarily labelled node (as all the neighbours of the permanently labelled nodes have been given temporary labels – unless they already have permanent labels). But no temporary label is smaller than that of A, and so the supposed shortest route has already covered a distance equal to A's temporary label. So it is not possible to improve on A's temporary label, and it can therefore be made permanent.

If more than one node shares the smallest temporary label, it doesn't matter which is made permanent.

The process is now repeated: the immediate neighbours of A are given temporary labels, or their temporary labels are improved on. The position after this step is shown in Figure 2.19.

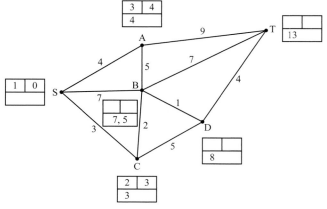

Figure 2.19

ACTIVITY 2.5
Complete this
procedure. (The solution
is shown in Figure 2.20.)

B now has the smallest temporary label, which is therefore made permanent.

The final position is shown in Figure 2.20.

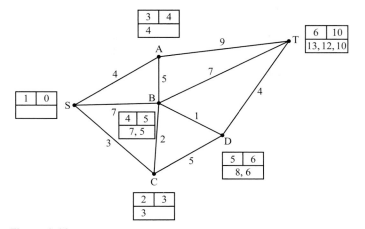

Figure 2.20

Discussion point

→ Why do you work
backwards from T?

Note

Dijkstra's algorithm can
be applied to networks
with directed arcs, but
not to networks with
negative weights.

The shortest distance from S to T is thus 10. Working backwards from T, the shortest route is determined by looking for neighbouring nodes for which the length of the arc between them equals the difference between their permanent labels.

In this example, the last stage has to be DT (since $10 - 6 = 4$, which is the arc length). Then BD = 1 is the next leg, followed by CB = 2, and finally SC = 3. Thus the shortest route is SCBDT, with a total distance of $3 + 2 + 1 + 4 = 10$ (which, as a check, equals the label of T).

Note that, although the aim was to find the shortest route from S to T, the algorithm also finds the shortest route from S to each of the other nodes.

Discussion point

→ How could you deal with the situation where there were several possible starting points (say, S_1, S_2, ...), and you wished to find the shortest route to a single end point (say, T)?

Exercise 2.3

① Use Dijkstra's algorithm to find a shortest path from S to T for the following networks (i), (ii) and (iii).

(i)

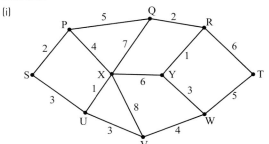

Figure 2.21

(ii)

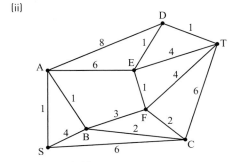

Figure 2.22

(iii)

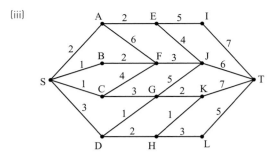

Figure 2.23

② Figure 2.24 shows the main railway lines across the USA and gives the approximate times in hours for the various journeys.

(i) Find the quickest route from Los Angeles to Chicago.

(ii) Find the quickest route from New Orleans to Denver.

(iii) If you can travel by road from El Paso to Santa Fe in 5 hours and from Santa Fe to Denver in 5 hours, would you save time on journey (i) or (ii) by using a mix of road and rail? (You should neglect connection times.)

③ The fire department in Westingham has a team fighting a large blaze at one of the town's hotels. They urgently need extra help from one of the neighbouring towns, A, B or C. The estimated times (in minutes) to travel along the various sections of road from A, B and C to Westingham are shown on the network below. Which town's firefighters should they call upon and how long will it take them to arrive at the fire?

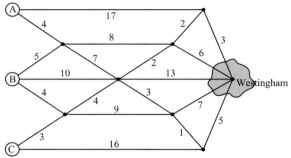

Figure 2.25

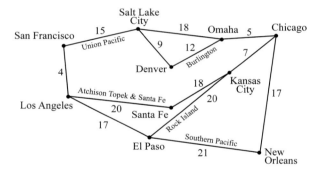

Figure 2.24

4 Floyd's algorithm

Whereas Dijkstra's algorithm finds the shortest route from a particular node to each of the other nodes, Floyd's algorithm finds the shortest route between every pair of nodes.

Consider the network in Figure 2.26.

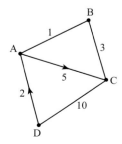

Figure 2.26

Note that the underlying graph here is directed. Floyd's algorithm can cope with directed arcs, but often there won't be any.

First of all, you create a table of distances between the nodes, based on arcs that lead directly from one node to another. The ∞ symbol is used to record the fact that there is no direct link between two nodes.

For the network in Figure 2.26 this gives the following.

To: From:	A	B	C	D
A	–	1	5	∞
B	1	–	3	∞
C	∞	3	–	10
D	2	∞	10	–

Table 2.9 Initial distance table

To accompany this **distance table**, you also create a **route table**, which records the first step on the journey between any two nodes. As you shall see shortly, initially this table will be of a trivial form, but it will become more meaningful when you have made improvements to the distance table.

For example, the shortest route from D to C will eventually be DABC, and this will be recorded in the route table by showing that the first step on the journey between D and C is A, that the first step on the journey between A and C is B, and that the first step on the journey between B and C is just C.

The route table corresponding to the initial distance table is as follows.

To: From:	A	B	C	D
A	A	B	C	D
B	A	B	C	D
C	A	B	C	D
D	A	B	C	D

Table 2.10 Initial route table

This table tells us that the first step on the journey between B and C (for example) is just C – because you are going directly from B to C. Note that, for convenience, the first step on the journey between C and A is recorded as A, even though the distance is ∞. Also for convenience, the first step on the journey between A and A is said to be A itself.

You now carry out the first iteration of the algorithm, by investigating whether the distances can be improved by taking an alternative route. You start by seeing what would happen if all routes went via A.

If you are starting from A anyway, then this has no effect (as you are already going via A). Also, if A is your destination then there is also no effect (as once again you are already going via A). It is therefore customary to highlight the first row and column, and to consider only the remaining cells in the table.

To: From:	A	B	C	D
A	–	1	5	∞
B	1	–	3	∞
C	∞	3	–	10
D	2	∞	10	–

Table 2.11 Distance table before the 1st iteration

You don't need to consider a journey from B to B, but for the journey from B to C, the distance table tells us the following.

You could travel from B to A, with a distance of 1, and then from A to C, with a distance of 5. As this isn't an improvement on the existing distance from B to C of 3, no change is made.

For B to D, no improvement is possible, as going via A would give a total distance of 1 (from B to A) + ∞ (from A to D).

Similarly, none of the routes from C can be improved on, owing to the presence of the ∞ in cell CA.

However, DB can be improved on by DA(2) + AB(1) = 3.

Also, DC can be improved on by DA(2) + AC(5) = 7.

Note that any potential improvement is found by looking horizontally and vertically to the highlighted cells, and adding them.

Any changes to the distance table can be indicated by enclosing the new distances in square brackets.

To: From:	A	B	C	D
A	–	1	5	∞
B	1	–	3	∞
C	∞	3	–	10
D	2	[3]	[7]	–

Table 2.12 Distance table after the 1st iteration

In the revised route table, cell DB needs to show the first step in the journey from D to B. As you are now going via A, this first step must be the first step on the journey from D to A, and this is just A – from the existing route table. Hence cell DB becomes [A] (the square brackets indicating a changed item), and similarly for cell DC.

To: From:	A	B	C	D
A	A	B	C	D
B	A	B	C	D
C	A	B	C	D
D	A	[A]	[A]	D

Table 2.13 Route table after the 1st iteration

For the second iteration, you consider any improvements obtained by travelling via B. As before, you can highlight the 2nd row and column, and consider only the remaining cells.

To: From:	A	B	C	D
A	–	1	5	∞
B	1	–	3	∞
C	∞	3	–	10
D	2	3	7	–

Table 2.14 Distance table before the 2nd iteration

You see that the following improvements can be made:

AC(5) can be replaced by AB(1) + BC(3) = 4
CA(∞) can be replaced by CB(3) + BA(1) = 4
DC(7) can be replaced by DB(3) + BC(3) = 6

To: From:	A	B	C	D
A	–	1	[4]	∞
B	1	–	3	∞
C	[4]	3	–	10
D	2	3	[6]	–

Table 2.15 Distance table after the 2nd iteration

To obtain the new route table, you look along to column B (in the previous route table), to see the first step on the journey from A to C (which is now going via B): this is just B (from cell AB). Similarly, for the journey from C to A. However, for the journey from D to C, note that the first step is now A (from cell DB).

To: From:	A	B	C	D
A	A	B	[B]	D
B	A	B	C	D
C	[B]	B	C	D
D	A	A	[A]	D

Table 2.16 Route table after the 2nd iteration

ACTIVITY 2.6

Perform the next two iterations (the answers are given over the page).

It may help to consider how the route from D to C has evolved so far. Initially you went directly from D to C (with a distance of 10). Then you found an improvement by going via A: this was the route DAC (with a distance of 2 + 5 = 7). And then you found a further improvement by going via B: this was the route DABC (with a distance of 2 + 1 + 3 = 6). This route via B has A as its first step. Having gone to A, the latest version of the route table (in cell AC) tells us to go B next, and then cell BC tells us to go straight to C.

To: From:	A	B	C	D
A	–	1	4	∞
B	1	–	3	∞
C	4	3	–	10
D	2	3	6	–

Table 2.17 Distance table before the 3rd iteration

To: From:	A	B	C	D
A	–	1	4	[14]
B	1	–	3	[13]
C	4	3	–	10
D	2	3	6	–

Table 2.18 Distance table after the 3rd iteration

To: From:	A	B	C	D
A	A	B	B	[B]
B	A	B	C	[C]
C	B	B	C	D
D	A	A	A	D

Table 2.19 Route table after the 3rd iteration

To: From:	A	B	C	D
A	–	1	4	14
B	1	–	3	13
C	4	3	–	10
D	2	3	6	–

Table 2.20 Distance table before the 4th iteration

To: From:	A	B	C	D
A	–	1	4	14
B	1	–	3	13
C	4	3	–	10
D	2	3	6	–

Table 2.21 Distance table after the 4th iteration (no changes)

To: From:	A	B	C	D
A	A	B	B	B
B	A	B	C	C
C	B	B	C	D
D	A	A	A	D

Table 2.22 Route table after the 4th iteration (no changes)

It can be shown that, having considered routes via each of A, B, C and D, this will then give the best solution.

The final distance and route tables can be checked against the network. For example, the shortest route from A to D is ABCD, and the route table confirms that the first step from A to D is B; then the first step from B to D is C; and the first step from C to D is just D.

Exercise 2.4

① Apply Floyd's algorithm to the networks represented by the following matrices in (i) and (ii).

(i)

	1	2	3	4
1	–	9	–	3
2	9	–	2	–
3	–	2	–	2
4	3	–	2	–

Table 2.23

(ii)

	1	2	3	4	5	6	7	8
1	–	9	–	3	–	–	–	–
2	9	–	2	–	7	–	–	–
3	–	2	–	2	4	8	6	–
4	3	–	2	–	–	–	5	–
5	–	7	4	–	–	10	–	9
6	–	–	8	–	10	–	7	12
7	–	–	6	5	–	7	–	10
8	–	–	–	–	9	12	10	–

Table 2.24

② Apply Floyd's algorithm to the following networks in (i), (ii) and (iii).

(i)

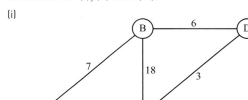

Figure 2.27

(ii)

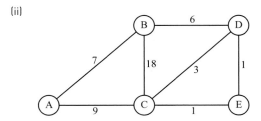

Figure 2.28

(iii)

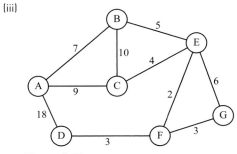

Figure 2.29

5 The travelling salesperson problem

In Chapter 1 a Hamiltonian cycle was defined as one that visits all of the nodes of a network exactly once and which returns to the starting point (another name for a Hamiltonian cycle is a **tour**). In the travelling salesperson problem, the aim is to find the shortest route that visits all of the nodes **at least once**. It may be that this route is a Hamiltonian cycle (i.e. where the nodes are not repeated), but the overriding priority is for the length to be minimised.

Consider, for example, the networks in Figure 2.30 and Figure 2.31.

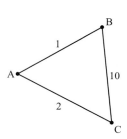

Figure 2.30

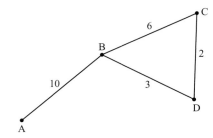

Figure 2.31

Note

The reason for the significance of the Hamiltonian cycle is that some of the algorithms that can be employed (and which you will be looking at shortly) are designed for Hamiltonian cycles.

In Figure 2.30, a Hamiltonian cycle exists (e.g. ABCA), but you are better off with ABACA, in order to minimise the length.

In Figure 2.31, if A is to be the start and end point, then you cannot avoid repeating B, so that the route will not be a Hamiltonian cycle.

A problem is said to be **classical** if the aim is to find a Hamiltonian cycle (i.e. no node is to be repeated), and it is called **practical** if each node is to be visited **at least** once before returning to the start.

However, a practical problem can always be converted to a classical one by the following device.

- For each pair of nodes in the network, establish the shortest distance between them (which may be along an indirect path).

- Then create a complete graph with the given nodes and attach these shortest distances to the appropriate arcs.

Note

When determining the shortest route between two nodes, the 'triangle inequality' in Geometry is sometimes referred to. This states that in the triangle ABC, $AC \leq AB + BC$. Applying this loosely to networks, we find the shortest route by looking for instances where the triangle inequality does not hold; i.e. where the shortest route involves $AB + BC$, instead of AC, and using this to make improvements to the route. Alternatively, Dijkstra's algorithm can be applied.

For example, the network in Figure 2.30 becomes the one in Figure 2.32, whilst the network in Figure 2.31 becomes the one in Figure 2.33.

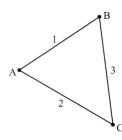

Figure 2.32

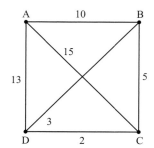

Figure 2.33

Unfortunately, there is no one algorithm that will enable you to find a shortest route. However, various methods exist for improving on a route that has already been found (i.e. one which passes through all the nodes, but is not of the shortest possible length).

The length associated with a route that has been found is called an **upper bound**, and so the aim is to reduce the upper bound.

There is also a method for finding a **lower bound** for the shortest distance. Once the upper bound is sufficiently close to the lower bound, you may decide that further effort is not worthwhile.

Finding an initial upper bound

Example 2.7

The network showing the distances in miles between various cities is repeated in Figure 2.34. Find a Hamiltonian cycle that is an upper bound for the optimal tour.

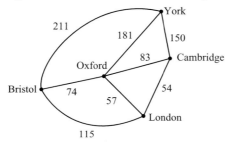

Figure 2.34

Solution

Three possible routes (with their total lengths) are as follows.
BYOCLB (211 + 181 + 83 + 54 + 115 = 644)
BYCOLB (211 + 150 + 83 + 57 + 115 = 616)
BOYCLB (74 + 181 + 150 + 54 + 115 = 574) ◄── The shortest length cannot be greater than 574, as you have already found a route of this length.
The upper bound (so far) is 574.

Finding a lower bound

You will now look at a method for finding a lower bound (often referred to as the **lower bound algorithm**). This method is only guaranteed to work if the network is complete.

Example 2.8

Use the lower bound algorithm to find a lower bound for a Hamiltonian cycle in the network shown in Figure 2.34.

Solution

Any Hamiltonian cycle will consist of two arcs from (say) B, together with three arcs linking O, L, C and Y.

The shortest possible total length of the two arcs from B is $74 + 115 = 189$.

To find the shortest possible total length of the arcs linking O, L, C and Y, you can find the minimum connector for these nodes.

By removing arcs in decreasing order, the length of the minimum connector for O, L, C and Y is found to be

$$(181 + 150 + 83 + 57 + 54) - 181 - 83 = 261.$$

Therefore the shortest possible total length of all the arcs (and a lower bound for a Hamiltonian cycle) is $189 + 261 = 450$.

So far, for the network shown in Figure 2.34, it has been established that the shortest possible length of a route that visits all the vertices lies between 450 and 574.

Further lower bounds can be established by dividing up the nodes differently. If node O is isolated instead of B, then the shortest possible total length of the two arcs from O is $57 + 74 = 131$, and using Kruskal's algorithm, for example, for the remaining nodes, you obtain a length of $54 + 115 + 150 = 319$, so that the lower bound is $131 + 319 = 450$ (again).

Isolating the other nodes in turn gives

L + BOCY: $(54 + 57) + (74 + 83 + 150) = 418$

C + BOLY: $(54 + 83) + (57 + 74 + 181) = 449$

Y + BOLC: $(150 + 181) + (54 + 57 + 74) = 516.$

The value of 516 supersedes the other, lower values: although it is true that the shortest route cannot be lower than 418, it is also true that it cannot be lower than 516.

You now have a lower bound of 516 and an upper bound of 574.

Using the nearest neighbour algorithm to find an upper bound

The **nearest neighbour algorithm** is a systematic way of finding a solution (and hence an upper bound). The method is only guaranteed to work if the network is complete.

Refer to Figure 2.34 again.

(i)   Start at any node (e.g. B).
(ii) Add the shortest arc leading to a new node: BO.
(iii) Repeat the process, to give BO + OL + LC + CY.

(iv)   Return directly to the start node, to give the cycle

BOLCYB $(74 + 57 + 54 + 150 + 211 = 546)$

(v)   Repeat the algorithm, with other starting points.

OLCYBO $(57 + 54 + 150 + 211 + 74 = 546)$

LCOBY: can't return to L.

CLOBY: can't return to C.

YCLOBY $(150 + 54 + 57 + 74 + 211 = 546)$

In general, you take the lowest of the values obtained.
You now have a lower bound of 516 and an upper bound of 546.
Therefore the solution is written as

> [This is not a solution if it does not give a tour.] →

$516 \leqslant$ optimal solution $\leqslant 546$

← [This will be a tour and it may be the optimal solution.]

It is easy to confuse Prim's algorithm with the nearest neighbour algorithm.
Make sure you know the difference.

Discussion point

→ What are the differences between the nearest neighbour algorithm and Prim's algorithm?

The nearest neighbour algorithm is another example of a 'greedy' algorithm.
You saw earlier that Prim's and Kruskal's are greedy algorithms. It doesn't usually give the best possible solution.

Solutions obtained by applying an algorithm can sometimes be improved on.

A possible **tour improvement algorithm** can be illustrated by referring to Figure 2.34 again. The three possibilities that were mentioned earlier were

BYOCLB $(211 + 181 + 83 + 54 + 115 = 644)$

BYCOLB $(211 + 150 + 83 + 57 + 115 = 616)$

BOYCLB $(74 + 181 + 150 + 54 + 115 = 574)$.

Note that BYOCLB is improved by swapping O and C, or by swapping Y and O. The algorithm consists of examining each sequence of four nodes, and seeing if an improvement can be obtained by swapping the middle two nodes.

Using computer language, the algorithm could be written as follows (where N_i denotes the ith node, and d denotes distance between nodes).

For $i = 1$ to n
If $d(N_i, N_{i+2}) + d(N_{i+1}, N_{i+3}) < d(N_i, N_{i+1}) + d(N_{i+2}, N_{i+3})$ then swap N_{i+1} and N_{i+2}
Next i

Example 2.9

Apply the lower bound algorithm to the network in Figure 2.35, by isolating Exeter.

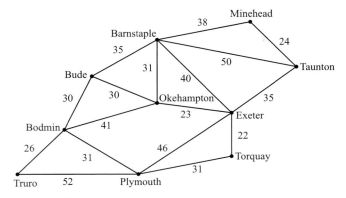

Figure 2.35

Solution

Exclude Exeter and all arcs connected to it.

Then find a minimum connector for the nodes that remain.

You can remove arcs in decreasing order, as follows (ensuring that the network remains connected).

Tru–Ply 52

Bar–Tau 50

Bod–Oke 41

Bud–Bar 35

This leaves the following arcs in the minimum connector.

Tor–Ply 31

Ply–Bod 31

Bod–Tru 26

Bod–Bud 30

Bud–Oke 30

Oke–Bar 31

Bar–Min 38

Min–Tau 24

The total weight is 241.

The two shortest arcs leading from Exeter are 22 and 23: add these to the total weight of the minimum connector.

So the lower bound for the length of the tour is $241 + 22 + 23 = 286$.

> ### Note
> ----------------
> The lower bound is made as high as possible (i.e. as close to the upper bound as possible) to reduce the interval in which the optimal solution lies.
>
> If the lower bound is equal to the upper bound, then the solution is optimal.

ACTIVITY 2.7

Apply the nearest neighbour algorithm to the network in Figure 2.35, with Taunton as the starting point.

Exercise 2.5

① Apply the lower bound algorithm to the network in Figure 2.10 (repeated in Figure 2.36), isolating each of the nodes in turn. What is the lower bound that it produces?

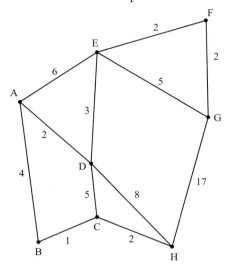

Figure 2.36

② Apply the nearest neighbour algorithm to the network in Figure 2.36, considering each of the nodes as a possible starting point. What is the upper bound that it produces?

③ Apply the lower bound algorithm to the network in Figure 2.37 (from question 3 of Exercise 2.1), isolating each of the nodes in turn. What is the lower bound?

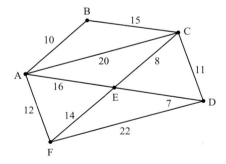

Figure 2.37

④ Apply the nearest neighbour algorithm to the network in Figure 2.37, considering each of the nodes as a possible starting point.

⑤ For the network in Figure 2.38, create the table of weights associated with the complete network obtained by finding the shortest distance between each pair of nodes (i.e. converting a practical problem to a classical problem).

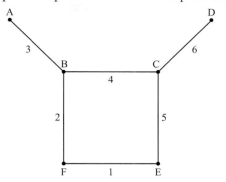

Figure 2.38

⑥ A group of tourists staying in Weston wishes to visit all the places shown on the following map.

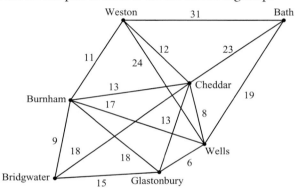

Figure 2.39

(i) Suggest a route that will minimise their total driving distance.

(ii) A tree has blocked the road between Weston and Cheddar, making it impassable for the whole day. Suggest an alternative route that will result in the least extra driving distance.

⑦ A depot located in Birmingham supplies goods to customers in Sheffield, Nottingham, Stoke, Shrewsbury, Hereford, Gloucester and Northampton.

(i) Plan a suitable route for the delivery lorry if it has to make deliveries in all of these towns on one trip. The distances involved are shown in Table 2.25 (overleaf).

(ii) Suggest two reasons why the shortest route may not be the best route for the lorry.

	Birmingham	Sheffield	Nottingham	Stoke	Shrewsbury	Hereford	Gloucester	Northampton
Birmingham	–	77	50	43	43	52	52	50
Sheffield	77	–	37	47	79	125	128	94
Nottingham	50	37	–	50	79	102	102	57
Stoke	43	47	50	–	34	83	89	85
Shrewsbury	43	79	79	34	–	52	75	93
Hereford	52	125	102	83	52	–	28	91
Gloucester	52	128	102	89	75	28	–	72
Northampton	50	94	57	85	93	91	72	–

Table 2.25

LEARNING OUTCOMES

Now you have finished this chapter, you should be able to

➤ understand and use the language of networks, including: node, arc and weight

➤ solve network optimisation problems using spanning trees

➤ find the shortest route between two nodes of a network using either Dijkstra's algorithm or Floyd's algorithm

➤ solve route inspection problems

➤ find and interpret upper bounds and lower bounds for the travelling salesperson problem

➤ evaluate, modify and refine models that use networks.

KEY POINTS

1 A network is a weighted graph.

2 The minimum connector problem is solved by creating a spanning tree with the minimum weight. The following methods can be employed.

- Remove arcs in order of decreasing weight.
- Apply Prim's algorithm.
- Apply Kruskal's algorithm.

3 Prim's algorithm can be applied to the table of weights.

4 Dijkstra's algorithm provides a procedure for determining the shortest route between two particular nodes of a network.

5 Floyd's algorithm finds the shortest route between every pair of nodes of a network.

6 The route inspection problem is to find the shortest route that covers all of the arcs at least once – returning to the starting point, if required. The problem is solved by classifying networks as:

- Eulerian if they have no odd nodes
- semi-Eulerian if they have two odd nodes
- neither Eulerian nor semi-Eulerian if they have four or more odd nodes.

7 The travelling salesperson problem is to find the shortest route that visits all of the nodes of a network at least once, returning to the starting point.

8 A problem is said to be classical if you aim to find a Hamiltonian cycle, and is practical otherwise. A practical problem can always be converted into a classical one.

9 The shortest possible route can be placed within bounds by applying the lower bound algorithm and the nearest neighbour algorithm.

10 Computers may employ a tour improvement algorithm.

3

Critical path analysis

→ Each morning Paul makes toast using a grill. The grill can take two slices of bread at a time and takes 1 minute to toast each side of the bread. How long does it take Paul to toast three slices of bread?

1 Constructing an activity network

Critical path analysis uses networks to help schedule projects involving a number of activities, some of which require other activities to take place before they can begin.

The starting point is the **precedence table** (also known as a dependence table), as shown in Table 3.1.

Activity	Immediately preceding activities	Duration (hours)
A	–	4
B	–	5
C	A, B	6
D	B	2
E	B	4
F	C, D	3
G	C, D, E	1

Table 3.1

From this you can construct a network that places the activities in their correct relation to each other, i.e. taking account of the precedences.

There are two conventions that can be adopted for the network. The one that you will employ in this chapter is called **activity-on-arc**. The alternative convention is called activity-on-node.

In this chapter, you will be using the terms nodes and arcs, rather than vertices and edges.

Example 3.1

Draw the network for the precedence table shown in Table 3.1.

Solution

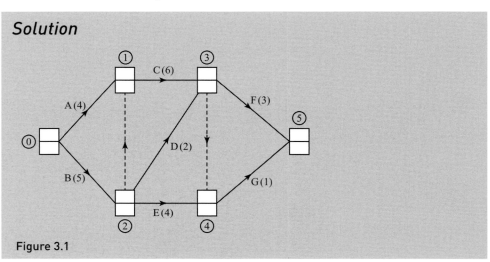

Figure 3.1

The network for the precedence table given in Table 3.1 is shown in Figure 3.1. The activities (on the arcs) lead into the nodes, which are referred to as **events**. The events are assigned two boxes, which will be explained shortly. The dotted lines, referred to as **dummy activities**, will also be explained shortly.

Events can only start once the activities that lead into them have been completed. For example, activity F can only start once activities C and D have been completed, and the event labelled 3 takes account of this.

Activity B needs to be completed before C, D and E can start, but this creates a problem. Suppose that you connect up the arcs as shown in Figure 3.2.

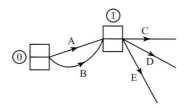

Figure 3.2

Although B leads into C, D and E, as required, Figure 3.2 implies that D and E depend on A, which is not correct.

Another issue is that, in Figure 3.2, A and B share both a start node and an end node. This creates a problem because activities are usually identified by their start and end nodes (by a computer, for example).

You get round both of these problems by creating a dummy arc leading from event 2 to event 1. Informally, you can think of a message being sent from event 2 to event 1, to say that the activities leading into event 2 have been completed.

The dummy arc leading from event 3 to event 4 represents the fact that G depends on both C and D, as well as E.

Dummy activities have duration zero.

Note that event 5 has been created to represent the end of the project. Only activities F and G need lead into it, as the other activities all lead into F or G, either directly or indirectly.

Determining earliest and latest event times

You are usually concerned with how soon the whole process can be completed. This is determined by making a **forward pass** through the network, recording the **earliest** (or **early**) **event times**.

Look at the network in Figure 3.1 in Example 3.1.

- Event 0 is given an earliest event time of 0.
- Event 1 cannot start until 5 hours have elapsed, in order that both the activities A and B have been completed. So 5 is entered in the upper box for event 1.
- 5 is entered in the upper box for event 2, as this only depends on activity B.
- Event 3 has to wait until 6 hours after event 1 has started, and also 2 hours after event 2 has started; i.e. not before $5 + 6 = 11$ and $5 + 2 = 7$ hours have elapsed, i.e. 11 hours.

ACTIVITY 3.1

How could the network be changed if activity G is no longer dependent on activity C?

Note

Whereas the route inspection and travelling salesperson problems involve an individual (for example) travelling through the network, so that they can only be in one place at a time, critical path analysis typically involves a number of people working simultaneously on different activities, so that different parts of the network are in operation at the same time.

- Event 4 has to wait until 4 hours after event 2 has started, and also until event 3 has started; i.e. not before 5 + 4 = 9 and 11 hours have elapsed, i.e. 11 hours.

- Finally, event 5 has to wait until 3 hours after event 3 has started, and also until 1 hour after event 4 has started; i.e. not before 11 + 3 = 14 and 11 + 1 = 12 hours have elapsed, i.e. 14 hours.

Figure 3.3 shows the situation once all the earliest event times have been determined. The whole process can be completed in 14 hours. This is the **minimum completion time** (or **critical time**).

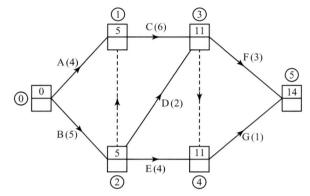

Figure 3.3

Some of the activities may have some slack available. For example, A could be delayed by up to 1 hour without increasing the duration of the project. Those activities that don't have any slack available are called **critical activities**.

In order to establish the extent of any available slack, you carry out a **backward pass**, starting at the end node.

- Place a 14 in the lower box for event 5, to indicate its **latest** (or **late**) **event time**.

- As activity G has a duration of 1, the latest time at which event 4 could end, in order to complete event 5 by time 14, is 13, which is therefore the latest event time.

- For event 3 it is 11, in order to complete event 4 by time 13 and event 5 by 14.

- For event 1 it is 5, in order to complete event 3 by time 11.

- For event 2 it is 5, in order to complete event 1 by time 5.

- And finally you expect the latest event time for event 0 to be 0.

Figure 3.4 shows the situation once all the latest event times have been determined.

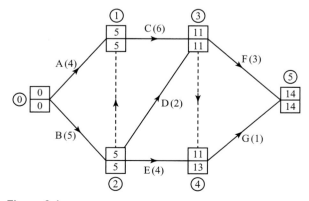

Figure 3.4

① Draw an activity-on-arc network to represent the following project.

Activity	Immediate predecessors	Duration
A	–	5
B	A	2
C	–	8
D	A, C	12
E	B, C	6

Table 3.2

② The table shows the precedences for the four tasks of a project. The duration of each task is also shown.

Task	Immediate predecessors	Duration (days)
A	–	2
B	–	1
C	A	1
D	A, B	3

Table 3.3

Draw an activity-on-arc network for the project, showing the earliest and latest event times. Give the minimum completion time.

Explain why a dummy activity is needed in the network.

③ Draw the activity-on-arc network for the project with the activities listed below.

Show the earliest and latest event times.

Activity	Immediate predecessors	Duration (days)
A	–	8
B	–	4
C	A	2
D	A	10
E	B	5
F	C, E	3

Table 3.4

④ The table shows the activities involved in building a short length of road to bypass a village. The table gives their durations and their immediate predecessors.

	Activity	Immediate predecessors	Duration (weeks)
A	Survey sites	–	8
B	Purchase land	A	22
C	Supply materials	–	10
D	Supply machinery	–	4
E	Excavate cuttings	B, D	9
F	Build bridges and embankments	B, C, D	11
G	Lay drains	E, F	9
H	Lay hardcore	G	5
I	Lay bitumen	H	3
J	Install road furniture	E, F	10

Table 3.5

Draw an activity-on-arc network for these activities, showing the earliest and latest event times. Give the minimum completion time.

⑤ A construction project involves nine activities. Their immediate predecessors and durations are listed in the table.

Activity	Immediate predecessors	Duration (days)
A	–	5
B	–	3
C	–	6
D	A	2
E	A, B	3
F	C, D	5
G	C	1
H	E	2
I	E, G	4

Table 3.6

Draw an activity-on-arc network for the project, showing the earliest and latest event times. Give the minimum completion time.

2 Critical paths and Gantt charts

Having found the earliest and latest event times (EET and LET), you can now establish the **earliest start and latest finish times** for the activities (be careful not to confuse these similar sounding terms). Note that the latest finish time means the latest time by which the activity must finish, in order not to affect the project completion time.

First of all, you can identify each activity by its start node i and end node j, writing (i, j).

Consider the part of a network involving activity (i, j), shown in Figure 3.5.

Figure 3.5

The earliest start time for (i, j) is 4 (in general, EET_i).

The latest finish time for (i, j) is 13 (in general, LET_j).

> The (total) **float** of an activity is the available slack, and is equal to (latest finish time − earliest start time) − duration of activity

In the example above, the float is $(13 - 4) - 2 = 7$.

> A **critical activity** has zero float.

This will only be possible if $\mathrm{LET}_i = \mathrm{EET}_i$, $\mathrm{LET}_j = \mathrm{EET}_j$, and $\mathrm{EET}_j = \mathrm{EET}_i + \text{duration}$.

Example 3.2

Establish the critical activities and floats for the network shown in Figure 3.4.

Solution

A: float of $5 - 0 - 4 = 1$

B: float of $5 - 0 - 5 = 0$; critical activity

C: float of $11 - 5 - 6 = 0$; critical activity

D: float of $11 - 5 - 2 = 4$

E: float of $13 - 5 - 4 = 4$

F: float of $14 - 11 - 3 = 0$; critical activity

G: float of $14 - 11 - 1 = 2$

ACTIVITY 3.2

Given that all of the activities in the network shown in Figure 3.4 over-run by 1 hour, find the new minimum completion time for the project.

The critical activities B, C and F form a path through the network, leading from the start to the end. Such a **critical path** will always exist, though there may be more than one.

The length of the critical path is the minimum completion time of the project. If there is more than one such path, they will all have the same length. These paths are the longest possible paths in the network (linear programming methods can use this property to solve critical path analysis problems).

It may be the case that the completion time of the project has to be reduced, and that this can be achieved by using extra workers to reduce the durations of the critical activities. This is sometimes referred to as **crashing the network**. Any such reductions may change the activities that make up the critical path.

Example 3.3

Table 3.7 shows the costs of reducing the durations of each of the activities in Example 3.1 by 1 hour, as well as the minimum duration that is possible for each activity.

Activity	Original duration (hours)	Cost of reducing duration by 1 hour	Minimum duration possible
A	4	£100	2
B	5	£200	4
C	6	£100	3
D	2	£300	1
E	4	£200	1
F	3	£200	2
G	1	–	1

Table 3.7

Suppose that it is necessary to complete the project as quickly as possible. Work out the extra cost involved in doing this.

Solution

One way of tackling this problem is to repeat the original process, using the minimum durations, and then to increase the durations of any non-critical activities.

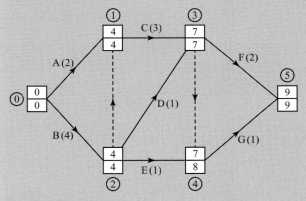

Figure 3.6

The new minimum completion time is 9 hours.

A: float of 2   E: float of 3
B: critical activity   F: critical activity
C: critical activity   G: float of 1
D: float of 2

You can now increase the durations of the non-critical activities, in order not to incur unnecessary costs. The results are shown in Table 3.8. Note that, for activities D and E, there is no need to increase the duration above the original figures.

Activity	Original duration (hours)	Cost of reducing duration by 1 hour	Minimum duration possible	New duration	Extra cost
A	4	£100	2	4	£0
B	5	£200	4	4	£200
C	6	£100	3	3	£300
D	2	£300	1	2	£0
E	4	£200	1	4	£0
F	3	£200	2	2	£200
G	1	–	1	1	£0

Table 3.8

The total extra cost is £700.

In addition to establishing the critical activities of an operation, it will usually be important to take account of the resources (people and equipment) required at different stages, and to try to make use of them in the most efficient way.

Example 3.4

Draw a **Gantt** (or cascade) **chart** to display the activities shown in the network in Figure 3.4 on page 60.

Solution

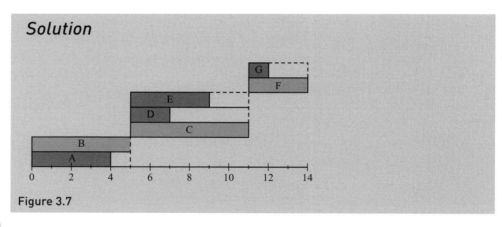

Figure 3.7

> ### Note
>
> Sometimes not all of the information about precedences can easily be reflected in the Gantt chart. For example, if activity A has to precede activity B, then if A is delayed it may also be necessary to delay B. Vertical dotted lines are sometimes introduced, to show the constraints on activities, but they may be difficult to interpret.

Gantt charts can be constructed in slightly different ways, but generally have the following features.

■ Activities are represented by horizontal bars, beginning at their earliest start times.

■ Each activity should be drawn on a separate line. However, critical activities can be drawn on a single horizontal line.

■ The bars are divided into two parts: the length of the first part is the duration of the activity, whilst the length of the second part is its float (the second part can be indicated by shading or a dotted border).

■ The number of workers required for an activity may be shown on the bar.

One use of the Gantt chart is to establish which activities definitely have to be taking place at a given point in time, i.e. activities that can't be shifted away from a particular vertical line.

Exercise 3.2

① A project is described in the table below.

Activity	Duration (days)	Immediate predecessors
A	8	–
B	4	–
C	2	A
D	10	A
E	5	B
F	3	C, E

Table 3.9

The duration of any of the activities can be reduced at a cost, as given in the table below.

Activity	Minimum duration	Cost (£) for each day by which duration is reduced
A	2	50
B	2	100
C	1	40
D	5	60
E	4	25
F	2	10

Table 3.10

Which activity durations should be reduced, and by how many days, to reduce the minimum project completion time by

(i)   2 days

(ii)   7 days

at minimum cost?

② Find the total float for each activity in this project.

Activity	Duration	Immediate predecessors
A	2	–
B	1	–
C	1	A
D	3	A, B

Table 3.11

[MEI adapted]

③ The activities involved in cooking a meal of toad-in-the-hole, potatoes and cabbage, followed by apple pie and custard, are shown in Table 3.12.

	Activity	Duration (mins)	Immediate predecessors
A	Grill sausages	8	–
B	Make batter	6	–
C	Make apple pie	15	–
D	Prepare potatoes	6	–
E	Prepare cabbage	4	–
F	Cook sausages and batter together	35	A, B
G	Cook potatoes	25	D
H	Cook cabbage	8	E
I	Cook apple pie	30	C
J	Make custard	8	–

Table 3.12

(i)   Draw an activity network to represent this project.

(ii)   Find the minimum project completion time, assuming that there are enough people available to carry out the activities.

(iii)   Which activities are critical?

④ The activity network below shows the durations (in days) of the nine activities of a project and the activities that precede them.

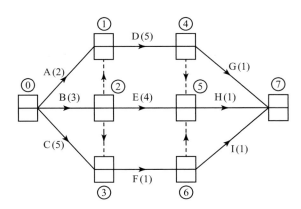

Figure 3.8

(i)   Produce a table showing, for each activity, the immediately preceding activities.

(ii)   Find the earliest start time and latest finish time for each activity. List the critical activities and give the minimum completion time.

(iii)   Draw a Gantt chart, given that all activities are scheduled to start as early as possible.

3 Using Gantt charts

A **resource histogram** can be drawn, based on the Gantt chart. It shows the number of workers required at any given time.

Example 3.5

Suppose that the activities of the network shown in Figure 3.4 on page 60 require the following numbers of workers.

A: 2   B: 3   C: 1   D: 5   E: 2   F: 4   G: 2

Draw the resource histogram based on the Gantt chart shown in Figure 3.7 on page 64.

ACTIVITY 3.3

Work out a timetable for each of the eight workers needed, according to this resource histogram. This timetable is called a **scheduling diagram**.

Solution

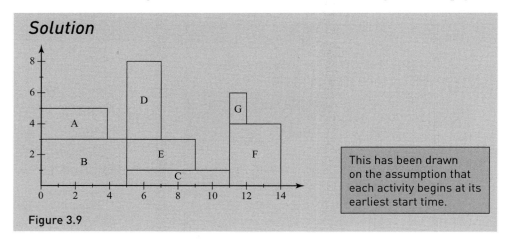

This has been drawn on the assumption that each activity begins at its earliest start time.

Figure 3.9

Resource problems

A factory is likely to employ a workforce on a full-time basis, and will want to keep its workers occupied, as far as possible. It wants to avoid taking on expensive temporary workers. For these reasons, it is desirable to smooth out the number of workers required over the duration of a project. This is referred to as **resource levelling**. It is an example of a **heuristic procedure** (when the solution is likely to be reasonably good, but is not guaranteed to be optimal).

The first step is to examine the resource histogram, to see if the floats allow activities to be shuffled around, in order to limit the number of workers required, without exceeding the critical time.

In the case of Figure 3.9 it is possible to schedule tasks D and E so they follow each other rather than being done in parallel. This gives the resource histogram in Figure 3.10.

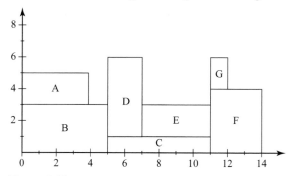

Figure 3.10

This means a maximum of six workers is needed, rather than eight. To reduce this further the duration of the project would need to be extended, or the activities modified to alter the precedences.

The lowest possible value for this limit can be established by considering areas in the resource histogram. The best you can hope for is that the resource levelling produces a rectangle, with an area equal to the sum of the areas of the blocks in the original resource histogram. This sum is

$$\sum(\text{duration of activity} \times \text{number of workers required for the activity})$$

where $\sum$ denotes summation over all the activities.

The height of the (ideal) rectangle is then obtained by dividing the area by the base, which is the critical time. A lower bound for the number of workers is obtained by rounding the height of the rectangle up to the nearest integer.

Once the resources have been allocated, the scheduling diagram may be constructed.

Note

The scheduling diagram gives a timetable for the project. Each worker is assigned a particular task at any given time (provided there is work available).

Example 3.6

Referring to the project in Example 3.1:

(i) Find the lowest possible value for the workforce needed in the case of Table 3.13.

(ii) Construct a scheduling diagram for the Gantt chart shown in Figure 3.11.

Solution

(i)

Activity	Duration (hours)	Workers needed	Duration × number of workers
A	4	2	8
B	5	3	15
C	6	1	6
D	2	5	10
E	4	2	8
F	3	4	12
G	1	2	2
			Total = 61

Table 3.13

This project is the same one as in Example 3.1 and so the minimum completion time is 14 hours.

The area of the ideal rectangle is $8 + 15 + 6 + 10 + 8 + 12 + 2 = 61$.

Dividing by the critical time gives $61 \div 14 = 4.36$

So a workforce of 5 is the smallest number needed. →

Note

However, as you have seen, the actual workforce needed is 6. This is close to the lower bound and may be acceptable in order not to increase the duration.

(ii) There is an indication of the number of workers required and it is clear what should be being done when.

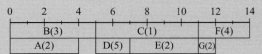

Figure 3.11

> ◀ **Note**
> --
> You will notice there are some similarities between the scheduling diagram and the Gantt chart and resource histogram. The critical activities are usually placed in one line, separate from the non-critical activities, so that it is easier to see where the project may over-run and where there is some float-time still available.

Exercise 3.3

① Harry wants to decorate a room. The activities involved are given in the table, together with their durations and immediate predecessors.

	Activity	Duration (days)	Immediate predecessors
A	Remove old wallpaper	1	–
B	Prepare wooden surfaces	0.25	–
C	Paint ceiling	0.75	A
D	Apply undercoat	1	A, B
E	Apply gloss paint	1	D
F	Paper walls	1	C, E

Table 3.14

(i) Represent the project as an activity network.

Harry decides to decorate three rooms. The activities, durations and predecessors for each room are as in the table above. Harry will be helped by his friend Nisha, but activities cannot be shared between Harry and Nisha.

(ii) Show how Harry and Nisha can decorate the three rooms when they only have 8 days available. [MEI adapted]

② Table 3.15 shows some information about the activities involved in a project.

(i) Calculate the minimum time in which this project can be completed and determine which activities are critical.

(ii) Calculate the float of the non–critical activities.

(iii) Draw a Gantt chart for the project.

(iv) Describe in detail the effect on the project if only five workers are available, each of whom can carry out any of the activities.

③ The table shows activities involved in a construction project, their durations, and their immediate predecessors.

	Activity	Immediate predecessors	Duration (weeks)
A	Obtain planning permission	–	6
B	Survey site	–	2
C	Dig foundations	A, B	6
D	Lay drains	A, B	3
E	Access work	A	10
F	Plumbing	C, D	2
G	Framework	C	6
H	Internal work	E, F, G	4
I	Brickwork	G	3

Table 3.16

Activity	A	B	C	D	E	F	G	H	I	J	K	L	M	N
Duration (days)	1	2	4	3	14	14	16	12	14	10	5	4	6	3
Immediate predecessors	–	A	B	A	C	C	C	D, G	D, G	D, G	H	I	J	E, F, K, L, M
Number of workers	1	1	1	1	1	2	2	2	3	1	1	2	1	2

Table 3.15

(i)   Draw an activity network for the project.

(ii)   Perform a forward pass and a backward pass to find earliest and latest event times. Give the critical path and the minimum time to completion.

(iii)   The contractor winning the contract has only one JCB (a digging machine) available. This is needed for activities C (digging foundations) and D (laying drains). Decide whether or not the contractor can complete the project within the minimum time found in (ii). Give reasons and working to support your conclusion.   [MEI]

④   The table shows the activities involved in a project, their durations, and their immediate predecessors.

Activity	A	B	C	D	E	F	G	H
Duration (days)	1	2	1	1	4	2	3	2
Immediate predecessors	–	–	A	B	B	C, D	E, F	E

Table 3.17

(i)   Draw an activity-on-arc network for the project.

(ii)   Perform a forward pass and a backward pass on your network to determine the earliest and latest event times. State the minimum time for completion and the activities forming the critical path.

(iii)   Draw a Gantt chart for the project, given that all the activities are scheduled to start as early as possible.

(iv)   The number of people needed for each activity is as follows.

Activity	A	B	C	D	E	F	G	H
People	1	4	2	3	1	2	3	2

Table 3.18

Activities C and F are to be scheduled to start later than their earliest start times so that only five people are needed at any one time, whilst the project is still completed in the minimum time. Specify the scheduled start times for activities C and F.   [MEI]

LEARNING OUTCOMES

Now you have finished this chapter, you should be able to

➤ construct, represent and interpret a precedence (activity) network using activity-on-arc

➤ understand the use of dummies and interpret them

➤ determine earliest and latest event times for an activity network

➤ determine earliest start and latest finish times for an activity

➤ identify critical activities, critical paths and the floats of non-critical activities

➤ refine models and understand the implications of possible changes in the context of critical path analysis

➤ construct and interpret Gantt (cascade) charts and resource histograms

➤ carry out resource levelling (using heuristic procedures) and evaluate problems where resources are restricted

➤ construct and modify schedules.

KEY POINTS

1 Critical path analysis uses networks to help schedule projects involving a number of activities.
2 Based on a precedence table, an activity-on-arc network is constructed.
3 Forward and backward passes are made to determine earliest and latest event times, and the minimum completion time.
4 A critical path is established.
5 Extra resources may be employed to reduce the durations of the critical activities.
6 Gantt charts and resource histograms can be used to display the activities.
7 Resource levelling may be employed to limit the number of workers used.

Linear programming

Tout est pour le mieux dans le meilleur des mondes possibles.

Voltaire, Candide

→ Think about a product that you might make to sell at a fundraising event. What factors affect how much profit you can make?

Formulating constrained optimisation problems

Linear programming is a way of solving logistical problems involving linear constraints, as in the following example.

Example 4.1

Millie bakes some cakes for a village fete. She makes cupcakes and chocolate cakes. She sells both types of cake for £1 each.

Each cupcake uses 2 units of sugar and 6 units of flour, and each chocolate cake uses 3 units of sugar and 5 units of flour.

She has only 12 units of sugar and 30 units of flour, and wants to make as much money as possible.

Formulate this as a linear programming problem.

> This is a **constrained optimisation** problem, and the first step is to formulate the constraints mathematically.

Solution

Let x be the number of cupcakes to be made, and y the number of chocolate cakes. The two constraints involving the ingredients become

$2x + 3y \leqslant 12$ (sugar)

$6x + 5y \leqslant 30$ (flour).

Also, $x \geqslant 0, y \geqslant 0$. ← The values of x and y can't be negative.

The total value of sales is $x \times 1 + y \times 1$, and so

$P = x + y$ is the **objective function** that you wish to maximise.

The variables x and y are referred to as the **control variables**.

1 Solving linear programming problems

The cake problem from Example 4.1 can be represented graphically, as shown in Figure 4.1.

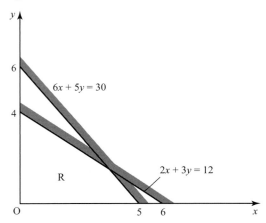

Figure 4.1

The region R in Figure 4.1 is the **feasible region**, where all the constraints are satisfied.

Note that it is the unwanted areas that are shaded. This makes it easier to identify the feasible region – especially where there are a number of constraints.

You now find which points of the feasible region maximise P.

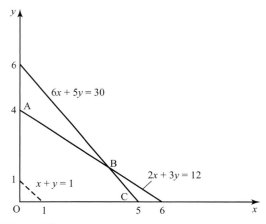

Figure 4.2

> **Note**
>
> It can help to use a ruler to represent the moving line, but if it still isn't obvious which vertex is required, you can evaluate the objective function at each vertex, to find the one with the largest value for P.

In Figure 4.2, the line $P = x + y$ is parallel to $x + y = 1$, and needs to be as far away from O as possible, in order to maximise P.

You need to visualise the objective line $x + y = 1$ being moved away from O, keeping its gradient the same, and find the point at which it is about to leave the feasible region. Therefore the maximum value of P will occur at one of the **vertices** (i.e. corners) of the feasible region (unless the line $P = x + y$ has the same gradient as one of the constraint lines). In this example it is B.

Example 4.2

Find the optimal solution for the following linear programming problem.

Maximise $P = x + y$
subject to $2x + 3y \leqslant 12$
$\qquad\qquad 6x + 5y \leqslant 30$
$\qquad\qquad x \geqslant 0,\ y \geqslant 0.$

Solution

Look at Figure 4.2.

At B, the lines $6x + 5y = 30$ ① and $2x + 3y = 12$ ② intersect.

Solve these simultaneously.

$3 \times$ ② $-$ ① $\Rightarrow 4y = 6 \Rightarrow y = \frac{3}{2}$

Then ② $\Rightarrow 2x = 12 - \frac{9}{2} \Rightarrow x = 6 - \frac{9}{4} = \frac{15}{4}$

$\Rightarrow P = x + y = \frac{21}{4} = 5.25$ at B $(3.75, 1.5)$.

At A, $P = 4$, and at C, $P = 5$, which confirms that B is the required vertex, so the optimal solution is $x = 3.75$ and $y = 1.5$.

In some contexts, non–integer solutions may be possible.

However, for the problem given in Example 4.1, only integer values are acceptable as x and y represent numbers of cakes. In this case, you need to consider integer points neighbouring $(3.75, 1.5)$, provided they are within the feasible region.

Example 4.3

Solve the linear programming problem given in Example 4.2 if the values of x and y can only take integer values.

Solution

The constraints are that

$6x + 5y \leqslant 30$ and $2x + 3y \leqslant 12$.

Maximise $P = x + y$.

Considering integer points neighbouring $(3.75, 1.5)$ gives

$(3, 1)$: $6x + 5y = 23$ and $2x + 3y = 9$; $P = 4$

$(3, 2)$: $6x + 5y = 28$ and $2x + 3y = 12$; $P = 5$

$(4, 1)$: $6x + 5y = 29$ and $2x + 3y = 11$; $P = 5$ ⟶ (4, 2) is not in the feasible region.

$(4, 2)$: $6x + 5y = 34$ (reject)

Note

(5, 0), vertex C, also gives $P = 5$, so 5 cupcakes is another solution that maximises the objective function, but with only one type of cake!

The points $(3, 2)$ and $(4, 1)$ give equally good solutions. However, that does not guarantee that this is the optimal solution.

Always state the solution in terms of the context of the problem.

So, in order to maximise the total value of sales, the output of cakes should be either 3 cupcakes and 2 chocolate cakes, or 4 cupcakes and 1 chocolate cake.

Instead of maximising sales or profit, you may want to minimise costs, for example. It may be possible to create a feasible region in this case, depending on the constraints.

Example 4.4

Create a feasible region for the following linear programming problem and use the objective line method to find the vertex that gives the optimal solution.

Minimise $P = 2x + y$
subject to $3x + 4y \geqslant 24$
$y \leqslant 3x$
$x \geqslant 0, y \geqslant 3$

Solution

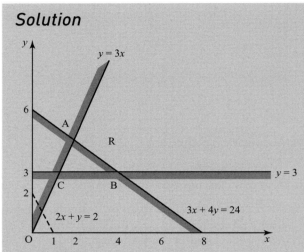

Figure 4.3

Figure 4.3 shows the feasible region, R.

In this case, the line $P = 2x + y$ needs to be parallel to $2x + y = 2$, but as near to the origin as possible.

The diagram shows that P is minimised at A.

ACTIVITY 4.1

Find the optimal solution for the linear programming problem given in Example 4.4, assuming that non-integer solutions are allowed.

Exercise 4.1

① Solve the following linear programming problem.

Maximise $\quad P = x + 2y$
subject to $\quad 4x + 5y \leqslant 45$
$4x + 11y \leqslant 44$
$x + y \leqslant 6.$

② A farmer grows two crops: wheat and beet. The number of hectares of wheat, x, and the number of hectares of beet, y, must satisfy

$10x + 3y \leqslant 52$
$2x + 3y \leqslant 18$
$y \leqslant 4.$

Determine the values of x and y for which the profit function, $P = 7x + 8y$, is a maximum. State the maximum value of P.

③ A robot can walk at $1.5\,\mathrm{m\,s^{-1}}$ or run at $4\,\mathrm{m\,s^{-1}}$. When walking it consumes power at 1 unit per metre, and when running it consumes power at three times this rate. If its batteries are charged to 9000 units, what is the greatest distance it can cover in half an hour?

④ A builder can build either luxury houses or standard houses on a plot of land. Planning regulations prevent the builder from building more than 30 houses altogether, and he wants to build at least 5 luxury houses and at least 10 standard houses. Each luxury house requires $300\,\mathrm{m^2}$ of land, and each standard house requires $150\,\mathrm{m^2}$ of land. The total area of the plot is $6500\,\mathrm{m^2}$.

Given that the profit on a luxury house is £14 000 and the profit on a standard house is £9000, find how many of each type of house he should build to maximise his profit.

⑤ Maximise $z = x + y$
   subject to $3x + 4y \leq 12$
   $2x + y \leq 4$
   x integer, y integer.

⑥ The Chief Executive of Leschester City Football Club plc has up to £4 million to spend following a good cup run. He has to decide on spending priorities.

Money needs to be spent on strengthening the playing squad and on extra support facilities (i.e. non-playing staff and stadium facilities).

The Coach, who is popular with the fans, has said that he will resign unless he gets at least £2 million to spend on new players.

The authorities require that at least £0.6 million be spent to remedy stadium deficiencies affecting crowd safety.

Club policy is that the amount to be spent on support facilities must be at least one quarter of the amount to be spent on the playing squad.

(i)   Let £x million be the amount to be spent on the playing squad and let £y million be the amount to be spent on support facilities. Write down four inequalities in terms of x and y representing constraints on spending.

(ii) Draw a graph to illustrate your inequalities.

(iii) Find the maximum amount that may be spent on the playing squad.

A report commissioned from a market research company indicates that fans regard both team performance and facilities as being important. The report states that the function $0.8x + 0.2y$ gives a measure of satisfaction with extra expenditure.

The Chief Executive proposes to spend £2.5 million on the playing squad and £1.5 million on support facilities.

(iv) Calculate the measure of satisfaction corresponding to the Chief Executive's proposals.

(v)   Add to your graph the line $0.8x + 0.2y = 2.3$, and explain what points on this line represent.

(vi) The Coach argues that the Chief Executive can achieve the same satisfaction score by spending less in total, but more on the playing squad. How much less and how much more?

[MEI]

⑦ Two products, X and Y, require three ingredients, A, B and C, for their manufacture. Table 4.1 summarises the amounts required and how much of each is available.

		Resource A	Resource B	Resource C
Amount required per unit of product	Product X	15	10	8
	Product Y	5	7	12
Amount available		600	560	768

Table 4.1

It is required to maximise the total output of the two products subject to the amounts available.

(i)   Identify variables and formulate an appropriate linear programming problem.

(ii) Solve your linear programming problem graphically, and interpret the solution.

(iii) The amount of B available is increased by 16. Show that the total output can be increased by 1 unit.

(iv) The amount of B available is increased by a further 16. Show that the total output cannot be increased any further.   [MEI]

⑧ Coal arrives at a coal preparation plant from an opencast site and from a deep mine. It is to be mixed to produce a blend for an industrial customer. The customer requires 20 000 tonnes per week of the blend, and will pay £20 per tonne. Deep-mined coal has a marginal cost of £10 per tonne and coal from the opencast site has a marginal cost of £5 per tonne.

The blend must contain no more than 0.17% chlorine, since otherwise the hydrochloric acid produced by burning would corrode the boilers.

The blend must contain no more than 2% sulphur, since this burns to produce sulphur dioxide which subsequently dissolves to give acid rain. Acid rain damages the environment.

The blend must produce no more than 20% ash when burnt, otherwise the boilers will clog.

The blend must contain no more than 10% water, since otherwise the calorific value is affected.

The deep-mined coal has a chlorine content of 0.2%, a sulphur content of 3%, ash of 35% and water 5%. The opencast coal has a chlorine content of 0.1%, sulphur of 1%, ash of 10% and a water content of 12%.

How much of each type of coal should be blended to satisfy the contract with maximum profit? Which constraint is critical and which constraints are redundant?

⑨ A furniture manufacturer produces tables and chairs. A table requires £20 worth of materials and 10 person hours of work. It sells for a profit of £15.

Each chair requires £8 of materials and 6 hours of work. The profit on a chair is £7.

Given that £480 and 300 worker hours are available for the next production batch, find how many tables and chairs should be produced to maximise the profit.

Why might the optimal solution not be a practical solution?

⑩ A clothing retailer stocks two types of jacket which cost her £10 and £30 to purchase. She sells them at £20 and £50 respectively. She needs to order at least 200 jackets and has £2700 to spend.

The cheaper jackets need 20 cm of hanging space. The expensive jackets need only 10 cm each. She has 40 m of hanging space.

(i)   Formulate a linear programming problem, assuming that all the jackets will be sold and that the retailer wishes to maximise her profit.

(ii) Solve the problem using a graphical method.

(iii) What would be the effect of trying to increase the order to satisfy a 10% increase in the demand for jackets? Explain your answer.

2 The Simplex algorithm

The Simplex algorithm provides an algebraic method for dealing with linear programming problems, suitable for use by a computer. It can also deal with problems involving more than two variables, which can't be represented graphically.

Example 4.5

Apply the Simplex algorithm to the linear programming problem from Example 4.1.

> This problem involves two variables only.

Solution

First convert the inequalities into equations. $2x + 3y \leqslant 12$ becomes $2x + 3y + s_1 = 12$, where $s_1 \geqslant 0$ is known as a **slack variable**.

The larger the value of s_1, the further you are from the constraint line, and the greater the amount of slack available.

> Slack variables are needed to turn inequalities into equations.

Including the objective function, the equations are

$$P - x - y \qquad\qquad = 0 \quad ①$$
$$2x + 3y + s_1 \qquad = 12 \quad ②$$
$$6x + 5y \qquad + s_2 = 30 \quad ③ \qquad\qquad (s_1, s_2 \geqslant 0)$$

Note

This is the expected form of presentation, but it can be awkward to read to start with. The method will be explained using the equations.

Note

Here it was chosen to set $x = 0$, but you could have chosen y, or any variable with a negative coefficient in the equation of the objective function (including in fact slack variables).

The ratio test ensures you are working within the feasible region.

These equations are set up so that all the variables appear on the left-hand side. The equations can also be presented using the **Simplex tableau**, as shown in Table 4.2.

P	x	y	s_1	s_2	Value	Equation
1	−1	−1	0	0	0	①
0	2	3	1	0	12	②
0	6	5	0	1	30	③

Table 4.2

Start with an initial 'solution' of $x = 0, y = 0$. This satisfies the equations above, and gives $P = 0, s_1 = 12, s_2 = 30$.

It corresponds to O in the feasible region in Figure 4.2.

To find a better solution, that gives a larger value for P, you notice that you can (for example) set $x = 0$, so that equations ① − ③ become

$P = y, 3y + s_1 = 12$ and $5y + s_2 = 30$.

This corresponds to working along the y-axis.

You now want to make y as large as possible. Noting the restriction that s_1 and s_2 have to be $\geqslant 0$, it will be possible to set y equal to the lower of $\frac{12}{3}$ and $\frac{30}{5}$, i.e. 4.

This step is referred to as the **ratio test**.

This gives $P = 4, x = 0, y = 4, s_1 = 0$ and $s_2 = 10$, which corresponds to vertex A of the feasible region. This is a feature of the Simplex method, where there are just two control variables. You are working your way round the vertices of the feasible region until no further improvement can be made.

Where the equation for the objective row is $P - 3x - 2y = 5$, for example, it is conventional to aim to maximise x (setting $y = 0$), because this gives the best chance of maximising P, on the grounds that, out of a choice of $5 + 3x$ and $5 + 2y, 5 + 3x$ is more likely to be the larger (though this may not prove to be the case).

Continuing with y as the variable to be maximised, the y column in the Simplex tableau is called the **pivot column**, and the row that provides the maximum value of y from the ratio test is called the **pivot row**. In this example, this is the row corresponding to equation ②.

The pivot row is used to consolidate the improvement in P, as follows.

The aim is to eliminate y from all of the rows except the pivot row. You use a method that a computer can easily apply. You first divide both sides of equation ② by 3, so that the coefficient of y becomes 1. Equation ② is now

$$\frac{2x}{3} + y + \frac{s_1}{3} = 4 \quad \text{②a}$$

Now eliminate y from equation ①, by adding equation ②a to equation ①, to give

$$P - \frac{x}{3} + \frac{s_1}{3} = 4$$

Notice that, by setting x and s_1 equal to zero, you can obtain the improved value of $P = 4$.

$\rightarrow$

You also eliminate y from equation ③, by subtracting 5 times equation ②ⓐ, to give

$$\frac{8x}{3} - \frac{5s_1}{3} + s_2 = 10.$$

To summarise, the new equations are (relabelling ②ⓐ as ⑤)

$$P - \frac{x}{3} \quad + \frac{s_1}{3} \quad = 4 \qquad ④ = ① + ⑤$$

$$\frac{2x}{3} + y + \frac{s_1}{3} \quad = 4 \qquad ⑤ = ② ÷ 3$$

$$\frac{8x}{3} \quad - \frac{5s_1}{3} + s_2 = 10 \qquad ⑥ = ③ - 5 × ⑤.$$

The Simplex tableau is now as follows.

P	x	y	s_1	s_2	Value	Equation
1	$-\frac{1}{3}$	0	$\frac{1}{3}$	0	4	④
0	$\frac{2}{3}$	1	$\frac{1}{3}$	0	4	⑤
0	$\frac{8}{3}$	0	$-\frac{5}{3}$	1	10	⑥

Table 4.3

Note that y now appears only once in the pivot column, with a coefficient of 1. Any value chosen for y will not affect the rows in which this variable has a zero coefficient. Similarly, for P and s_2. These variables are termed **basic** variables, whilst the variables that have coefficients in more than one row are termed **non-basic**.

At the end of each stage of the Simplex method, you can obtain the (current) improved solution by setting the non-basic variables to zero. This means that the values of the basic variables will be those in the right-hand column.

So $P = 4$, $x = 0$, $y = 4$, $s_1 = 0$ and $s_2 = 10$.

This corresponds to point A on the graphical representation.

> **Note**
>
> Although the solution has been improved, there is still scope for further improvement, as can be seen from the fact that there is a negative coefficient of x in the (new) objective row of the tableau.

Example 4.6

Apply a second iteration of the Simplex algorithm, to obtain an improved value for P.

Solution

Take x as the pivot column, and apply the ratio test. You see that equation ⑤ gives $\frac{4}{\left(\frac{2}{3}\right)} = 6$, whilst equation ⑥ gives $\frac{10}{\left(\frac{8}{3}\right)} = \frac{15}{4} < 6$.

> Always show your working for the ratio test and write down the pivot row.

So equation ⑥ is the pivot row.

Ensure that the coefficient of x is 1, then obtain new equations by eliminating x from ④ and ⑤, giving

$$P + \quad \frac{s_1}{8} + \frac{s_2}{8} = \frac{21}{4} \qquad ⑦ = ④ + \frac{1}{3} × ⑨$$

$$y + \frac{3s_1}{4} - \frac{s_2}{4} = \frac{3}{2} \qquad ⑧ = ⑤ - \frac{2}{3} × ⑨$$

$$x - \frac{5s_1}{8} + \frac{3s_2}{8} = \frac{15}{4} \qquad ⑨ = \frac{3}{8} × ⑥.$$

The Simplex tableau is now as follows.

P	x	y	s_1	s_2	Value	Equation
1	0	0	$\frac{1}{8}$	$\frac{1}{8}$	$\frac{21}{4}$	⑦
0	0	1	$\frac{3}{4}$	$-\frac{1}{4}$	$\frac{3}{2}$	⑧
0	1	0	$-\frac{5}{8}$	$\frac{3}{8}$	$\frac{15}{4}$	⑨

Table 4.4

Now P, x and y are the basic variables, and the improved solution is

$$P = \frac{21}{4}, x = \frac{15}{4}$$

$$y = \frac{3}{2}, s_1 = 0 \text{ and } s_2 = 0,$$

which corresponds to vertex B of the feasible region.

As the coefficients of s_1 and s_2 in the objective row are both positive, there is no further scope for increasing P.

> Note that the value for y has reduced from 4 to $\frac{3}{2}$; i.e. the maximum value wasn't needed in the end.

In the previous example, the aim was to maximise P. If, instead, you wish to minimise P, then this can sometimes be done by maximising $-P$ as in the following example. This also features three control variables (and so couldn't be solved by a graphical method). At this point, a couple of restrictions on the Simplex method should be mentioned. Firstly, inequalities need to be of the form $2x + 3y \leqslant 12$, rather than $2x + 3y \geqslant 12$. This ensures that the initial solution $x = 0, y = 0$ satisfies the constraints. (There are variations of the Simplex method that allow for $\geqslant$ inequalities: the 'two-stage' Simplex and the 'big M' method, which are covered in the next section.) Secondly, when the equations are set up for the constraints, the values on the right-hand side need to be non-negative. This ensures that the ratio test can be carried out in the same way each time. This doesn't apply to the objective row.

Example 4.7

Minimise $2x + y - 3z$, subject to the following constraints.

$x - 4y + z \leqslant 4$

$3x + 2y - z \geqslant -2$

$x \geqslant 0, y \geqslant 0, z \geqslant 0$

> **Note**
>
> Notice that $(0, 0, 0)$ is a feasible solution, which can be taken as the starting point.

Solution

Step 1 Rewrite the problem as

Maximise $P = -2x - y + 3z$

subject to $x - 4y + z \leqslant 4$

and $-3x - 2y + z \leqslant 2$.

> Note that the inequalities are now of the $\leqslant$ type, and that the right-hand values are non-negative.

Step 2 Create equations, with slack variables.

$$P + 2x + y - 3z \qquad\qquad = 0 \quad ①$$
$$x - 4y + z + s_1 \qquad = 4 \quad ②$$
$$-3x - 2y + z \qquad + s_2 = 2 \quad ③$$

Step 3 Represent the equations in a Simplex tableau.

P	x	y	z	s_1	s_2	Value	Equation
1	2	1	−3	0	0	0	①
0	1	−4	1	1	0	4	②
0	−3	−2	1	0	1	2	③

Table 4.5

Step 4 Choose z as the pivot column (as it is the only variable in the objective row with a negative coefficient), and apply the ratio test.

② with $x = y = s_1 = 0 \Rightarrow z = 4$

③ with $x = y = s_2 = 0 \Rightarrow z = 2$

As $2 < 4$, ③ is the pivot row (indicated by circling the coefficient of z in equation ③ in the table below).

P	x	y	z	s_1	s_2	Value	Equation
1	2	1	−3	0	0	0	①
0	1	−4	1	1	0	4	②
0	−3	−2	①	0	1	2	③

Table 4.6

Step 5 Eliminate z from equations ① and ②.

P	x	y	z	s_1	s_2	Value	Equation
1	−7	−5	0	0	3	6	④ = ① + 3 × ⑥
0	4	−2	0	1	−1	2	⑤ = ② − ⑥
0	−3	−2	1	0	1	2	⑥ = ③

Table 4.7

Step 6 As x now has the largest negative coefficient in the new objective row (equation ④), you choose this as the next pivot column.

You would normally apply the ratio test now, but you note that the coefficient of x in equation ⑥ is negative. As explained in the following note (which you may wish to omit on a first reading), any such row can be excluded when establishing the pivot row.

Note

The ratio test

In Step 6 of Example 4.7, you are trying to maximise x, so that when y and s_2 are set equal to zero in equation ④, P (equal to $6 + 7x$) will be increased by as much as possible.

When maximising x you need to ensure that all the constraint equations are satisfied. For equation ⑤, you set s_1 equal to zero (you have already set y and s_2 to zero in equation ④), to leave you with $4x = 2$. This places an upper limit of $\frac{2}{4} = \frac{1}{2}$ on x (x could be less than $\frac{1}{2}$, as it would always be possible to introduce another slack variable, giving $4x + s_3 = 2$).

In equation ⑥, the coefficient of x is negative, and this row cannot be chosen as the pivot row: such a choice would require us to subtract a multiple of the pivot row from the objective row (in order to eliminate x from it), and this would cause the value of the objective row to fall. This assumes that the values in the right-hand column of the constraint rows are non-negative (which is a requirement of the method). So, when applying the ratio test, you only need to consider constraint equations where the coefficient of the pivot variable is positive.

So you take the pivot row to be equation ⑤, and divide by 4 before eliminating x from the other equations, to give equations ⑦–⑨.

P	x	y	z	s_1	s_2	Value	Equation
1	−7	−5	0	0	3	6	④ = ① + 3 × ⑥
0	④	−2	0	1	−1	2	⑤ = ② − ⑥
0	−3	−2	1	0	1	2	⑥ = ③

Table 4.8

P	x	y	z	s_1	s_2	Value	Equation
1	0	$-8\frac{1}{2}$	0	$1\frac{3}{4}$	$1\frac{1}{4}$	$9\frac{1}{2}$	⑦ = ④ + 7 × ⑧
0	1	$-\frac{1}{2}$	0	$\frac{1}{4}$	$-\frac{1}{4}$	$\frac{1}{2}$	⑧ = ⑤ ÷ 4
0	0	$-3\frac{1}{2}$	1	$\frac{3}{4}$	$\frac{1}{4}$	$3\frac{1}{2}$	⑨ = ⑥ + 3 × ⑧

Table 4.9

Step 7 There are no further variables that have negative coefficients in the objective row and positive coefficients elsewhere in their columns, so you have reached the end of the process.

The variables with a single 1 (and otherwise zeros) in their columns are the basic variables, and their values can be read off the right-hand column, whilst the other (non-basic) variables are set to zero.

Solution: $x = 0.5$, $y = 0$, $z = 3.5$, $s_1 = 0$, $s_2 = 0$.

The maximised value of $-2x - y + 3z$ is 9.5 and so the minimised value of $2x + y - 3z$ is −9.5.

Step 8 Check:
$x - 4y + z = 4$ ($\leqslant 4$) and $3x + 2y - z = -2$ ($\geqslant -2$).

Exercise 4.2

① Use the Simplex algorithm to solve the following linear programming problem.

Maximise $P = 9x + 10y + 6z$

subject to $2x + 3y + 4z \leqslant 3$

$6x + 6y + 2z \leqslant 8$

$x \geqslant 0, y \geqslant 0, z \geqslant 0.$

② Use the Simplex algorithm to solve the following linear programming problem.

Maximise $P = 3w + 2x$

subject to $w + x + y + z \leqslant 150$

$2w + x + 3y + 4z \leqslant 200$

$w \geqslant 0, x \geqslant 0, \ y \geqslant 0, z \geqslant 0.$

③ Use the Simplex algorithm to solve the following linear programming problem.

Maximise $P = 3w + 2x$

subject to $w + x + y + z \leqslant 150$

$2w + x + 3y + 4z \leqslant 200$

$w \geqslant x$ (rewrite this as $x - w \leqslant 0$)

$w \geqslant 0, x \geqslant 0, y \geqslant 0, z \geqslant 0.$

④ The 'Cuddly Friends Company' produces soft toys. For one day's production run it has available $11\,m^2$ of furry material, $24\,m^2$ of woolly material and 30 glass eyes. It has three soft toys that it can produce:

The 'Cuddly Aardvark', each of which requires $0.5\,m^2$ of furry material, $2\,m^2$ of woolly material and two eyes. Each sells at a profit of £3.

The 'Cuddly Bear', each of which requires $1\,m^2$ of furry material, $1.5\,m^2$ of woolly material and two eyes. Each sells at a profit of £5.

The 'Cuddly Cat', each of which requires $1\,m^2$ of furry material, $1\,m^2$ of woolly material and two eyes. Each sells at a profit of £2.

An analyst formulates the following linear programming problem to find the production plan that maximises profit.

Maximise $\quad 3a + 5b + 2c$

subject to $\quad 0.5a + b + c \leqslant 11$

$\qquad\qquad 2a + 1.5b + c \leqslant 24$

$\qquad\qquad 2a + 2b + 2c \leqslant 30$

(i) Explain how this formulation models the problem, and say why the analyst has not simplified the last inequality to $a + b + c \leqslant 15$.

(ii) The final constraint is different from the others in that the resource is integer valued. Explain why that does not impose an additional difficulty for this problem.

(iii) Solve this problem using the Simplex algorithm.

Interpret your solution and say what resources are left over. [MEI adapted]

⑤ A publisher is considering producing three books over the next week: a mathematics book, a novel and a biography. The mathematics book will sell at £10 and costs £4 to produce. The novel will sell at £5 and costs £2 to produce. The biography will sell at £12 and costs £5 to produce. The publisher wants to maximise profit, and is confident that all books will be sold.

There are constraints on production. Each copy of the mathematics book needs 2 minutes of printing time, 1 minute of packing time, and $300\,cm^3$ of temporary storage space.

Each copy of the novel needs 1.5 minutes of printing time, 0.5 minutes of packing time, and $200\,cm^3$ of temporary storage space.

Each copy of the biography needs 2.5 minutes of printing time, 1.5 minutes of packing time, and $400\,cm^3$ of temporary storage space.

There are 10000 minutes of printing time available on several printing presses, 7500 minutes of packing time, and $2\,m^3$ of temporary storage space.

(i) Explain how the following initial feasible tableau models this problem.

P	x	y	z	s_1	s_2	s_3	Value
1	−6	−3	−7	0	0	0	0
0	2	1.5	2.5	1	0	0	10000
0	1	0.5	1.5	0	1	0	7500
0	300	200	400	0	0	1	2000000

Table 4.10

(ii) Use the Simplex algorithm to solve your linear programming problem, and interpret your solution.

(iii) The optimal solution involves producing just one of the three books. By how much would the price of each of the other books have to be increased to make them worth producing? [MEI adapted]

3 Advanced Simplex methods

The basic Simplex method assumes that all the constraints are of the $\leqslant$ type (apart from $x \geqslant 0$, $y \geqslant 0$ etc.).

A constraint such as $3x + 2y - z \geqslant -2$ can just be rewritten as $-3x - 2y + z \leqslant 2$, but the constraint $3x + 2y - z \geqslant 2$ could not be dealt with in this way, as it would leave us with a negative value on the right-hand side, and the Simplex procedure requires the values on the right-hand side to be positive.

Another issue is that, in some cases, the feasible region does not contain the origin, and this means that you cannot start the procedure with the provisional solution $x = 0$, $y = 0$.

There are two methods for dealing with these problems: the two-stage Simplex method and the big M (Simplex) method.

These advanced Simplex methods also enable us to cope with constraints that are expressed as equalities (for example, $x + y = 10$), by writing them as a pair of inequalities ($x + y \leqslant 10$ and $x + y \geqslant 10$).

The two-stage Simplex method

Example 4.8

Maximise $P = x + y$

subject to $2x + 3y \leqslant 12$

$6x + 5y \leqslant 30$

$x + y \geqslant 4$

Solution

The feasible region is shown in Figure 4.4 and does not contain the origin.

You create slack variables as usual, but introduce a temporary artificial variable for the $x + y \geqslant 4$ constraint (explained below).

$$P - x - y = 0 \qquad \text{①}$$

$$2x + 3y + s_1 = 12 \qquad \text{②}$$

$$6x + 5y + s_2 = 30 \qquad \text{③}$$

$$x + y - s_3 + a_1 = 4 \qquad \text{④}$$

$$(s_1, s_2, s_3, a_1 \geqslant 0)$$

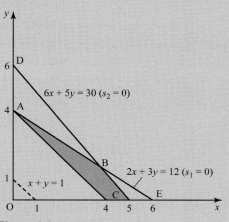

Figure 4.4

> **Note**
>
> Here the slack variable s_3 is referred to as a **surplus** variable. It corresponds to the surplus produced from the sum of x and y, and so has to be subtracted.

a_1 is needed because $x + y - s_3 = 4$ doesn't allow $x = y = 0$, since $s_3 \geqslant 0$; but with the artificial variable you can now start with $x = y = s_3 = 0$ and $a_1 = 4$.

Initial solution:

$x = y = s_3 = 0$; $s_1 = 12$, $s_2 = 30$, $a_1 = 4$, $P = 0$.

The aim is to minimise a_1, so that (if possible) the solution moves into the feasible region. This is the first stage of the process.

Create a new objective: minimise $A = a_1$.

From ④, rewrite $A = a_1$ as $A + x + y - s_3 = 4$ ⑤

Relabelling the rows:

> **Note**
>
> It might seem a bit unnecessary to create another variable with the same value as a_1, but it enables the method to be extended easily to cases where there are two or more artificial variables, as seen later.

A	P	x	y	s_1	s_2	s_3	a_1	Value	Equation
1	0	1	1	0	0	−1	0	4	①
0	1	−1	−1	0	0	0	0	0	②
0	0	2	3	1	0	0	0	12	③
0	0	6	5	0	1	0	0	30	④
0	0	1	1	0	0	−1	1	4	⑤

Table 4.11

Referring to the Simplex tableau above:

1st row: new objective (1st stage of method)

2nd row: original objective (2nd stage of method)

$\rightarrow$

Each stage of the method involves applying the ordinary Simplex method.

To minimise A: the positive coefficients of x and y mean that x or y could be increased (as $A + x + y - s_3 = 4$, this would cause A to be reduced). Alternatively, you could maximise $-A$, as you did before.

Choose x as the pivot column (for example) and apply the ratio test:

3rd row: $\frac{12}{2} = 6$, 4th row: $\frac{30}{6} = 5$, 5th row: $\frac{4}{1} = 4$

Thus the pivot row is row 5.

A	P	x	y	s_1	s_2	s_3	a_1	Value	Equation
1	0	0	0	0	0	0	−1	0	⑥ = ① − ⑩
0	1	0	0	0	0	−1	1	4	⑦ = ② + ⑩
0	0	0	1	1	0	2	−2	4	⑧ = ③ − 2 × ⑩
0	0	0	−1	0	1	6	−6	6	⑨ = ④ − 6 × ⑩
0	0	1	1	0	0	−1	1	4	⑩ = ⑤

Table 4.12

As $A = 0$ (referring to the value on the right-hand side), the 1st stage has been successfully completed.

Now remove the 1st row, and the columns for A and a_1 (a_1 is a non-basic variable and is being set to 0).

Solution so far: $x = 4$, $y = 0$, $P = 4$.

The 2nd stage is now to maximise P, in the usual way. You may like to complete this as an exercise. (The solution is $x = \frac{15}{4}$, $y = \frac{3}{2}$, $P = \frac{21}{4}$.)

The big M (Simplex) method

This starts off in the same way as the two-stage method, to give the same equations as before:

$$P - x - y = 0 \qquad ①$$
$$2x + 3y + s_1 = 12 \qquad ②$$
$$6x + 5y + s_2 = 30 \qquad ③$$
$$x + y - s_3 + a_1 = 4 \qquad ④$$

$(s_1, s_2, s_3, a_1 \geqslant 0)$

You now modify the objective to:

maximise $P = x + y - Ma_1$,

where M is a large number (e.g. 1000).

This ensures that minimising a_1 is given first priority, as the Ma_1 term has the largest effect on P.

Then rewrite as $P = x + y - M(4 - x - y + s_3)$,

giving $P - (1 + M)x - (1 + M)y + Ms_3 = -4M$,

and the Simplex tableau becomes

P	x	y	s_1	s_2	s_3	a_1	Value	Equation
1	$-(1+M)$	$-(1+M)$	0	0	M	0	$-4M$	①
0	2	3	1	0	0	0	12	②
0	6	5	0	1	0	0	30	③
0	①	1	0	0	-1	1	4	④

Table 4.13

> **Note**
>
> To minimise $P = x + y$ instead, modify to minimising $x + y + Ma_1$ (instead of maximising $x + y - Ma_1$).

You now carry out the Simplex method as usual, and you should find that the right-hand value of the objective row becomes free of M.

Choose x as the pivot column (for example) and apply the ratio test:

2nd row: $\frac{12}{2} = 6$, 3rd row: $\frac{30}{6} = 5$, 4th row: $\frac{4}{1} = 4$ (as before).

> **Note**
>
> Artificial variables may be needed for more than one constraint. In this case, let
> $A = a_1 + a_2 + \ldots$ for the two-stage Simplex method, and have
> $-M(a_1 + a_2 + \ldots)$ in place of $-Ma_1$ for the big M method.

P	x	y	s_1	s_2	s_3	a_1	Value	Equation
1	0	0	0	0	-1	$1 + M$	4	⑤ = ① + (1+M) × ⑧
0	0	1	1	0	2	-2	4	⑥ = ② − 2 × ⑧
0	0	-1	0	1	6	-6	6	⑦ = ③ − 6 × ⑧
0	1	1	0	0	-1	1	4	⑧ = ④

Table 4.14

Now that M only appears in the a_1 column, you can remove that column, arriving at the same tableau as at the end of the 1st stage of the two-stage method (and then continue as before).

Exercise 4.3

① Use the two-stage Simplex method to solve the following linear programming problem.

Maximise $P = 16x + 24y$

subject to $2x + 3y \leq 24$

$\quad\quad\quad 2x + y \leq 16$

$\quad\quad\quad x \geq 0, 2 \leq y \leq 6$.

② Use the two-stage Simplex method to solve the following linear programming problem.

Maximise $P = 9x + 10y + 6z$

subject to $2x + 3y + 4z \leq 3$

$\quad\quad\quad 6x + 6y + 2z \leq 8$

$\quad\quad\quad x + y + z \geq 1$

$\quad\quad\quad x \geq 0, y \geq 0, z \geq 0$.

③ Use the two-stage Simplex method to solve the following linear programming problem.

Maximise $P = 3w + 2x$

subject to $w + x + y + z \leq 150$

$\quad\quad\quad 2w + x + 3y + 4z \leq 200$

$\quad\quad\quad y + z \geq 50, w \geq 0, x \geq 0,$

$\quad\quad\quad y \geq 0, z \geq 0$.

④ Use the two-stage Simplex method to solve the following linear programming problem.

Maximise $P = 3w + 2x$

subject to $w + x + y + z \leq 150$

$\quad\quad\quad 2w + x + 3y + 4z \leq 200$

$\quad\quad\quad w \geq x$ (rewrite this as $x - w \leq 0$)

$\quad\quad\quad y + z \geq 50, w \geq 0, x \geq 0, y \geq 0, z \geq 0$.

⑤ Use the big M method to solve the following linear programming problem.

Maximise $P = 16x + 24y$

subject to $2x + 3y \leqslant 24$

$2x + y \leqslant 16$,

$x \geqslant 0, 2 \leqslant y \leqslant 6$.

⑥ Use the big M method to solve the following linear programming problem.

Maximise $P = 9x + 10y + 6z$

subject to $2x + 3y + 4z \leqslant 3$

$6x + 6y + 2z \leqslant 8$

$x + y + z \geqslant 1$

$x \geqslant 0, y \geqslant 0, z \geqslant 0$.

⑦ Use the big M method to solve the following linear programming problem.

Maximise $P = 3w + 2x$

subject to $w + x + y + z \leqslant 150$

$2w + x + 3y + 4z \leqslant 200$

$y + z \geqslant 50$

$w \geqslant 0, x \geqslant 0, y \geqslant 0, z \geqslant 0$.

⑧ Use the big M method to solve the following linear programming problem.

Maximise $P = 3w + 2x$

subject to $w + x + y + z \leqslant 150$

$2w + x + 3y + 4z \leqslant 200$

$w \geqslant x$ (rewrite this as $x - w \leqslant 0$)

$y + z \geqslant 50, w \geqslant 0, x \geqslant 0, y \geqslant 0, z \geqslant 0$.

LEARNING OUTCOMES

Now you have finished this chapter, you should be able to

➤ formulate constrained optimisation problems

➤ solve constrained optimisation problems via graphical methods

➤ use the Simplex algorithm for optimising (maximising and minimising) an objective function, including the use of slack variables

➤ interpret a Simplex tableau

➤ use the two-stage and big M Simplex methods.

KEY POINTS

1 Linear programming is concerned with solving logistical problems involving linear constraints – constrained optimisation problems.

2 The first step is to formulate the constraints mathematically.

3 The objective function is the item that you wish to maximise (or minimise).

4 The feasible region is the region of the graph where all the constraints are satisfied.

5 The objective function is generally maximised (or minimised) at one of the vertices of the feasible region.

6 Neighbouring points may need to be considered if an integer-valued solution is required.

7 The Simplex algorithm provides an algebraic method for dealing with linear programming problems.

   ■ Inequalities are converted into equations using slack variables.

   ■ A Simplex tableau can be used to standardise the process.

   ■ At each stage of the process, a pivot column is established, and the ratio test is used to identify the pivot row.

   ■ After each stage, the values of any basic variables can be read from the tableau, and the non-basic variables are set to zero.

8 The two-stage and big M Simplex methods both introduce a surplus variable and a temporary artificial variable to cope with $\geqslant$ inequalities.

5

Allocation problems

→ The times (in minutes) taken by four workers A–D to complete four tasks P–S are shown in the table below. Find an allocation of workers to tasks (where each worker carries out a different task), such that the overall time is minimised.

	P	Q	R	S
A	6	4	7	5
B	5	3	6	5
C	4	8	6	7
D	5	9	7	6

Table 5.1

1 Cost matrix reduction

Allocation (or assignment) problems are an extension of matching problems where, for example, a number of workers are each to be allocated a particular task. In the matching problem, you take account of the fact that a particular worker may only be able to do certain tasks. In the allocation problem, each worker can often carry out any of the tasks, but will take a certain amount of time to perform each task.

Example 5.1

Three workers (A, B and C) are to carry out three tasks (P, Q and R). The times they take for the tasks (in minutes) are shown in the matrix in Table 5.2.

	P	Q	R
A	9	8	6
B	11	8	7
C	10	8	7

Table 5.2

Allocate the workers to the tasks in such a way as to minimise the total time taken. Each worker should carry out one task only, and each task should be carried out by just one worker.

Note

The maximising problem will be dealt with in Section 3.

Note

Had all the times been 10 times greater, then you could have divided them all by 10 without changing the nature of the problem (effectively, the unit of measurement has just been changed). But note that you cannot divide one row's elements by 10, leaving the other rows unchanged, as this distorts the problem.

Note

There will often be more than one optimum allocation.

ACTIVITY 5.1

Find any other optimum allocations for this example, and in each case verify that the time taken is the same as for the solution already found.

Discussion point

→ What is the reasoning behind the check?

Note

It is conventional to reduce by rows before reducing by columns. However, there are circumstances when it would be better to reduce by columns first (as will be seen shortly).

Solution

Assuming that a solution is not obtainable by inspection (which would be more difficult for larger matrices), you can convert the problem to an equivalent simpler one by reducing all the elements of row A by 6 (so that the smallest element is 0), all the elements of row B by 7, and all the elements of row C by 7. You can do this because it is the relative times that are important.

After **reducing by rows** in this way, the new matrix is shown in Table 5.3.

	P	Q	R
A	3	2	0
B	4	1	0
C	3	1	0

Table 5.3

At this point, you can see by inspection that, for example, the following allocation minimises the total time: AP, BQ and CR. To find the total time you refer back to the original matrix: AP: 9, BQ: 8, CR: 7, giving a total of 24.

Inspection is made easier if you can match each worker to a task with zero time (with the other times in the matrix being positive). At the moment, it is only task R that has zero times, but you can make further progress by reducing the matrix by columns, by subtracting 3 from column P and 1 from column Q, to give Table 5.4.

	P	Q	R
A	0	1	0
B	1	0	0
C	0	0	0

Table 5.4

And now it is possible to allocate each worker to a different task with zero time; for example, AP, BQ and CR (as before).

A check can be made on the minimum time, as follows.

The zeros were obtained by reducing the rows by a total time of 6 + 7 + 7 = 20, and by reducing the columns by a total time of 3 + 1 + 0 = 4, giving an overall reduction of 24, which is the minimum time.

However, in some cases, after you have reduced by both rows and columns, it may not be possible to allocate each worker to a different task with zero time, as happens with the cost matrix in Table 5.5.

	P	Q	R
A	3	5	6
B	4	2	1
C	2	4	6

Table 5.5

ACTIVITY 5.2

Reduce the matrix in Table 5.5 by rows, and then (if necessary) by columns (the solution is given in the text that follows).

After reducing by rows you obtain

	P	Q	R
A	0	2	3
B	3	1	0
C	0	2	4

Table 5.6

Then, reducing by columns gives

	P	Q	R
A	0	1	3
B	3	0	0
C	0	1	4

Table 5.7

Note

For the cost matrix in Table 5.5, you can of course still find an optimum allocation by inspection. This will involve using ones when you can't use zeros.

However, you are now unable to allocate each worker to a different task with zero time, as A and C can both only be allocated to P. Nevertheless, an optimum allocation will exist, and you shall see in the next section how the Hungarian algorithm can be applied in this case.

The reason why you cannot allocate each worker to a different task with zero time in Table 5.7 is due to the fact that all of the zeros in the matrix can be covered by fewer than three rows and/or columns (in general, by either two rows, two columns, or one row and one column). Here you can cover the zeros with the second row and the first column.

ACTIVITY 5.3

Find an optimum solution for the cost matrix in Table 5.5.

For an $n \times n$ matrix, it will only be possible to allocate each worker to a different task with zero time (after row and column reductions) if the zeros require n rows and/or columns to cover them.

Exercise 5.1

For questions 1–4, find the allocation that minimises the total, reducing first by rows, unless specified otherwise.

①

Task	P	Q	R
A	3	7	5
B	4	6	2
C	1	5	3

Table 5.8

 ②

Task	P	Q	R	S
A	5	3	7	4
B	4	2	8	6
C	7	1	2	3
D	6	6	5	2

Table 5.9

③ (i) Reduce by rows, then columns.
(ii) Reduce by columns, then rows.

Task	P	Q	R	S
A	4	6	2	7
B	4	2	5	5
C	7	4	6	8
D	10	5	5	7

Table 5.10

④

Task	P	Q	R
A	210	180	150
B	190	270	240
C	170	200	260

Table 5.11

⑤ A family is planning to visit some tourist attractions whilst on holiday. They intend to visit a different type of attraction in each town, but want to keep walking time to a minimum. The table shows the walking times from each town's car park to the different attractions. Which attraction should they visit in each town?

	Castle	Steam railway	Musuem	Zoo	Fun fair
Okestock	4	1	7	6	5
Exbridge	9	7	10	8	9
Tormouth	3	2	5	1	4
Barnsworthy	8	6	4	4	7
Plymquay	2	5	5	1	6

Table 5.12

2 The Hungarian algorithm

The Hungarian algorithm provides a method for dealing with cases such as in Table 5.7. The procedure involves back-tracking a bit, so that some of the elements of the matrix are increased, to enable others to be reduced. The net effect will be that there are more reductions than increases, so that you will have made progress, and created more zeros.

As already mentioned, Table 5.7 can be solved by inspection, by using ones when you can't use zeros. Using the Hungarian algorithm, you will manipulate the matrix in such a way as to convert these ones to zeros.

This is done by first of all shading the necessary rows/columns (or crossing them out, if handwritten), in order to cover up all the zeros, to give Table 5.13.

> **Note**
>
> There could be more than one way of crossing out the rows and columns, and it is best to choose the way that gives rise to the largest non-zero element amongst the elements that aren't crossed out – as should become clear shortly.

	P	Q	R
A	0	1	3
B	3	0	0
C	0	1	4

Table 5.13

You then add 1 (in general, the smallest value that hasn't been crossed out) to each element in a crossed-out row or column (noting that this won't change the relative values), to give Table 5.14.

	P	Q	R
A	1	1	3
B	5	1	1
C	1	1	4

Table 5.14

Note that this means that any element that is an intersection of a crossed-out row and a crossed-out column is increased twice. Now there are no zeros, and you can reduce every element of the matrix by 1, to give Table 5.15. This process is sometimes referred to as **augmenting** the matrix. Now three rows/columns are needed to cover the zeros, and so you have finished (apart from identifying the allocations).

	P	Q	R
A	0	0	2
B	4	0	0
C	0	0	3

Table 5.15

A shortcut can be applied to the augmenting process by noting that the overall effect is to reduce the uncovered elements by 1 (for the above example) and increase any intersections of crossed-out lines by 1, leaving the other elements unchanged.

Summary of the overall process

(i)   Reduce the matrix by rows and columns (having divided all elements by the same number, if this is possible).

(ii) Cover the zero elements with as many rows and/or columns as are necessary. If the number of crossed-out rows/columns equals the size of the matrix, then you can find a solution by inspection: workers and tasks are matched up so that there is a zero time in each case in the reduced matrix. The actual times are then found by referring to the original matrix.

(iii) If the number of crossed-out rows/columns is less than the size of the matrix, you establish the smallest non-covered element: S (say). This value S is then added to each element of a crossed-out row or column (so adding twice for any intersections), and finally S is subtracted from every element of the matrix. (Alternatively, you can employ the shortcut mentioned above.) Then apply step (ii).

Example 5.2

Find the allocation that minimises the total for the following matrix.

Task	P	Q	R	S
A	140	180	160	150
B	170	200	130	200
C	150	190	190	180
D	210	200	140	180

Table 5.16

Solution

Step 1: Divide all the elements by 10, to give

Task	P	Q	R	S
A	14	18	16	15
B	17	20	13	20
C	15	19	19	18
D	21	20	14	18

Table 5.17

➜

Step 2: Reduce by rows, to give

Task	P	Q	R	S	Deducted
A	0	4	2	1	14
B	4	7	0	7	13
C	0	4	4	3	15
D	7	6	0	4	14

Table 5.18

Step 3: Reduce by columns, to give

Task	P	Q	R	S
A	0	0	2	0
B	4	3	0	6
C	0	0	4	2
D	7	2	0	3
Deducted		4		1

Table 5.19

Step 4: As only three rows and/or columns are needed to cover the zeros, the Hungarian algorithm can be applied. Using the shortcut, reduce the uncovered elements by 2 (the smallest uncovered element), and increase the intersections of rows and columns by 2, to give

Task	P	Q	R	S
A	0	0	4	0
B	2	1	0	4
C	0	0	6	2
D	5	0	0	1

Table 5.20

Step 5: Now four rows and/or columns are needed to cover the zeros, and you can look for an allocation. In fact, the only possible one is: BR, DQ, CP, AS.

Referring back to the original matrix, the solution is

A: 150, B: 130, C: 150, D: 200 (total of 630)

Step 6: The check mentioned earlier can be adapted to allow for the Hungarian algorithm, as follows.

Having divided all the elements by 10, the total of the row deductions was 56, and the total of the column deductions was 5. A further zero was then created by subtracting 2. (The addition of 2 to the intersections of the rows and columns didn't involve one of the eventual zeros, and so has no effect on the allocations.)

The total of 630 can then be arrived at as follows: $(56 + 5 + 2) \times 10 = 630$.

① What is the smallest number of rows and/or columns that can cover the zeros in the following matrix?

	P	Q	R	S	T	U	V	W
A	3	2	0	2	1	0	4	2
B	4	1	5	0	3	2	1	1
C	2	4	0	3	0	4	0	3
D	2	3	1	0	1	0	2	6
E	0	5	4	2	0	1	5	4
F	3	0	1	0	2	2	3	0
G	2	1	0	6	3	0	4	4
H	3	2	1	0	4	3	1	6

Table 5.21

For questions 2–5, find the allocation that minimises the total, reducing first by rows.

②

Task	P	Q	R
A	9	7	12
B	15	8	10
C	7	10	6

Table 5.22

③

Task	P	Q	R
A	120	70	90
B	80	40	100
C	50	60	60

Table 5.23

④

Task	P	Q	R	S
A	4	7	5	5
B	6	3	8	7
C	9	6	4	5
D	5	3	9	6

Table 5.24

⑤

Task	P	Q	R	S	T
A	7	7	3	4	3
B	3	7	4	2	6
C	4	4	1	4	3
D	8	10	9	5	4
E	5	5	7	3	5

Table 5.25

3 Modifications

(i)   Problems where the total value needs to be maximised, rather than minimised.

In this case, you could just multiply each element by −1, and then aim to minimise the values. Suppose that the most negative value was then −10, for example. Adding 10 to each element then results in the normal situation where the elements are all non-negative values, and the optimum allocation involves choosing elements that are as small as possible.

However, a shortcut for this procedure is to subtract each element from the largest value in the matrix.

(ii)   Non-square matrices.

These are dealt with by adding in one or more **dummy rows** or **columns**, to create a square matrix. The elements in each dummy row (or column) are all the same, so that the dummy has no effect on the nature of the problem. The dummy values are often taken to be the largest value in the matrix. For example, in Table 5.26, you can add a further column of 9s.

Task	P	Q	R
A	7	5	8
B	6	6	4
C	5	8	3
D	9	3	6

Table 5.26

> **ACTIVITY 5.4**
> Why might it be best to reduce by rows next?

Note that one of A, B, C and D will not be selected when the allocation is optimised (i.e. the one that is matched to the dummy column).

(iii) It may be the case that some of the possible allocations are not allowed. This can be dealt with by inserting a large number (relative to the values in the matrix, e.g. twice the largest value) as the relevant elements. This makes these elements unattractive, so that they won't appear in the solution(s).

Exercise 5.3

① Add a column of 9s to Table 5.26 and find the allocation with the smallest total by first reducing the matrix by rows. Then carry out the process again, by first reducing the matrix by columns instead.

② Find the allocation that maximises the total for the following matrix.

Task	P	Q	R
A	4	5	3
B	5	7	3
C	6	5	5

Table 5.27

③ Find the allocation that minimises the total for the following matrix.

Task	P	Q	R	S
A	5	–	7	4
B	–	3	5	2
C	6	4	5	–
D	3	–	4	6

Table 5.28

④ A team in a television reality show has to complete five tasks, with each task being managed by a different member of the team. The suitability of each team member to manage the various tasks (on a scale of 1 to 10, where 10 is the best) is recorded in the table below. Find the best matching of team members to tasks.

How can the result be checked?

Task	1	2	3	4	5
Ant	6	4	7	2	5
Brian	9	6	8	7	8
Camilla	3	4	5	2	6
Dot	7	7	4	5	5
Eva	8	4	6	8	7

Table 5.29

⑤ Find the allocation that maximises the total for the following matrix.

Task	P	Q	R	S
A	–	14	20	18
B	15	22	–	12
C	13	–	17	16

Table 5.30

4 Formulation as a linear programming problem

It is possible to tackle allocation problems by linear programming methods.

Consider the initial example, repeated in Table 5.31, with a change of notation.

	1	2	3
A	9	8	6
B	11	8	7
C	10	8	7

Table 5.31

Define A1, A2, A3, B1, B2, ... , C3 to be **binary variables** (i.e. taking the values 0 or 1).

For example, A2 = 1 means that worker A is allocated to task 2.

The objective function to be minimised will be

$P = 9A1 + 8A2 + 6A3 + 11B1 + ... + 7C3$

If the solution involves A2 = 1, you will expect to find that A1 = 0 and A3 = 0, and also that B2 = 0 and C2 = 0, This is covered by the following constraints:

A1 + A2 + A3 = 1 and A1 + B1 + C1 = 1

B1 + B2 + B3 = 1 and A2 + B2 + C2 = 1

C1 + C2 + C3 = 1 and A3 + B3 + C3 = 1

The standard method for dealing with constraints that are equalities is to write them as inequalities.

For example, A1 + A2 + A3 = 1 becomes A1 + A2 + A3 $\leqslant$ 1 and A1 + A2 + A3 $\geqslant$ 1.

Because of the large number of constraints (12 in this case), this problem would usually be dealt with by running a computer program using the Simplex method.

Exercise 5.4

① The table shows the cost of allocating individuals A, B, C to tasks X, Y, Z. Each individual has to do one task and each task must be done by one individual.

	X	Y	Z
A	3	6	4
B	7	4	6
C	6	4	5

Table 5.32

Formulate a linear programming problem to find the minimum cost allocation.

② The annual cost of supplying six warehouses from six depots is £8000 plus the costs given in Table 5.33. Each warehouse is to be supplied from exactly one depot and each depot is to supply exactly one warehouse.

Formulate a linear programming problem to find the minimum cost allocation.

③ Reformulate the minimum allocation problem in question 3 of Exercise 5.3 as a linear programming problem.

④ Reformulate the maximum allocation problem in question 5 of Exercise 5.3 as a linear programming problem.

Warehouses

	Cost (£100)	1	2	3	4	5	6
Depots	A	6	5	3	0	1	2
	B	1	2	5	0	3	0
	C	10	7	0	2	0	3
	D	0	0	0	4	1	5
	E	6	3	2	0	5	4
	F	3	7	0	3	2	1

Table 5.33

LEARNING OUTCOMES

Now you have finished this chapter, you should be able to

➤ minimise the total value of an allocation by reducing the cost matrix

➤ apply the Hungarian algorithm, where necessary

➤ modify the procedure to maximise the total value of an allocation

➤ deal with non-square matrices

➤ deal with situations where some allocations are not allowed

➤ use linear programming methods to tackle allocation problems.

KEY POINTS

1 It may be possible to divide all elements by the same number.

2 The cost matrix can be reduced by rows and/or columns.

3 It is conventional to reduce by rows before reducing by columns.

4 There will often be more than one optimum allocation.

5 A check can be made on the minimum value by finding the sum of the row and column reductions.

6 For an $n \times n$ matrix, it will only be possible to allocate each worker to a different task with zero time if the zeros require n rows and/or columns to cover them.

7 Hungarian algorithm:

- Cover the zero elements with as many rows and/or columns as are necessary.

- Establish the smallest non-covered element, S. If there is more than one way of covering the zero elements, choose the way that gives rise to the largest value of S.

- Add S to each element of a crossed-out row or column (so adding twice for any intersections).

- Then subtract S from every element of the matrix.

- Alternatively, apply the shortcut of reducing the uncovered elements by S and increasing any intersections of crossed-out lines by S, leaving the other elements unchanged.

8 To maximise the total value of an allocation, subtract each element from the largest value in the matrix, and minimise the total value.

9 Non-square matrices are dealt with by adding in one or more dummy rows or columns.

10 Allocations that are not allowed can be dealt with by inserting a large number as the relevant elements.

11 To reformulate as a linear programming problem, create binary variables for each element, with appropriate constraints.

6

Recurrence relations

➔ Work through this algorithm, starting with the word 'mathematics'.

Step 1 Think of an English word and write it down.

Step 2 Write, as a word, the number of letters in the word you have just written.

Step 3 If the last two words you have written down are the same, stop.

Step 4 Go back to Step 2.

➔ Repeat this for several different words. Do you always get the same answer? What happens if you do it in French? Or in other languages like Spanish or Welsh?

In the problem above you will have produced a sequence of answers, each of which became the starting point for the next run through.

$$\text{mathematics} \to \text{eleven} \to \text{six} \to \text{three} \to \dots$$

A single run through such an algorithm is called an **iteration**.

In this case, the algorithm is given as a sequence of numbered instructions, rather like a computer program, except that it is written in English. This is not the only way of writing an iteration, or indeed the most common. In mathematical examples the algorithm for an iteration is often written in the form of a **recurrence relation**, the rule for going from one term to the next. You also need to know the first term so that you can get started.

Here is an example of an iteration given as a recurrence relation.

$x_{n+1} = \dfrac{x_n^2 + 9}{2x_n}$ with starting value $x_0 = 1$

Working through this, the algorithm proceeds as follows, to calculator accuracy.

$$x_0 = 1$$

$$x_1 = \frac{1^2 + 9}{2} = 5$$

$$x_2 = \frac{5^2 + 9}{2 \times 5} = 3.4$$

$$x_3 = \frac{3.4^2 + 9}{2 \times 3.4} = 3.023529412$$

$$x_4 = \frac{3.023529412^2 + 9}{2 \times 3.023529412} = 3.000091554$$

$$x_5 = \frac{3.000091554^2 + 9}{2 \times 3.000091554} = 3.000000001$$

$$x_6 = \frac{3.000000001^2 + 9}{2 \times 3.000000001} = 3$$

$$x_7 = \frac{3^2 + 9}{2 \times 3} = 3$$

ACTIVITY 6.1

Work through this algorithm again, this time replacing the number 9 on the top line by 25. What do you think is happening? Does changing the starting value, x_0, make any difference to the final outcome? What happens if you change 9 to a negative number, say −4?

1 Solving first-order recurrence relations

A bank pays interest at 5% per annum on deposit accounts. In one account a deposit of £1000 is left to grow over a number of years.

To model this account mathematically you can use a recurrence relation in which the time period is one year and in which you start counting when the first deposit is made at time 0. (Sometimes it makes more sense to start at 1 rather than at 0. The resulting formulae then look slightly different.)

A recurrence relation to model the account is

$$u_n = 1.05u_{n-1} \qquad u_0 = 1000$$

In a second account, annual deposits of £1000 are made.

A recurrence relation to model this second account is

$$u_n = 1.05u_{n-1} + 1000 \qquad u_0 = 1000$$

> **Note**
> ----------
> The recurrence relations are **linear** because the power of every u term is 1.
>
> In general, the **order** of a recurrence relation is the difference between the highest and lowest subscripts in the equation.

Both of these are **first-order linear recurrence relations** because u_n is expressed as a linear function of its immediate predecessor, u_{n-1} only. If u_{n-2} had also been involved, but no earlier terms, then the recurrence relation would have been of **second order**.

The first recurrence relation consists entirely of u terms. It is called **homogeneous**.

The second has a term not involving u. It is called **non-homogeneous**.

In each case, you would like to know how much money is in the account after n years, for whatever value you choose for n. That is, you would like to have an explicit expression for u_n, not involving u_{n-1} or earlier terms. Such an expression is called a solution of the recurrence relation.

First-order linear homogeneous recurrence relations

Here is one way, from first principles, to solve a recurrence relation of this form.

If $\qquad u_n = au_{n-1}$

then $\qquad u_n = a(au_{n-2}) = a^2u_{n-2}$ (since $u_{n-1} = au_{n-2}$)

$\qquad\qquad u_n = a^2(au_{n-3}) = a^3u_{n-3}$

$\qquad\qquad \vdots$

$\qquad\qquad u_n = a^nu_0 \longleftarrow$ $\boxed{\text{This is the solution.}}$

A more efficient way to solve a recurrence relation like $u_n = 3u_{n-1}$, $u_0 = 6$, $n \geqslant 1$) is to notice that the solution of an equation like this is of the form $u_n = x^n$.

So $u_{n-1} = x^{n-1} \Rightarrow x^n = 3 \times x^{n-1}$

Simplifying gives the equation $x = 3$. ◄——— $x = 3$ is called the **auxiliary equation**.

So the solution to the auxiliary equation is $x = 3$.

$u_n = 3^n$ satisfies the recurrence relation $u_n = 3u_{n-1}$ as $3^n = 3 \times 3^{n-1}$.

It does not satisfy the initial condition, $u_0 = 6$, as $3^0 = 1 \neq 6$.

A constant, k, is included in the **general solution** $u_n = k \times 3^n$.

This still satisfies the original recurrence relation, $k \times 3^n = 3 \times k \times 3^{n-1}$.

Substituting into the initial condition $u_0 = k \times 3^0 \Rightarrow 6 = k$.

So, the solution of the recurrence relation is $u_n = 6 \times 3^n$.

To summarise the steps when solving a first-order linear homogeneous recurrence relation:

- find the auxiliary equation by using a solution of the form $u_n = x^n$
- solve the auxiliary equation
- write down the general solution
- use the initial condition to find the solution.

First-order linear non-homogeneous recurrence relations

The recurrence relation may have other terms in addition to the u term and would then be described as non-homogeneous, taking the form $u_n = ku_{n-1} + f(n)$.

The homogeneous part is solved using the method above to determine a **complementary function**. The 'extra bit', $f(n)$, is dealt with by trying out various trial functions to find a **particular solution**. This process could potentially be time-consuming but here is some guidance.

$f(n)$	Trial function
c	p
cn	$pn + q$
cn^2	$pn^2 + qn + r$
ck^n	pk^n (or pnk^n when the complementary function is of the form dk^n)
cn^2k^n	$k^n(pn^2 + qn + r)$

Table 6.1

In Decision Mathematics 2 you will only deal with functions that are constant. The others are included for completeness and you will meet them in the Further Pure Mathematics 2 unit.

For trial functions with several unknowns, use different values of n to generate equations to determine them.

Example 6.1

Solve the recurrence relation $u_n = 2u_{n-1} + 7$, $u_0 = 4$, $n \geqslant 1$.

Solution

Treat the two parts of the recurrence relation separately.

First solve $u_n = 2u_{n-1}$.

The solution is of the form $u_n = x^n$.

Substituting into $u_n = 2u_{n-1}$

$\Rightarrow x^n = 2 \times x^{n-1}$ so $x = 2$ is the auxiliary equation, with solution $x = 2$, and the general solution is $u_n = k \times 2^n$.

> $k \times 2^n$ is the complementary function.

Note

The complementary function $u_n = k \times 2^n$ satisfies $u_n - 2u_{n-1} = 0$, and the particular solution $u_n = -7$ satisfies $u_n - 2u_{n-1} = 7$, so that when $u_n = k \times 2^n - 7$, $u_n - 2u_{n-1} = 0 + 7 = 7$.

Since $f(n) = 7$, the trial function is p, a constant.

Substituting into $u_n = 2u_{n-1} + 7$ gives $p = 2p + 7 \Rightarrow p = -7$.

The general solution is $u_n = k \times 2^n - 7$.

> The two functions are added to give the overall general solution.

This must satisfy the initial condition, $u_0 = 4$.

$u_0 = k \times 2^0 - 7 = 4 \Rightarrow k = 11$

The final solution of the recurrence relation is thus $u_n = 11 \times 2^n - 7$. This can be checked.

$u_n = 11 \times 2^n - 7$ and $u_{n-1} = 11 \times 2^{n-1} - 7$

$u_n = 2u_{n-1} + 7 = 2 \times \left(11 \times 2^{n-1} - 7\right) + 7$

$\qquad\qquad = 2 \times 11 \times 2^{n-1} - 2 \times 7 + 7$

$\qquad\qquad = 11 \times 2^n - 7$, as required.

$u_0 = 11 \times 2^0 - 7 = 4$, as required.

To summarise the steps when solving a first-order linear non-homogeneous recurrence relation:

- find the general solution of the homogeneous part
- use a trial function to find a particular solution of the non-homogeneous relation
- add the two functions to obtain the general solution of the recurrence relation
- use the initial condition to find the final solution.

Example 6.2

£1000 is invested at a compound interest rate of 5%.

(i)   Write a recurrence relation for u_n, the amount at the end of the nth year.

(ii)   Solve the recurrence relation.

(iii) How many years will it take the money to double in value?

Solution

(i) $u_n = 1.05u_{n-1}$, $u_0 = 1000$

(ii) The auxiliary equation is $x = 1.05 \Rightarrow u_n = k \times 1.05^n$ ◀ This is the general solution.

Use the initial condition, $u_0 = 1000$, to determine the final solution.

$u_0 = k \times 1.05^0 = 1000 \Rightarrow k = 1000$.

Thus $u_n = 1000 \times 1.05^n$

(iii) $1000 \times 1.05^n > 2000$

$\Rightarrow 1.05^n > 2$

Solve the inequality using logs or by trialling values to obtain $n = 15$. The money takes 15 years to double in value.

Example 6.3

£1000 is deposited each year in an account paying 5% compound interest per annum.

(i)   Write a recurrence relation for u_n, the amount at the end of the nth year.

(ii) Solve the recurrence relation.

(iii) How many years will it take the accumulated amount to exceed £20 000?

Solution

(i) $u_n = 1.05u_{n-1} + 1000$, $u_0 = 1000$

(ii) This is non–homogeneous.

The general solution to $u_n = 1.05u_{n-1}$ is $u_n = k \times 1.05^n$ so $k \times 1.05^n$ is the complementary function.

$f(n) = 1000$, so the trial function is p, a constant.

Substituting into $u_n = 1.05u_{n-1} + 1000$,

$p = 1.05p + 1000 \Rightarrow p = -20\,000$

So the general solution is $u_n = k \times 1.05^n - 20\,000$

$u_0 = 1000 = k \times 1.05^0 - 20\,000 \Rightarrow k = 21\,000$

$u_n = 21\,000 \times 1.05^n - 20\,000$ is the solution of the recurrence relation.

(iii) Solve the inequality $21\,000 \times 1.05^n - 20\,000 > 20\,000$.

Simplifying: $21 \times 1.05^n > 40$

Solve $1.05^n > \dfrac{40}{21}$ using logs or trialling values to get 14 years.

An alternative method that works for first-order linear, non-homogeneous recurrence relations with a constant term is similar to the first method for the homogeneous ones.

If $u_n = au_{n-1} + b$, $a \neq 1$

so that $u_{n-1} = au_{n-2} + b$

then $u_n = a^2 u_{n-2} + ab + b$

Repeating the process,

$$u_n = a^2(au_{n-3} + b) + ab + b$$
$$= a^3 u_{n-3} + a^2 b + ab + b$$

Eventually

$$u_n = a^n u_0 + a^{n-1}b + a^{n-2}b + \ldots + ab + b$$
$$= a^n u_0 + b(a^{n-1} + a^{n-2} + \ldots + a + 1)$$

The expression in brackets is the sum of the first n terms of a geometric progression with first term 1 and common ratio a. It can be written as $\dfrac{1 - a^n}{1 - a}$ or $\dfrac{a^n - 1}{a - 1}$.

(The first is more convenient if $a < 1$ and the second if $a > 1$.)

Therefore $u_n = a^n u_0 + \dfrac{b(a^n - 1)}{a - 1}$, $a \neq 1$.

Exercise 6.1

① Solve

(i) $u_n = 4u_{n-1}$, $u_0 = 7$ $(n \geqslant 1)$

(ii) $u_n = 0.5u_{n-1}$, $u_0 = 1$ $(n \geqslant 1)$

(iii) $u_n = 10u_{n-1} + 8$, $u_0 = 2$ $(n \geqslant 1)$

(iv) $u_n = 2u_{n-1} + 5n$, $u_0 = 20$ $(n \geqslant 1)$

② (i) Solve the recurrence relation $u_{n+1} = au_n + b$ (where a and b are constants), $u_0 = c$ and $a \neq 1$.

(ii) Sketch a graph of u_n against n in the case where $a = 0.5$ and $b = 10$.

③ The birth rate of a type of insect is 20% of the existing population each year. The growth of a population of these insects is modelled by the recurrence relation $u_n = 1.2u_{n-1} - 15$, $u_0 = 100$ $(n \geqslant 1)$.

(i) State what is represented by $u_0 = 100$ in the model.

(ii) Explain what the constant term represents in the recurrence relation.

(iii) Solve the recurrence relation.

(iv) Is the population increasing? Justify your answer.

④ Calculate the equal annual repayments which are required to pay off a £10 000 loan over 10 years with interest at 8% per annum.

⑤ Model the sequence 7, 17, 37, 77, 157, ... with a recurrence relation, and solve it to give an expression for the nth term in terms of n.

⑥ In the 'Tower of Hanoi' the object is to transfer a pile of rings from one needle to another, one ring at a time, in as few moves as possible, with never a larger ring sitting upon a smaller ring.

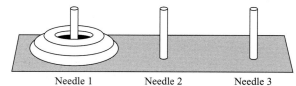

Needle 1   Needle 2   Needle 3

Figure 6.1

In the Temple of Benares, each day a priest moves a ring from an original pile of 64 according to the Tower of Hanoi rules. A novice priest asks for instruction on how to continue with the task.

He is told:

'To move one ring from needle 1 to needle 2 or 3, move it directly. To move n rings, where $n > 1$, from needle 1 to needle 3, first move $n - 1$ rings from needle 1 to needle 2, then move the nth ring from needle 1 to needle 3, then move the $n - 1$ rings from needle 2 to needle 3.'

(i) Apply the recursive procedure defined by the instructions to move three rings from needle 1 to needle 3. Show each move.

(ii) Calculate how many days it will take for the priests of Benares to complete their task.

⑦ The cooling system of my car has a capacity of 10 litres. It contains antifreeze at a concentration of 0.25, so there are 2.5 litres of ethylene glycol and 7.5 litres of water. The system leaks 0.1 litres per week.

I wish to top it up weekly with 0.1 litres of undiluted ethylene glycol, until the concentration reaches 0.5. Thereafter I shall use a diluted top-up (concentration 0.5) to maintain the concentration.

(i) Derive a recurrence relation for v_k, the volume of ethylene glycol in the cooling system immediately after the kth top-up.

Hence show that the recurrence relation for the concentration of ethylene glycol is $c_{k+1} = 0.99c_k + 0.01$, where c_k is the concentration immediately after the kth top-up.

(ii) Solve the recurrence relation for c_k. Find the concentration after four weeks and find how many weeks are required for the concentration to reach 0.5.

⑧ Each month Ann puts £400 into her bank account and allows herself to spend 20% of what was in the account at the end of the previous month.

(i) Letting u_n be the amount in the account at the end of month n, write down a recurrence relation for u_{n+1} in terms of u_n.

(ii) Find a general expression for u_n, given that $u_1 = 400$.

(iii) Starting with an empty account, how much will Ann have in her account

(a) after 12 months

(b) in the long run?

2 Solving second-order recurrence relations

Second-order recurrence relations

Rabbits breed quickly! Suppose that you start with one newborn pair and that every month any mature pair gives birth to a new pair. It takes two months for a newborn pair to mature.

The progression of the population is shown in the table below.

Time (months)	0	1	2	3	4	5	6	...
Number of newborn pairs	1	0	1	1	2	3	5	...
Number of 1-month-old pairs	0	1	0	1	1	2	3	...
Number of mature pairs ($\geqslant$ 2 months old)	0	0	1	1	2	3	5	...
Total number of pairs (u_n)	1	1	2	3	5	8	13	...

Table 6.2

The sequence u_n is attributed to Fibonacci (c. 1170–1250).

The recurrence relation which describes the sequence is

$$u_{n+2} = u_{n+1} + u_n, \qquad u_0 = 1, u_1 = 1$$

This is a second-order recurrence relation. Note that it requires two initial conditions.

Second-order, linear, homogeneous recurrence relations

A recurrence relation of this type has the form

$$u_{n+2} = au_{n+1} + bu_n$$

Try the solution $u_n = Am^n$, where A and m are constants. This would give

$$Am^{n+2} = aAm^{n+1} + bAm^n$$

This collects and factorises to

$$Am^n(m^2 - am - b) = 0.$$

Since you cannot have $A = 0$ or $m = 0$, it must be the case that

$$m^2 - am - b = 0.$$

This is known as the auxiliary equation. It is a quadratic equation with two, possibly complex, solutions. Let the solutions be m_1 and m_2.

There are three possibilities to consider:

- $m_1 \neq m_2$ and both are real
- $m_1 = m_2$ (in which case it is real)
- $m_1 \neq m_2$ and both are complex.

$m_1 \neq m_2$ and both are real

In this case, both $u_n = m_1^n$ and m_2^n are solutions.

It can be shown that any linear combination (i.e. a sum of multiples) of the two solutions is also a solution. Furthermore, it can be shown that any solution of the recurrence relation is of this form, i.e.

$$u_n = Am_1^n + Bm_2^n$$

Example 6.4

Find the solution of

$$u_{n+2} = u_{n+1} + 6u_n \qquad u_0 = 0, u_1 = 1.$$

Solution

The auxiliary equation is

$$m^2 - m - 6 = 0$$

$$\Rightarrow (m - 3)(m + 2) = 0$$

so $m = 3$ or -2.

The general solution is

$$u_n = A3^n + B(-2)^n. \quad \longleftarrow \quad \boxed{\text{This is the complementary function.}}$$

$$u_0 = 0 \Rightarrow \qquad 0 = A + B$$

$$u_1 = 1 \Rightarrow \qquad 1 = 3A - 2B$$

Solving gives $A = \frac{1}{5}$, $B = -\frac{1}{5}$

So the solution is

$$u_n = \frac{1}{5} \times 3^n - \frac{1}{5}(-2)^n.$$

Check:

n	0	1	2	3	4	5
u_n	0	1	1	7	13	55

Table 6.3

e.g. $u_5 = \frac{1}{5} \times 3^5 - \frac{1}{5}(-2)^5$

$= \frac{1}{5}(243 - (-32))$

$= \frac{1}{5} \times 275 = 55$

$m_1 = m_2$ (= m, say)

In this special case, it can be shown that the general solution is

$$u_n = Am^n + Bnm^n$$

Example 6.5

Find the solution of

$$u_{n+2} = 8u_{n+1} - 16u_n \qquad u_0 = 1, u_1 = 1.$$

Solution

The auxiliary equation is

$$m^2 - 8m + 16 = 0$$
$$\Rightarrow \qquad (m - 4)^2 = 0$$
$$\text{so} \qquad m = 4$$

The general solution is

$$u_n = A4^n + Bn4^n$$
$$u_0 = 1 \Rightarrow \qquad 1 = A$$
$$u_1 = 1 \Rightarrow \qquad 1 = 4A + 4B$$

Solving gives $A = 1$, $B = -\frac{3}{4}$.

So the solution is

$$u_n = 4^n - \frac{3}{4}n4^n$$

$$= (1 - \frac{3n}{4})4^n.$$

Check:

n	0	1	2	3	4	5
u_n	1	1	−8	−80	−512	−2816

Table 6.4

e.g. $u_5 = (1 - \frac{15}{4})4^5$

$= -2816$

$m_1 \neq m_2$ and both are complex

In this case, the solution looks similar to the real case, i.e. $u_n = Am_1^{\ n} + Bm_2^{\ n}$.

Although m_1 and m_2 are complex numbers, the expression produces a real answer. Complex number theory allows the general solution to be written in terms of sines and cosines, showing it to be cyclic in nature.

You are not required to be able to produce an analytical (i.e. theoretical) solution in this case.

ACTIVITY 6.2

Use a spreadsheet to investigate the behaviour of
$$u_{n+2} = u_{n+1} - 2u_n$$
for various values of u_0 and u_1.

Second-order, linear, non-homogeneous recurrence relations

A recurrence relation of this type has the form

$$u_{n+2} = au_{n+1} + bu_n + \mathrm{f}(n).$$

It can be shown that the general solution is

$$u_n = \left(\begin{array}{c} \text{general solution to the associated} \\ \text{homogenous equation} \end{array} \right) + \left(\begin{array}{c} \text{a particular solution} \\ \text{for the full equation} \end{array} \right)$$

For example, look at

$$u_{n+2} = u_{n+1} + 6u_n + (n+2) \qquad u_0 = 1, u_1 = 1.$$

You know from Example 6.4 that the general solution to the homogeneous equation $u_{n+2} = u_{n+1} + 6u_n$ is

$$u_n = A3^n + B(-2)^n.$$

You now need a particular solution for the full equation. Try $u_n = pn + q$ so that

$$u_{n+1} = p(n+1) + q \text{ and } u_{n+2} = p(n+2) + q.$$

For this to work you need (substituting these expressions into the recurrence relation)

$$p(n+2) + q = p(n+1) + q + 6(pn+q) + n + 2$$
$$pn + (2p+q) = (7p+1)n + (p+7q+2)$$

So you will need (looking at the coefficients of n)
$$p = 7p + 1, \text{ giving } p = -\frac{1}{6}$$

and (looking at the constant terms)

$$2p + q = p + 7q + 2, \text{ giving } q = \frac{p-2}{6} = -\frac{13}{36}.$$

You now have the general solution

$$u_n = A3^n + B(-2)^n - \frac{1}{6}n - \frac{13}{36}.$$

Finally, use the initial conditions to find the final solution.

$$u_0 = 1 \Rightarrow \qquad 1 = A + B - \frac{13}{36}$$

so $\qquad A + B = \frac{49}{36}$

$$u_1 = 1 \Rightarrow \qquad 1 = 3A - 2B - \frac{1}{6} - \frac{13}{36}$$

so $\qquad 3A - 2B = \frac{55}{36}$

Solving gives $A = \frac{17}{20}, B = \frac{23}{45}$.

So the final solution is

$$u_n = \frac{17}{20} \times 3^n + \frac{23}{45}(-2)^n - \frac{n}{6} - \frac{13}{36}.$$

Check:

n	0	1	2	3	4	5
u_n	1	1	9	18	76	189

Table 6.5

e.g. $u_5 = \frac{17}{20} \times 3^5 + \frac{23}{45}(-2)^5 - \frac{5}{6} - \frac{13}{36} = 189.$

Exercise 6.2

① Find the general solutions of
   (i) $u_{n+2} = 4u_{n+1} - 4u_n$
   (ii) $u_{n+2} - 6u_{n+1} + 9u_n = 0$.

② Find the solution of
   $$u_{n+2} - 6u_{n+1} + 9u_n = 0$$
   when $u_1 = 1$ and $u_2 = 5$.

③ Solve the recurrence relation $u_{n+2} = u_{n+1} + 12u_n$ with $u_0 = 1$ and $u_1 = 3$.

④ Find an expression for the nth Fibonacci number.

⑤ Paving slabs of dimensions $1\,\text{m} \times 0.5\,\text{m}$ are to be laid to make a path which is $1\,\text{m}$ wide. Show that the recurrence relation $u_{n+2} = u_{n+1} + u_n$ models the number of possible ways of laying such a path.

⑥ Find the solution of
   $$u_{n+1} - 5u_n + 6u_{n-1} = 1 + (n + 1)^2$$
   when $u_0 = 2$ and $u_1 = 3$.

⑦ Victoria has an income of £1000 per month, which goes into her bank account on the first day of each month. On the first day of each month she withdraws spending money from the account. Also at the beginning of each month interest of 1% of the amount in the account during the previous month is added into the account. Throughout the rest of each month the amount in her account remains constant.

After the £1000 deposit, withdrawal of spending money and payment of interest on 1st January, she had a balance of £2000 in the account.

Victoria decided that she would withdraw spending money of £500 on 1st February. Thereafter on the first of each month she would withdraw 25% of the amount in her account (after income, withdrawal and interest) two months previously. Thus on 1st March she would again transfer £500, because 25% of £2000 is £500, but on 1st April she would transfer 25% of the balance (after income, withdrawal and interest) on 1st February.

(All withdrawals and interest payments are computed to the nearest penny.)

(i) (a) Find how much she has in her account during February.

   (b) Find how much she has in her account during March.

(ii) (a) Show that she withdraws £630 on 1st April.

   (b) Find how much she withdraws on 1st May.

(iii) Counting January as month 1, if u_n is the balance in her account during month n, explain why, for $n \geqslant 1$,

$$u_{n+2} = 1.01u_{n+1} - 0.25u_n + 1000.$$

(iv) By setting $u_{n+2} = u_{n+1} = u_n$, find the long-term balance in Victoria's account. Say how much she withdraws to spend each month in the long term.

(v) If Victoria were to decide to transfer 50% of the balance instead of 25%, then her balances for the first three months would be £2000, £2520 and £2545.20. Say what the amount in her account would be in the long term. Say how much she would withdraw to spend each month in the long term.

⑧ A piece of coral has four new branches. During each year, one new branch develops on each branch which is more than one year old.

The number of branches after n years is denoted by u_n. Thus $u_0 = 4$, $u_1 = 4$ and $u_2 = 8$.

(i) Find u_3, the number of coral branches after three years.

(ii) Explain why $u_{n+1} = u_n + u_{n-1}$ ($n \neq 1$).

(iii) (a) Solve the recurrence relation to find an exact expression for u_n in terms of n.

(b) Verify that your expression gives $u_2 = 8$ exactly.

(iv) Construct a spreadsheet model for u_n. Use it and adapt it to answer the following questions.

(a) How many branches are there at the end of year 5 (i.e. u_5) and how many of these are more than one year old (i.e. u_4)?

At the end of year 5 a number of old branches are removed (without losing any of the newer branches), so that the total number of branches at the end of year 6 is 34.

(b) How many old branches are removed at the end of year 5?

(c) If no further branch removal takes place, how many branches will there be at the end of year 10, and how many at the end of year 20?

(d) At the end of year 6, how many of the 34 branches are old and how many are new? Show that it is not possible to achieve between 120 and 126 branches at the end of year 10 by removing old branches at the end of year 6.

3 Generating functions

You have seen that a recurrence relation defines a sequence $u_0, u_1, u_2, u_3, ..., u_n$ in terms of previous terms of the sequence and one or more of the initial terms in that sequence.

A **generating function** is a polynomial whose coefficients are the terms of that sequence. Thus, the generating function contains information about the sequence and gives rise to a technique for solving the associated recurrence relation.

This is the generating function.

→ The polynomial is given by $u(x) = u_0 + u_1 x + u_2 x^2 + u_3 x^3 + ... + u_n x^n$

Example 6.6

Use the generating function $u(x) = u_0 + u_1 x + u_2 x^2 + u_3 x^3 + \dots + u_n x^n$ to solve the second-order linear homogeneous recurrence relation given by

$$u_{n+2} = u_{n+1} + 6u_n,\ u_0 = 0,\ u_1 = 1.$$

Note

This is the recurrence relation solved in Example 6.4.

Solution

First write the recurrence relation in the form $u_{n+2} - u_{n+1} - 6u_n = 0,\ u_0 = 0,\ u_1 = 1$.

Now work out the next couple of terms in the sequence using the recurrence relation:

$u_2 = u_1 + 6u_0 = 1$ and $u_3 = u_2 + 6u_1 = 7$.

The generating function can now be written as

$u(x) = 0 + x + x^2 + 7x^3 + \dots + u_n x^n$.

> The coefficient of u_{n+1} is –1 in the rewritten form.

Now consider the function $u(x) - xu(x) - 6x^2 u(x)$.

> The coefficient of u_n is –6 in the rewritten form.

Discussion point

Why do the terms of ① simplify to zero after the term in x?

$$u(x) = 0 + x + x^2 + 7x^3 + \dots$$
$$-xu(x) = \qquad\quad - x^2 - x^3 - 7x^4 + \dots$$
$$-6x^2 u(x) = \qquad\qquad\quad -6x^3 - 6x^4 + \dots$$
$$u(x) - xu(x) - 6x^2 u(x) = 0 + x + 0x^2 + 0x^3 + \dots \quad ①$$

> All of the other terms simplify to zero.

$$u(x)(1 - x - 6x^2) = x$$

> Factorise left-hand side.

$$u(x) = \frac{x}{1 - x - 6x^2}$$

> This is the generating function for the recurrence relation.

The generating function, in this form, can now be manipulated to give a solution to the recurrence relation.

$$u(x) = \frac{x}{1 - x - 6x^2} = \frac{x}{(1 - 3x)(1 + 2x)} = \frac{\frac{1}{5}}{1 - 3x} - \frac{\frac{1}{5}}{1 + 2x}$$

> Partial fractions.

$$u(x) = \frac{1}{5}\left[(1 - 3x)^{-1} - (1 + 2x)^{-1} \right]$$

$$= \frac{1}{5}\left[\begin{array}{l} (1 + 3x + (3x)^2 + \dots + (3x)^n + \dots) \\ \qquad - (1 - 2x + (-2x)^2 + \dots + (-2x)^n + \dots) \end{array} \right]$$

$$= \frac{1}{5}\left[\sum_0^\infty 3^n x^n - \sum_0^\infty (-2)^n x^n \right]$$

$$= \frac{1}{5}\left[\sum_0^\infty (3^n - (-2)^n) x^n \right]$$

ACTIVITY 6.3

Work out u_4 and u_5. Hence work out the next two terms in the generating function and check that the further terms generated in equation ① are zero.

So the solution to the recurrence relation is $u_n = \frac{1}{5}(3^n - (-2)^n)$.

Generating functions may also be used to solve non-homogeneous recurrence relations.

Example 6.7

Use the generating function $u(x) = u_0 + u_1 x + u_2 x^2 + u_3 x^3 + \ldots + u_n x^n$ to solve the second-order linear non-homogeneous recurrence relation given by

$$u_{n+2} = u_{n+1} + 2u_n + 3, \quad u_0 = 1, \quad u_1 = 1.$$

Solution

First write the recurrence relation in the form

$$u_{n+2} - u_{n+1} - 2u_n = 3, \quad u_0 = 1, \quad u_1 = 1.$$

Now work out the next few terms in the sequence using the recurrence relation:

$$u_0 = 1, \quad u_1 = 1, \quad u_2 = 6, \quad u_3 = 11, \quad u_4 = 26.$$

The generating function can now be written as

$$u(x) = 1 + x + 6x^2 + 11x^3 + 26x^4 + \ldots + u_n x^n$$

Now consider the function $u(x) - xu(x) - 2x^2 u(x)$.

$$u(x) = 1 + x + 6x^2 + 11x^3 + 26x^4 + \ldots$$

$$-xu(x) = \quad -x - \quad x^2 - \quad 6x^3 - 11x^4 + \ldots$$

$$-2x^2 u(x) = \qquad\qquad -2x^2 \quad -2x^3 - 12x^4 + \ldots$$

> The other terms do not simplify to zero.

$$u(x) - xu(x) - 2x^2 u(x) = 1 + 3x^2 + 3x^3 + 3x^4 + \ldots$$

(2)

$$u(x)(1 - x - 2x^2) = 1 + 3x^2(1 + x + x^2 + \ldots)$$

> The other terms form an infinite series.

$$u(x) = \frac{1}{1 - x - 2x^2} + \frac{3x^2}{1 - x - 2x^2}(1 + x + x^2 + \ldots)$$

$$= \frac{1}{(1 + x)(1 - 2x)} + \frac{3x^2}{(1 + x)(1 - 2x)(1 - x)}$$

> $1 + x + x^2 + \ldots = \dfrac{1}{1 - x}$

$$= \tfrac{5}{6}(1 + x)^{-1} + \tfrac{5}{3}(1 - 2x)^{-1} - \tfrac{3}{2}(1 - x)^{-1}$$

> Using partial fractions and simplifying.

$$= \frac{5}{6}\sum_{0}^{\infty}(-x)^n + \frac{5}{3}\sum_{0}^{\infty}(2x)^n - \frac{3}{2}\sum_{0}^{\infty}x^n$$

> Using binomial expansions.

$$= \sum_{0}^{\infty}\left(\tfrac{5}{6}(-1)^n + \tfrac{5}{3} \times 2^n - \tfrac{3}{2} \times 1^n\right)x^n$$

So the solution to the recurrence relation is

$$u_n = \tfrac{5}{6}(-1)^n + \tfrac{5}{3} \times 2^n - \tfrac{3}{2}.$$

> $1^n = 1$ for all n.

ACTIVITY 6.4

Work out the first five terms of the recurrence relation $u_n = \frac{5}{6}(-1)^n + \frac{5}{3} \times 2^n - \frac{3}{2}$.

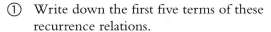

Exercise 6.3

① Write down the first five terms of these recurrence relations.

(i) $u_{n+2} = 2u_{n+1} + 3u_n$, $u_0 = 1$, $u_1 = 2$

(ii) $u_{n+2} = 2u_{n+1} + 8u_n + 5$, $u_0 = 0$, $u_1 = 1$

② Write down the generating functions in polynomial form for the recurrence relations in question 1 up to the term in x^4.

③ Write down the generating functions as the sum of partial fractions for the recurrence relations in question 1.

④ The generating function for a recurrence relation is $u(x) = \dfrac{2}{1 + 2x} - \dfrac{3}{1 - 5x}$.

Solve the recurrence relation.

⑤ Solve the recurrence relations in question 1.

⑥ Use the generating function to solve the recurrence relation
$$u_{n+2} - 3u_{n+1} + 2u_n = 0, \ u_0 = 2, \ u_1 = 1.$$

⑦ Use the generating function to solve the recurrence relation
$$u_{n+2} - 4u_{n+1} - 5u_n = 3, \ u_0 = 1, \ u_1 = 1.$$

⑧ Use the generating function to solve the recurrence relation
$$u_{n+2} - 5u_{n+1} + 6u_n = n, \ u_0 = 1, \ u_1 = 2.$$

LEARNING OUTCOMES

Now you have finished this chapter, you should be able to

➤ use recurrence relations to model appropriate problems

➤ detect problems in context which could be modelled with a recurrence relation

➤ recognise and describe associated sequences using a recurrence relation

➤ classify a recurrence relation by its order

➤ solve a first-order recurrence relation

➤ apply solutions to first-order recurrence relations to problems in context

➤ obtain the solution of any linear homogeneous second-order recurrence relation

➤ use generating functions to solve non-homogeneous second-order recurrence relations

➤ apply solutions to second-order recurrence relations to problems in context.

KEY POINTS

1 Situations involving sequences may be expressed as recurrence relations.

2 First-order recurrence relations only involve u_n and u_{n-1}, or equivalent.

3 Second-order recurrence relations only involve u_n, u_{n-1} and u_{n-2}, or equivalent.

4 The order of any recurrence relation is the difference between the highest and lowest subscripts in the equation.

5 The solution to a first-order linear homogeneous recurrence relation is of the form $u_n = k \times a^n$.

6 The general solution to a first-order linear non-homogeneous recurrence relation is of the form $u_n = a^n u_0 + \dfrac{b(a^n - 1)}{a - 1}$.

7 Solving a recurrence relation means finding an expression for u_n that does not involve other u terms.

8 The first step in solving homogeneous recurrence relations is to find the auxiliary equation, by substituting the likely form of the solution into the recurrence relation, giving the general solution.

9 The second step is to solve the auxiliary equation.

10 The third step is to use the initial conditions to determine any unknown constants to find the final solution.

11 The first step in solving non-homogeneous recurrence relations is to find the complementary function by solving the homogeneous part.

12 The second step is to find a particular solution to the recurrence relation, using a trial function that depends on the form of $f(n)$:

f(n)	Trial function
c	p
cn	$pn + q$
cn^2	$pn^2 + qn + r$
ck^n	pk^n (or pnk^n when the complementary function is of the form dk^n)
cn^2k^n	$k^n(pn^2 + qn + r)$

13 The third step is to add the complementary function and the particular solution, and use the initial conditions to determine the final solution.

Network flows

'Oh, could I flow like thee,
and make thy stream my
great example, as it is my
theme!'

Sir John Denham,
Cooper's Hill

→ List all the possible paths from A to D in the network below.

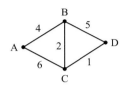

1 The language of network flows

A common problem that may need to be solved is finding the maximum flow that is possible through a network. For example, you might consider the hourly rate of traffic passing from one point to another, or the rate of flow of water through a system of pipes.

Figure 7.1 shows a directed network. In the context of network flows, the weights on the arcs are called **capacities**.

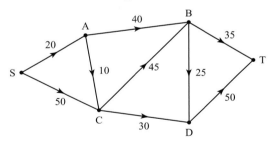

Figure 7.1

However, it is important to note that these weights could represent one of two things: either the actual flow along an arc, or the maximum flow allowed along an arc (i.e. its maximum capacity). In this chapter the terms 'capacity' and 'upper capacity' will both mean the maximum flow allowed along an arc (and you will see shortly that an arc may have a 'lower capacity'). Any actual flows will be described as such (rather than as 'capacities').

Figure 7.1 shows the upper capacities, and the task is to establish the actual flows needed along all the arcs, so that the flow through the whole network is maximised. Note that when the word 'flow' is used, it means a flow in a given time period, i.e. a rate of flow.

> ## Note
> A flow through a network must satisfy both the **feasibility condition**: the flow along an arc must not exceed the capacity of that arc, and the **conservation condition**: the total flow into a node must equal the total flow out of that node.

The starting node is called the **source** (usually denoted by S) and the end node is called the **sink** (usually denoted by T). Sources are nodes that have all directed arcs pointing outwards, whilst sinks are nodes that have all directed arcs pointing inwards. There may be more than one source or sink.

Example 7.1

Determine the maximum flow across the network given in Figure 7.1.

Solution

Start by noting that a flow of 30 is possible, by just using the path SCDT (i.e. with no flow along the other arcs). This gives the network in Figure 7.2.

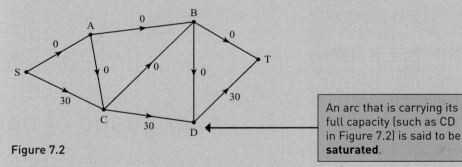

Figure 7.2

> An arc that is carrying its full capacity (such as CD in Figure 7.2) is said to be **saturated**.

This flow of 30 can be increased by using other arcs.

For example, SABT provides an additional flow of 20, to give a total of 50.

You can improve this by using SCBT (this can support a flow of 35), together with SABDT (which can support a flow of 20), to give a total of 55.

A further improvement can then be made by also using SCDT (noting that you have already used a flow of 35 along SC, as well as a flow of 20 along DT), and this gives us a further flow of 15, and hence a total of 70.

To summarise, the following flows are possible.

SCBT: 35

SABDT: 20

SCDT: 15

These flows are combined in Figure 7.3.

Note
As a check, note that the total flow out of each node equals the total flow into that node (except for the source and sink).

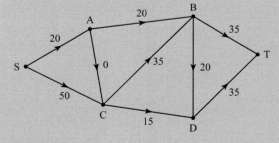

Figure 7.3

Maximum flow–minimum cut theorem

A useful device for maximising the flow is the **cut**. In general, a cut is any line or curve that divides the network into two parts, separating S and T. It must not pass through a node.

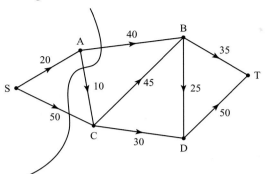

Figure 7.4

An example is shown in Figure 7.4. Imagine that you are dealing with a network of roads in neighbouring countries, and that the cut is the border between the countries.

A cut can be specified in the form: {source-side nodes}/{sink-side nodes}.

The cut in Figure 7.4 would be written as {S, A}/{B, C, D, T}.

The **value** of the cut (also known as the capacity of the cut) in Figure 7.4 is $40 + 10 + 50 = 100$.

This is the maximum flow across the border (in a given time period), arising from the three crossing points.

> Note that the flows that you are using for the cut are the maximum allowed flows along the various arcs.

This is a simple case, where the three flows are all crossing the border in the same direction (i.e. from the left-hand country to the right-hand country).

Figure 7.5 shows a cut where one of the arcs (DB) has a flow from the right-hand country to the left-hand country. As you are trying to maximise the flow from left to right, there is no need to have any flow from B to D (as this will reduce the total flow), and so the value of the cut is defined as the sum of the flows from left to right only, i.e. $40 + 45 + 50 = 135$.

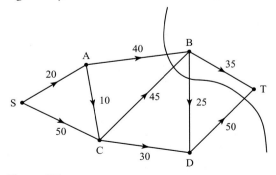

Figure 7.5

Considering the example of the two countries again (A and B, say), you can interpret S and T as their capital cities. Suppose that the location of the border has yet to be decided. The possible cuts in the network are where the border could be placed. The number of tourists, for example, that can pass from S to T in a given time period cannot exceed the number that pass from country A to country B across any particular border, represented by a cut.

> **Note**
>
> In Example 7.1, a flow of 70 was found by inspection. As the cut {S}/{A, B, C, D, T} has a value of 70, you know that this flow of 70 cannot be improved upon.

In general, the maximum possible flow across a network can be determined by finding the cut that has the smallest value. This is the **maximum flow–minimum cut theorem**.

> The value of the maximum flow = the value of the minimum cut.

However, for large networks it may be time-consuming to establish all the possible cuts.

Although there is no algorithm associated with this particular theorem that enables the maximum flow to be found, the theorem does mean that if you can find a flow and a cut of the same value, then you will have found the maximum flow (as it is not possible for the flow to exceed the value of the cut). However, you will see that an algorithm does exist for finding the maximum flow.

Exercise 7.1

①
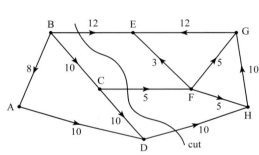

Figure 7.6

(i) In the network shown above, identify the source and the sink.

(ii) Find the capacity of the indicated cut.

② (i) Find minimum cuts for each of these networks.

(a)

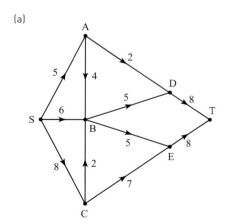

Figure 7.7

(b)

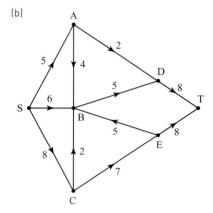

Figure 7.8

(ii) Confirm that your cuts are minimum cuts by finding a flow of the same value in each network.

③ List all the cuts in the network shown in Figure 7.9, and find their values. Hence determine the maximum flow through the network, and find a flow pattern that has this maximum value.

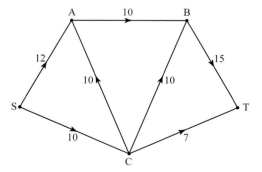

Figure 7.9

④ The following diagram shows capacities in a network.

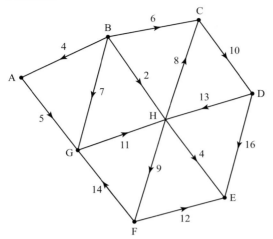

Figure 7.10

(i) Identify the source and sink.

(ii) Find the values of the cuts
{A, B, G}/{C, D, E, F, H} and
{B, C, H}/{A, D, E, F, G}.

(iii) What do these values tell us about the maximum flow through the network?

⑤ The following diagram shows actual flows in a network. Determine a, b, c, d and e.

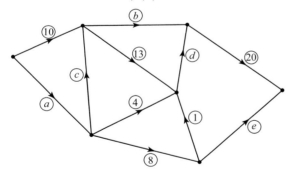

Figure 7.11

⑥ The following diagram shows capacities in a network.

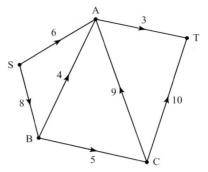

Figure 7.12

(i) Identify all the possible cuts and give their values.

(ii) Hence determine the value of the maximum flow.

(iii) Find a flow that has this maximum value.

2 Flow augmenting

The algorithm referred to earlier for finding the maximum flow involves a process known as **flow augmenting** (or the labelling procedure).

Using our earlier example, you start with any flow that you can find, such as the one in Figure 7.2, with a flow of 30 along SCDT. For each arc of the network, you note how much scope there is for increasing and decreasing the flow. These two figures (i.e. the potential increase and the potential decrease) are then indicated on a new version of the network, by means of 'forward' and 'backward' arrows, respectively, as shown in Figure 7.13.

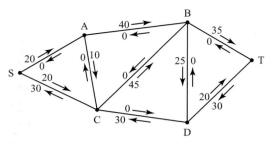

Figure 7.13

You then look for any flow within this network of potential changes, for example the flow of 20 along SABT (as found previously). You note this change, and modify the network of potential changes, to give Figure 7.14.

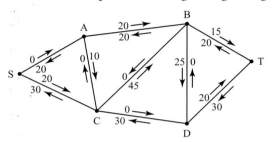

Figure 7.14

So, for example, because you are now increasing the flow along AB by 20, the scope for a further increase along this arc has reduced from 40 to 20, whilst the scope for decreasing the flow along this arc has risen from 0 to 20.

In general:

■ when the flow along an arc is increased, the amount is subtracted from the value on the forward arrow for that arc and added to the value on the backward arrow

■ the forward arrow shows the spare capacity of an arc, i.e. the amount by which the flow along it can be increased

■ the backward arrow shows the current flow along an arc, which is the amount by which the flow can be decreased

■ both forward and backward arrows can be used to find a route, but there must be a positive amount in the direction in which you want to change the flow.

At this point the algorithm diverges from the earlier method by inspection, as it doesn't allow for one path being replaced by another. However, you can easily spot an additional flow of 20 along the path SCBDT. The new network of potential changes is shown in Figure 7.15.

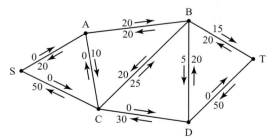

Figure 7.15

The arcs leading from S are both of capacity zero, and this means that no further improvements are possible.

The flows that are introduced during the process are often displayed in a table, as in Table 7.1.

Route	Flow
SCDT	30
SABT	20
SCBDT	20
Total	70

Table 7.1

This agrees with the total flow of 70, found previously. However, the combined effect of these flows, as shown in Figure 7.16, is different from that found by inspection.

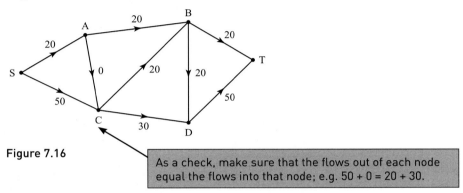

Figure 7.16

As a check, make sure that the flows out of each node equal the flows into that node; e.g. 50 + 0 = 20 + 30.

The flow augmenting procedure can sometimes involve **backflows**. This occurs when the flow that was initially chosen along a particular arc needs to be reduced (or removed entirely), in order to re-route the flow along a different arc and thereby increase the overall flow. This is illustrated in the next example.

Example 7.2

Figure 7.17 shows the capacity for each arc of a network and Figure 7.18 shows an initial flow for this network.

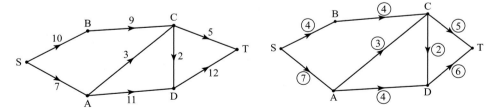

Figure 7.17

Figure 7.18

Show that the total flow can be increased to 14.

Solution

Figure 7.18 shows an initial flow that has been chosen by inspection, so that the flow along each arc doesn't exceed its capacity, and the total of the flows leading from each node is equal to the total of the flows leading into it. The total flow across the network is 11.

➜

Figure 7.19 shows the network of potential changes. For example, for the arc leading from S to B, the 'forward' flow of 6 brings you up to the maximum capacity of 10, whilst the 'backward' flow of 4 is the most that the flow could be reduced by (being the current flow along the arc).

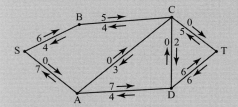

Figure 7.19

Note that there is no scope for increasing the flow from S to A. But you can follow the route SBCADT: an additional flow of 3 is possible. This involves a backflow along CA. After making the change, you obtain Figure 7.20.

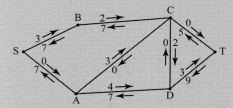

Figure 7.20

All the arcs leading from C now have zero value, and so no further improvements can be made. Figure 7.21 shows the new version of the actual flow. The total flow across the network has increased to 14.

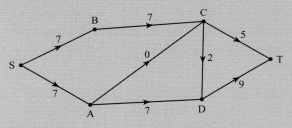

Figure 7.21

① For the network in question 1 of Exercise 7.1

   (i)   use flow augmentation to find a flow pattern that gives a maximum total flow

   (ii) prove that your total flow is a maximum.

② For the network in question 3 of Exercise 7.1, use flow augmentation to find a flow pattern that gives a maximum total flow.

③ The diagram in Figure 7.22 shows a pipe network. The numbers on the arcs give the capacities of the pipes.

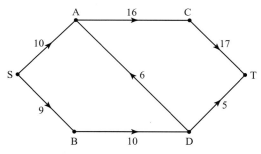

Figure 7.22

   (i)   Find the maximum flow through the network, showing the steps in your working.

   (ii) Prove that your flow is a maximum.

④ The diagram below shows the capacities of the edges in a directed distribution network and the flows currently established in the network. The capacity of each pipe is given by the number not circled on each arc. The number inside the circle on each arc represents the actual flow.

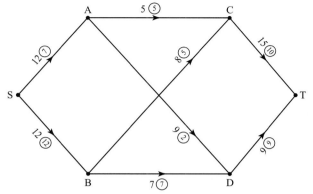

Figure 7.23

(i) Find a minimum cut and give its capacity.

(ii) Say why the established flows do not give a maximum total flow through the network.

(iii) Find and give a flow-augmenting path, and give a set of flows that do produce a maximum flow through the network.

⑤ Figure 7.24 shows a directed flow network with capacities and established flows. The capacity of each pipe is given by the number not circled on each arc. The number inside the circle on each arc represents the actual flow.

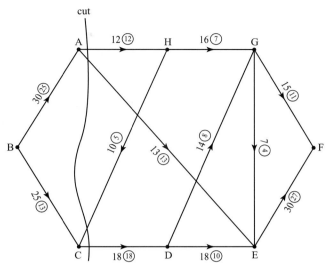

Figure 7.24

(i) Use flow augmentation to find the maximum flow.

(ii) Explain how the cut marked on the diagram confirms that the flow you have found is a maximum.

3 Refinements

Multiple sources and sinks

Figure 7.25 shows an example where there is more than one source, and more than one sink. This situation can easily be dealt with by introducing a **supersource** and a **supersink**. This is shown in Figure 7.26. Large capacities (relative to those for the existing arcs) are introduced for the new arcs created, so that they don't affect the solution. Alternatively, the capacity of SS_1 could just be set to 40 (10 + 30), as this is the maximum flow that could leave S_1. Also the capacity of T_2T could just be set to 50 (20 + 30), and similarly for the other sources and sinks.

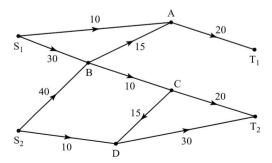

Figure 7.25

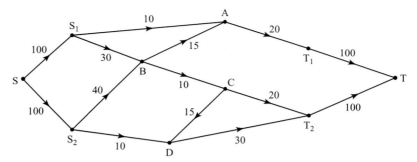

Figure 7.26

Nodes of restricted capacity

It is possible that an upper limit exists for the flow that can pass through a particular node. This can be dealt with by replacing the node with two (unrestricted) nodes, connected by an arc of capacity equal to the limit placed on the original node. Figure 7.27 shows the network in Figure 7.1, where there is now a limit of 20 placed on the flow through node B.

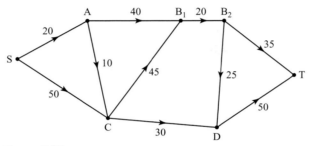

Figure 7.27

Arcs with lower capacities

In some situations, the flow for a particular arc may not be allowed to fall below a certain value. When labelling the original network, you now need to show lower and upper capacities, as for example in Figure 7.28 (which also shows some possible cuts).

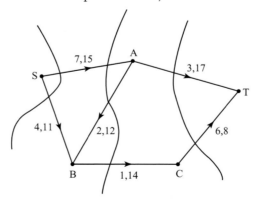

Figure 7.28

ACTIVITY 7.1

Maximise the flow across the network shown in Figure 7.28 by inspection.

ACTIVITY 7.2

Find a cut with a value of 21 in Figure 7.28.

As before, you can try to maximise the flow through the network by inspection. Finding a cut of the same value will confirm the maximum flow.

When determining the value of a cut, you can no longer exclude any arcs where the flow is towards the source. Instead, the lower capacities of these arcs are subtracted from the total maximum flow leading away from the source. The example of the border between two countries should make this clear: if it is a requirement that there is some traffic going back towards the source along a particular arc, then the amount of this traffic will reduce the net flow across the border in the direction of the sink.

Applying this to Figure 7.28, the cut $\{S\}/\{A, B, C, T\}$ has value $15 + 11 = 26$; the cut $\{S, B\}/\{A, C, T\}$ has value $15 - 2 + 14 = 27$, and the cut $\{S, A, B, C\}/\{T\}$ has value $17 + 8 = 25$.

This means that the maximum flow cannot exceed 25.

Example 7.3

Apply the flow augmenting process to the network shown in Figure 7.28.

Solution

The procedure is the same as used previously, except that the initial flow chosen must take account of any lower capacities – as must the potential increases and decreases for the arcs.

Suppose that you start with the following flow.

SABCT   4

SAT   11

SBCT   4,

with a total of 19.

This gives rise to the network of potential changes in Figure 7.29.

ACTIVITY 7.3

Identify a flow through the network of potential changes in Figure 7.29.

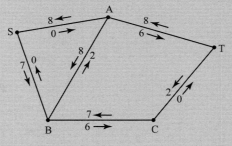

Figure 7.29

Exercise 7.3

① Find a flow pattern that gives a maximum total flow for the network in Figure 7.27.

② A gas distribution network consisting of three supply points, A, B and C, three intermediate pumping stations, P, Q and R, and two delivery points, X and Y, as well as connecting pipes, is shown in Figure 7.30.

The figures by A, B and C are measures of the daily availability of gas at the supply points.

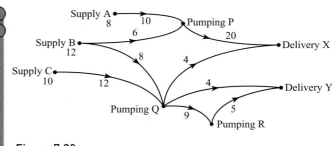

Figure 7.30

(i) Introduce a single source and a single sink and draw the revised network. The links from the source should reflect the supply availabilities.

(ii) By inspection, find the maximum daily flow through the network, listing the flows in each pipe.

(iii) Prove that your flow is a maximum.

A new pipeline is proposed, with a capacity of 5 units per day, connecting P and Q.

(iv) Apply the flow augmenting procedure to find the new maximum flow.

(v) R is now a delivery point. Explain how to adapt the approach used in (i) to find the maximum daily flow of gas in total that can be delivered to R, X and Y. You do not need to calculate this flow.

③ Find a flow pattern that gives a maximum total flow for the network in Figure 7.31.

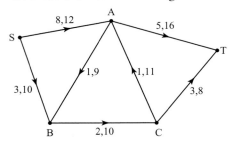

Figure 7.31

④ Gas is supplied to three locations, T_1, T_2 and T_3, from two sources S_1 and S_2. The rate of supply from S_1 cannot exceed 20 units. The rate of supply from S_2 cannot exceed 30 units. There are no constraints on the rate of flow into T_1, T_2 and T_3. The transmission network is shown in Figure 7.32, pipe capacities giving the maximum permissible rates of flow.

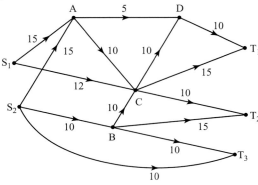

Figure 7.32

(i) Add a supersource together with appropriate capacitated arcs to model the supply constraints.

(ii) Add a supersink together with appropriate arcs.

(iii) Find the maximum total flow through the network, saying how much is delivered to each of T_1, T_2 and T_3.

⑤ The matrix below represents capacities of roads (thousands of cars per hour) in a road network.

	A	B	C	D	E	F	G
A	–	3	3	–	–	2	–
B	3	–	–	5	1	–	–
C	3	–	–	2	–	3	–
D	–	5	2	–	–	1	2
E	–	1	–	–	–	–	1
F	2	–	3	1	–	–	2
G	–	–	–	2	1	2	–

Figure 7.33

(i) Draw the network.

(ii) Find the maximum hourly flow of cars from B to F, showing how this may be achieved. Prove that this is a maximum.

⑥ The network below shows a system of pipes. The numbers represent the capacities of the pipes.

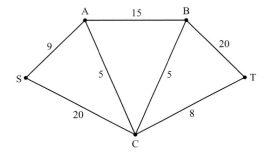

Figure 7.34

(i) Show that a flow of 27 units from S to T is possible.

(ii) Find a cut with capacity 27 units. Explain its significance.

(iii) If there must be a flow of at least 2 from A to C in AC what will be the maximum flow from S to T, and what flow will be needed in SC to achieve that maximum?

⑦ In the following network the arcs have capacities in the directions indicated by the arrows. The capacity of each pipe is given by the number not circled on each arc. The number inside the circle on each arc represents the actual flow.

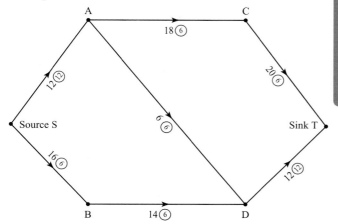

Figure 7.35

(i) Find the minimum cut and explain why it shows that the existing flow is not a maximum flow. Show the flows along the arcs that give the maximum flow from S to T.

Suppose that the flow along the arc AD may now be in either direction.

(ii) Explain why the maximum flow from S to T is now greater than in part (i) and state the value of the new maximum. Show the flows along the arcs that give that maximum flow from S to T.

LEARNING OUTCOMES

Now you have finished this chapter, you should be able to

➤ interpret flow problems represented by a network of directed arcs
➤ find the value of a cut and understand its meaning
➤ use and interpret the maximum flow–minimum cut theorem
➤ introduce supersources and supersinks to a network
➤ augment flows and determine the maximum flow in a network
➤ determine the value of a cut for a network containing arcs that have both upper and lower capacities
➤ solve problems involving arcs with upper and lower capacities
➤ refine network flow problems, including using nodes of restricted capacity.

KEY POINTS

1 The aim is to find the maximum possible flow through a network, from a source to a sink.
2 A cut divides a network into two parts, separating the source and the sink.
3 The value of a cut places a limit on the maximum flow possible, and this gives rise to the maximum flow–minimum cut theorem.
4 Supersources and supersinks may be introduced to deal with multiple sources and sinks.
5 The flow augmenting algorithm may be employed to identify the maximum possible flow.
6 Adjustments can be made to allow for nodes of restricted capacity and arcs with lower capacities.

8

Game theory

→ **Matching pennies** is the name for a simple game used in **game theory**. It is played between two players, Even and Odd. Each player has a penny and must secretly turn the penny to heads or tails. The players then reveal their choices simultaneously. If the pennies match (both heads or both tails), then Even keeps both pennies, so wins one from Odd (+1 for Even, −1 for Odd). If the pennies do not match (one heads and one tails), Odd keeps both pennies, so receives one from Even (−1 for Even, +1 for Odd).

1 Pay-off matrices

Game theory aims to model situations involving competitors (or **players**), where each player's gain (or loss) depends not only on their decisions, but also the decisions of their competitors. It can be applied in areas such as business negotiations, election campaigns, and warfare.

This chapter is about **zero-sum** games between two players. This means that if player 1 wins a certain amount, then player 2 loses that amount. For example, suppose that both players have two options: A and B. The amount (in £) won by player 1 (and lost by player 2) is given by the **pay-off matrix** in Table 8.1.

	Player 2 plays A	Player 2 plays B
Player 1 plays A	1	0
Player 1 plays B	−5	10

The pay-off matrix shows player 1's gains and player 2's losses.

Table 8.1

The elements in the pay-off matrix are given from player 1's point of view (this is the standard convention).

If player 1 wants to have a chance of winning £10, they must choose option B, and accept the risk of losing £5 if player 2 chooses option A. The safer course of action is to choose option A and either win £1 or break even.

Because this is a zero-sum game, to consider things from player 2's point of view, you transpose the matrix and reverse the signs of the elements in the matrix, to give the matrix in Table 8.2.

	Player 1 plays A	Player 1 plays B
Player 2 plays A	−1	5
Player 2 plays B	0	−10

Table 8.2 (player 2's gains)

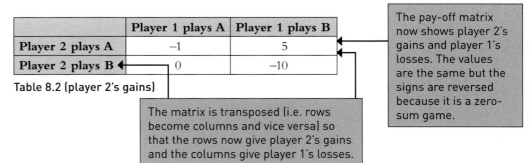

The matrix is transposed (i.e. rows become columns and vice versa) so that the rows now give player 2's gains and the columns give player 1's losses.

The pay-off matrix now shows player 2's gains and player 1's losses. The values are the same but the signs are reversed because it is a zero-sum game.

Option A offers player 2 the chance of winning £5, with the risk of losing £1, and choosing option B means either breaking even or losing £10.

The following factors may affect the choices made by each player.

■ How risk averse is the player? Player 1 may be able to afford to lose £5, but the situation might be different for £5000.

■ Will the game be repeated many times? A player may then be able to bear an occasional loss.

■ Can the choice of the other player be predicted? For example, if the game is repeated, the other player may always make the same choice.

Predicting the other player's choice is of particular interest in game theory.

For the current example, player 1 may conclude that player 2 is more likely to choose option A, and so player 1 may decide to choose option A themselves, and win £1 (rather than lose £5). Player 2 will then lose £1.

If player 2 discovers player 1's intention to choose option A, then it is better for player 2 to choose option B, and so break even.

Play-safe strategies

A **play-safe strategy** is where a player chooses the option with the best worst outcome. In other words, they assume that the other player penalises them the most by their choice.

In the previous example, if both players adopt a play-safe strategy, player 1 chooses option A (which has a worst outcome of £0, compared to the worst outcome of −£5 for option B), and player 2 also chooses option A (which has a worst outcome of −£1, compared to the worst outcome of −£10 for option B).

The result is that player 1 wins £1, and player 2 loses £1. It is assumed that both players have to play the game.

Now consider the pay-off matrix in Table 8.3, where player 1 has two choices and player 2 has three.

	Player 2 plays A	Player 2 plays B	Player 2 plays C
Player 1 plays A	2	−1	1
Player 1 plays B	1	−2	−3

Table 8.3

As usual, these are the pay-offs for player 1. The pay-offs for player 2 are shown in Table 8.4.

	Player 1 plays A	Player 1 plays B
Player 2 plays A	−2	−1
Player 2 plays B	1	2
Player 2 plays C	−1	3

Table 8.4 (player 2's gains)

The matrix has been transposed and the signs have been reversed.

The worst outcomes for player 1 can be shown in an additional column, as in Table 8.5 with the better option (from player 1's point of view) circled.

	Player 2 plays A	Player 2 plays B	Player 2 plays C	Worst
Player 1 plays A	2	−1	1	(−1)
Player 1 plays B	1	−2	−3	−3

Table 8.5

The worst outcomes for player 2 can also be shown in an additional column, as in Table 8.6, where the best option (from player 2's point of view) is circled.

	Player 1 plays A	Player 1 plays B	Worst
Player 2 plays A	−2	−1	−2
Player 2 plays B	1	2	(1)
Player 2 plays C	−1	3	−1

Table 8.6 (player 2's gains)

The play-safe strategy for player 1 is option A, whilst for player 2 it is option B.

If both players adopt the play-safe strategy, player 1 will not want to change their choice (assuming that player 2 doesn't change from option B), as −1 is better than −2.

Similarly, player 2 will not want to change their choice (assuming that player 1 doesn't change from option A), as 1 is better than either −2 or −1.

This is known as a **stable solution**. It is also called a **saddle point**, and the game is said to be in equilibrium. The stable solution exists because, in player 1's matrix, −1 is below both 2 and 1 (in row A), whilst −1 is above −2 (in column B).

So, where a stable solution exists, it is in both players' interests for them to adopt the play-safe strategy. The **value of the game** is defined as player 1's pay-off.

Although you considered player 2's matrix in the previous discussion, the standard procedure for identifying a stable solution is based on player 1's matrix.

You establish the worst outcomes for player 1, and place these in a column to the right of the pay-off matrix. These are called the **row minima** (i.e. the column shows the minimum for each row).

Because the elements of the matrix are now player 2's outcomes with the sign reversed, the column of worst outcomes for player 2 now becomes the row of maximum values for each of the columns. These are called the **column maxima**.

This new system of labelling is shown in Table 8.7.

	A	B	C	Row minima
A	2	−1	1	(−1) ←
B	1	−2	−3	−3
Column maxima	2	(−1)	1	

Table 8.7

This is called the min (column maxima).

This is called the max (row minima).

A stable solution occurs because −1 is the minimum value in row A, and also the maximum value in column B.

In general, a stable solution occurs when the maximum of the row minima equals the minimum of the column maxima.

A zero-sum game has a stable solution if and only if

> the max (row minima) = the min (column maxima)

If a stable solution exists, it is the best strategy for both players.

Exercise 8.1

① The pay-off matrix for a zero-sum game between players 1 and 2 is as follows.

	A	B	C
A	2	0	1
B	−1	3	−4

Table 8.8

(i) Determine the pay-off matrix from player 2's point of view.

(ii) What is the most that player 2 can win?

(iii) What is the most that player 2 can lose?

② The pay-off matrix for a zero-sum game between players 1 and 2 is as follows.

	A	B	C
A	0	1	1
B	−1	5	2
C	4	−2	−3

Table 8.9

(i) What will be the outcome if both players play safe?

(ii) What will be the outcome if player 1 plays safe, and player 2 hears of player 1's intention?

(iii) What will be the outcome if (instead) player 2 plays safe, and player 1 hears of player 2's intention?

③ The pay-off matrix for a zero-sum game between players 1 and 2 is as follows.

	A	B	C
A	4	−1	2
B	0	−3	−2
C	−3	−2	6
D	−5	−4	3

Table 8.10

Show that this game has a stable solution, and give the value of the game.

④ For each of the following pay-off matrices for zero-sum games, determine the play-safe strategies for player 1 and player 2, or say if there is no stable solution.

(i)

	A	B
A	1	−1
B	2	0

Table 8.11

(ii)

	A	B	C	D
A	3	2	0	1
B	1	−2	−1	0

Table 8.12

(iii)

	A	B	C
A	−2	1	4
B	0	2	−1
C	3	−3	0

Table 8.13

(iv)

	A	B
A	1	3
B	2	0
C	4	−1

Table 8.14

⑤ For the pay-off matrices in question 4, identify any stable solutions and give the values of the games in these cases.

⑥ Show that if $a < b < c < d$, then a stable solution will exist for the zero–sum game pay-off matrix shown in Table 8.15.

	A	B
A	a	b
B	d	c

Table 8.15

2 Dominated strategies

Where a stable solution doesn't exist, it may be possible to devise a strategy for both players where neither player's choices are predictable. This is referred to as a **mixed strategy**, and is considered in the next section.

However, before adopting this strategy, there is one simplifying process that can often be applied. This involves the idea of **dominance**.

	A	**B**	**C**
A	1	2	2
B	−2	1	2
C	3	−1	0

Table 8.16

Referring to the pay-off matrix in Table 8.16 (which, by convention, is from player 1's point of view), you see that player 2 would never choose option C, because option B would always be either better or of equal value (from player 2's point of view), whatever choice player 1 made. Column B is said to **dominate** column C, and the pay-off matrix can be reduced to that in Table 8.17.

	A	**B**
A	1	2
B	−2	1
C	3	−1

Table 8.17

Similarly, for the new matrix in Table 8.17, player 1 would never choose option B, as row A dominates row B, and you can reduce the matrix further to that in Table 8.18.

	A	**B**
A	1	2
C	3	−1

Table 8.18

As will be seen in Exercise 8.2, using the idea of dominance sometimes leads to a 1 × 1 matrix, which gives the value of the game directly.

Exercise 8.2

① Consider the following pay-off matrix.

	A	**B**	**C**	**D**
A	2	1	3	3
B	0	0	−1	0
C	1	1	0	0

Table 8.19

(i) Which option(s) should player 1 never choose?

(ii) Which option(s) should player 2 never choose?

② For each of the pay-off matrices in question 4 of Exercise 8.1, identify any dominated strategies, and give the reduced matrix in these cases.

③ (i) Show that there is a stable solution for the following pay-off matrix, without reducing the matrix. Give the value of the game.

	A	B	C	D	E
A	1	0	−1	2	3
B	1	2	0	1	2
C	2	1	−1	4	3

Table 8.20

(ii) Reduce the pay-off matrix, as far as possible.

④ Reduce the following pay-off matrix as much as possible, and show that there is no stable solution to the game.

	A	B	C	D
A	2	−1	0	4
B	0	6	2	2
C	4	0	1	1
D	1	−3	−1	2
E	−2	3	1	−3

Table 8.21

⑤ For what values of x can the following pay-off matrix be reduced?

	A	B	C
A	2	x	1
B	1	4	0

Table 8.22

3 Optimal mixed strategies

In a mixed strategy the players select their options with a certain probability, so that their expected outcomes are optimised. Because the games are zero-sum, the expected outcome of one player is the expected outcome of the other, with the sign reversed.

A mixed strategy can be employed whenever the pay-off matrix is of order $2 \times n$ (where $n \geqslant 2$), after the matrix has been reduced due to any dominance.

You start by looking at the 2×2 case.

Example 8.1

Establish whether there is a stable solution for the zero-sum game given by the following pay-off matrix.

	A	B	Row minima
A	1	2	①
C	3	−1	−1
Column maxima	3	②	

Table 8.23

> Compare the max (row minima) with the min (column maxima).

Solution

Max (row minima) = 1

Min (column maxima) = 2

As these values are not equal, there is not a stable solution.

> **Note**
>
> In Table 8.23, you see that if player 1 plays safe, they choose option A, as this guarantees that the worst outcome is 1 (as opposed to a worst outcome of −1 if option C is chosen).
>
> Similarly, player 2 will choose option B, as this guarantees a worst outcome of −2 (2 for player 1), compared with the worst outcome of −3 if option A is chosen.
>
> This means that the actual outcome is 2 for player 1 and −2 for player 2.
>
> If player 1 knows that player 2 will always choose option B, then they are happy to choose option A (as 2 > −1). But if player 2 knows that player 1 will always choose option A, then player 2 will want to change their choice to option A (as 1 < 2, or −1 > −2 from player 2's point of view).
>
> But if player 1 knows that player 2 will choose option A, then player 1 will now want to choose option C, and so on. It can be shown that a stable solution is never obtained.

The following problems occur when there is no stable solution.

- Neither player can safely assume what the other player's choice will be.

- Where the game is repeated, one player may take advantage of the other, if their choice becomes predictable.

It is possible to find a strategy for each player that avoids these problems, by deliberately introducing an element of uncertainty, so that each player makes their choice with certain probabilities. This is the mixed strategy already mentioned.

For the 2×2 matrix in Table 8.23, suppose that player 1 adopts option A with probability p, and option C with probability $1 - p$.

Player 1's expected pay-off depends on player 2's choice.

- If player 2 chooses option A, then player 1's expected pay-off is

  $1p + 3(1 - p) = 3 - 2p.$

- If, instead, player 2 chooses option B, then player 1's expected pay-off is

  $2p + (-1)(1 - p) = 3p - 1.$

These expected pay-offs are functions of p, and can be shown graphically, as in Figure 8.1.

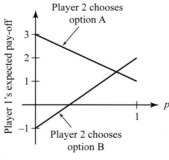

Figure 8.1

You see that player 1 can maximise their expected pay-off (obtaining 3) when player 2 chooses option A, by setting $p = 0$. However, they would risk receiving a pay-off of only −1 if player 2 chose option B. Similarly, if player 2 chooses option B, player 1's expected gain is maximised (obtaining 2) by setting $p = 1$, but they risk obtaining only 1 if player 2 chooses option A instead.

The safest strategy is to assume that player 2's choice always results in the worst possible outcome for player 1, so that whatever you set p equal to, player 1's expected pay-off is given by the lower of the two lines.

This means that you need to look for the value of p such that the lower of the two lines is as high as possible, and this occurs where the two lines intersect.

Example 8.2

Find the required value of p for the zero-sum game shown by the pay-off matrix in Table 8.23.

Note

It does not matter whether the game is repeated: the expected pay-off for each game is 1.4, regardless of the number of games played.

Solution

$$3 - 2p = 3p - 1 \Rightarrow 4 = 5p \Rightarrow p = 0.8$$

> To find where the two lines intersect you need to solve their equations simultaneously.

With this value for p, player 1 does not mind what player 2 does: if the game is repeated, player 2 might choose the same option all the time, or they might themselves choose their option according to a probability rule.

Player 1's expected pay-off is $3 - 2p$ (or $3p - 1$) $= 1.4$

Example 8.3

Find the probability rule that player 2 should adopt, and their expected pay-off.

Solution

Suppose that player 2 adopts option A with probability q, and option B with probability $1 - q$.

If player 1 chooses option A, then player 2's expected pay-off is

$$-\{1q + 2(1 - q)\} = q - 2$$

> The minus sign is needed because the values in the pay-off matrix show player 2's losses, not gains.

If, instead, player 1 chooses option C, then player 2's expected pay-off is

$$-\{3q + (-1)(1 - q)\} = 1 - 4q$$

It is not essential to draw the graphs. However, they are shown in Figure 8.2.

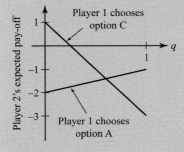

Figure 8.2

You then find the required value of q from $q - 2 = 1 - 4q \Rightarrow 5q = 3 \Rightarrow q = 0.6$

Player 2's expected pay-off is $q - 2$ (or $1 - 4q$) $= -1.4$

As this is a zero-sum game, it is no surprise that player 2's expected pay-off is just player 1's expected pay-off with the sign reversed.

$2 \times n$ and $n \times 2$ matrices

This method can be extended to $2 \times n$ matrices, i.e. where player 2 has n choices.

In the case of $n \times 2$ matrices, where player 1 has n choices, the method cannot be used to find player 1's probability rule, as this would require more than one probability variable (instead of the single p).

However, the value of the game can be established by swapping the roles of player 1 and player 2, to obtain a $2 \times n$ matrix, and then find player 1's probability rule.

Example 8.4

Find expressions, in terms of p, for player 1's expected pay-off, for each of player 2's three options, for the pay-off matrix in Table 8.24.

Draw the graphs of the corresponding straight lines on a single diagram.

	A	B	C
A	0	−1	2
B	2	3	−2

Table 8.24

Solution

The first step is always to check if the matrix can be reduced, due to any dominance of either rows or columns. Here there is no dominance.

As before, suppose that player 1 adopts option A with probability p and option B with probability $1 - p$.

If player 2 chooses option A, then player 1's expected pay-off is

$0p + 2(1 - p) = 2 - 2p$

If player 2 chooses option B, then the expected pay-off is

$(-1)p + 3(1 - p) = 3 - 4p$

If player 2 chooses option C, the expected pay-off is

$2p + (-2)(1 - p) = 4p - 2$

The graphs of the three straight lines are shown in Figure 8.3.

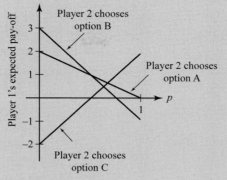

Figure 8.3

Once again, you need to look for the value of p such that the lowest of the lines is as high as possible. This occurs where the lines for options B and C intersect. Note that it was necessary to draw the graphs in order to see this.

Hence $3 - 4p = 4p - 2$, so that $5 = 8p$ and $p = \frac{5}{8}$.

With this value of p, the expected pay-off for player 1 is $3 - 4p$ (or $4p - 2$) $= \frac{1}{2}$ (this is the value of the game).

The following example shows a device that can be used to find player 2's probability rule, where player 2 has three options.

Example 8.5

Find player 2's probability rule for the pay-off matrix (Table 8.24) of Example 8.4.

Solution

Suppose that player 2 adopts options A, B and C with probabilities q, r and $1 - q - r$, respectively.

If player 1 chooses option A, then player 2's expected pay-off is

> The minus sign is needed because the values in the pay-off matrix show player 2's losses, not gains.

$-\{0q + (-1)r + 2(1 - q - r)\} = -2 + 2q + 3r$

If, instead, player 1 chooses option B, then player 2's expected pay-off is

$-\{2q + 3r + (-2)(1 - q - r)\} = 2 - 4q - 5r$

As usual, the probability rule is chosen in such a way that the expected pay-offs are the same, whichever option player 1 chooses, and both are equal to the value of the game from player 2's point of view. (This corresponds to the intersection of the lines in the simple 2×2 case.)

So $-2 + 2q + 3r = 2 - 4q - 5r = -\frac{1}{2}$ (as the value of the game from player 1's point of view is $\frac{1}{2}$, from Example 8.4).

These equations can be written as

$-4 + 4q + 6r = -1$ and $4 - 8q - 10r = -1$
or $4q + 6r = 3$ ① and $8q + 10r = 5$ ②.

$2 \times$ ① $-$ ② gives $2r = 1$, so that $r = 0.5$, and $q = 0$.

> Remember to always state the probabilities at the end of your calculation.

Thus the probability rule for player 2 is to never choose option A and choose options B and C with equal probability (0.5).

135

① (i) Show that there is no stable solution for the following pay-off matrix.

	A	B
A	3	2
B	1	4

Table 8.25

(ii) Use a mixed strategy to find the value of the game.

② (i) Consider the game with the following pay-off matrix.

	A	B
A	1	2
B	3	0
C	−1	0
D	−1	4

Table 8.26

Are there any choices that either player should never make?

(ii) Find the value of the game.

③ Use a mixed strategy to find the values for player 1 of the games having the following pay-off matrices.

(i)

	A	B
A	1	4
B	5	3

Table 8.27

(ii)

	A	B	C
A	−1	2	5
B	9	7	3

Table 8.28

(iii)

	A	B
A	−1	5
B	2	4
C	7	3

Table 8.29

④ Determine optimal strategies for both players for the game with the following pay-off matrix, and draw a graph to illustrate the situation from player 1's point of view.

	A	B
A	3	−1
B	2	4

Table 8.30

⑤ Determine the value of the game with the following pay-off matrix.

	A	B	C
A	5	2	−3
B	−1	4	6

Table 8.31

⑥ Determine optimal strategies for both players for the game with the following pay-off matrix, and establish the value of the game.

	A	B	C
A	4	3	2
B	−2	1	4
C	2	1	5

Table 8.32

4 Converting games to linear programming problems

So far, you have established methods for dealing with the following situations:

- 2×2 pay-off matrices
- cases where there is dominance, so that the pay-off matrix can be reduced
- $2 \times n$ or $n \times 2$ pay-off matrices.

For other orders of matrices, you can turn to linear programming methods.

In order to illustrate the method, consider the pay-off matrix in Table 8.33. This uses the same numbers as in Table 8.24 (swapping the roles of the two players in Table 8.24), and the value of the game can be found to be $\frac{1}{2}$.

Note

This is a new example, where player 1 now has three options.

		A	B
A		0	2
B		−1	3
C		2	−2

Table 8.33

Suppose that player 1 chooses the three options with probabilities p_1, p_2 and p_3.

Let v be the value of the game.

In order for the Simplex method to work, you require the control variables to be non-negative. The probabilities are non-negative, but you also want $v \geqslant 0$. Suppose that the pay-off matrix is of the general form shown in Table 8.34, and that any dominance has been removed.

		A	B
A		λ_1	μ_1
B		λ_2	μ_2
C		λ_3	μ_3

Table 8.34

Then, as before, v will be found from the intersection of $\lambda_1 p_1 + \lambda_2 p_2 + \lambda_3 p_3$ and $\mu_1 p_1 + \mu_2 p_2 + \mu_3 p_3$,

so that $v = \lambda_1 p_1 + \lambda_2 p_2 + \lambda_3 p_3 = \mu_1 p_1 + \mu_2 p_2 + \mu_3 p_3$

In order for the Simplex method to work, you need to have positive values for the λ_i and μ_i. The reason for this will be explained shortly.

As it is only the relative values of the elements that are important, you can add any amount to all of the elements, provided you subtract it from the expected pay-off. For the present example, you can add 3 to each element, to produce the matrix in Table 8.35.

		A	B
A		3	5
B		2	6
C		5	1

Table 8.35

Using this new matrix, the expected pay-offs for player 1 are $3p_1 + 2p_2 + 5p_3$ or $5p_1 + 6p_2 + 1p_3$, depending on whether player 2 chooses option A or option B.

As before, assume the worst-case scenario; namely that, whatever probabilities are adopted, player 2's choice will always result in v being the lower of $3p_1 + 2p_2 + 5p_3$ and $5p_1 + 6p_2 + 1p_3$. Given this constraint, aim to maximise v.

Also, $p_1 + p_2 + p_3 = 1$, but for the purpose of linear programming an inequality is required. However, it is possible to write $p_1 + p_2 + p_3 \leqslant 1$, for the following reason:

Suppose that v has been maximised with $p_1 + p_2 + p_3 < 1$. Then it would be possible to increase one of the probabilities, and thereby increase both $3p_1 + 2p_2 + 5p_3$ and $5p_1 + 6p_2 + 1p_3$, so that the lower of these expressions would be increased, giving a higher value for v, which contradicts the assumption that v has been maximised. So $p_1 + p_2 + p_3 < 1$ isn't possible, and therefore $p_1 + p_2 + p_3 = 1$.

Note that, in the above argument, when one of the probabilities is increased, the expressions for v (in general, $\lambda_1 p_1 + \lambda_2 p_2 + \lambda_3 p_3$ and $\mu_1 p_1 + \mu_2 p_2 + \mu_3 p_3$) can only be guaranteed to increase if the λ_i and p_i are all positive.

The linear programming problem can therefore be expressed as

maximise $p = v - 3$ subject to

$v \leqslant 3p_1 + 2p_2 + 5p_3$
$v \leqslant 5p_1 + 6p_2 + 1p_3$
$p_1 + p_2 + p_3 \leqslant 1$
$p_1, p_2, p_3 \geqslant 0.$

This can be solved using the Simplex method.

Example 8.6

Use the Simplex method to find the value of the game with the following pay-off matrix.

		A	B
		A	**B**
A		1	2
B		3	−1

Table 8.36

> You have already found this value to be 1.4 in Example 8.2.

Solution

Add 2 to each element, so that all elements are positive, to give the following matrix.

		A	B
		A	**B**
A		3	4
B		5	1

Table 8.37

Maximise $P = v - 2$, subject to the constraints

$v \leqslant 3p_1 + 5p_2, v \leqslant 4p_1 + p_2, p_1 + p_2 \leqslant 1$ $(p_1, p_2 \geqslant 0, v > 0).$

Introducing slack variables, the Simplex equations are

$P - v = -2$

$v - 3p_1 - 5p_2 + s_1 = 0$

$v - 4p_1 - p_2 + s_2 = 0$

$p_1 + p_2 + s_3 = 1$

The Simplex tableau is shown in Table 8.38.

P	v	p_1	p_2	s_1	s_2	s_3	Value	Equation
1	−1	0	0	0	0	0	−2	①
0	①	−3	−5	1	0	0	0	②
0	1	−4	−1	0	1	0	0	③
0	0	1	1	0	0	1	1	④
1	0	−3	−5	1	0	0	−2	⑤ = ① + ⑥
0	1	−3	−5	1	0	0	0	⑥ = ②
0	0	−1	④	−1	1	0	0	⑦ = ③ − ⑥
0	0	1	1	0	0	1	1	⑧ = ④
1	0	$-\dfrac{17}{4}$	0	$-\dfrac{1}{4}$	$\dfrac{5}{4}$	0	−2	⑨ = ⑤ + 5 × ⑪
0	1	$-\dfrac{17}{4}$	0	$-\dfrac{1}{4}$	$\dfrac{5}{4}$	0	0	⑩ = ⑥ + 5 × ⑪
0	0	$-\dfrac{1}{4}$	1	$-\dfrac{1}{4}$	$\dfrac{1}{4}$	0	0	⑪ = ⑦ ÷ 4
0	0	$\left(\dfrac{5}{4}\right)$	0	$\dfrac{1}{4}$	$-\dfrac{1}{4}$	1	1	⑫ = ⑧ − ⑪
1	0	0	0	$\dfrac{3}{5}$	$\dfrac{2}{5}$	0	$\dfrac{7}{5}$	⑬ = ⑨ + $\dfrac{17}{4}$ × ⑯
0	1	0	0	$\dfrac{3}{5}$	$\dfrac{2}{5}$	0	$\dfrac{17}{5}$	⑭ = ⑩ + $\dfrac{17}{4}$ × ⑯
0	0	0	1	$-\dfrac{1}{5}$	$\dfrac{1}{5}$	$\dfrac{1}{5}$	$\dfrac{1}{5}$	⑮ = ⑪ + $\dfrac{1}{4}$ × ⑯
0	0	1	0	$\dfrac{1}{5}$	$-\dfrac{1}{5}$	$\dfrac{4}{5}$	$\dfrac{4}{5}$	⑯ = ⑫ × $\dfrac{4}{5}$

Table 8.38

The maximised value of P is $\dfrac{7}{5} = 1.4$, as before.

Also, as a check, $p_1 + p_2 = 1$, where $p_1 = \dfrac{4}{5}$ and $p_2 = \dfrac{1}{5}$, also as before.

Exercise 8.4

① Formulate the linear programming problem that can be used to find the value of the game with the following pay-off matrix.

	A	B
A	1	3
B	2	0
C	4	−1

Table 8.39

② Use the Simplex method to find the value of the game in question 1 of Exercise 8.3, with the following pay-off matrix.

	A	B
A	3	2
B	1	4

Table 8.40

③ Use the Simplex method to find the values of the games in question 3 of Exercise 8.3.

④ Formulate the linear programming problem that can be used to find the value of the game with the following pay-off matrix. Write down the initial Simplex equations.

	A	B
A	−2	−1
B	−3	0
C	1	−2

Table 8.41

⑤ Establish the initial Simplex tableau that can be used to find the value of the game with the following pay-off matrix.

	A	B
A	4	−3
B	−1	2

Table 8.42

⑥ For what value(s) of x is there a stable solution for the following pay-off matrix?

	A	B
A	2	x
B	0	3
C	1	2

Table 8.43

⑦ A mathematical board game for two players is being trialled. When player 1 lands on a particular square, the amount he or she wins is the highest common factor of two numbers. These numbers are chosen from three specified numbers, with each player choosing one of the numbers (they can both choose the same number). Player 2 is trying to minimise the amount that player 1 wins.

Janet and John are playing this game, and Janet lands on a square with the numbers 24, 30 and 45.

(i) Which numbers should Janet and John choose if they adopt play-safe strategies, and how much will Janet win in that case?

(ii) If (unknown to Janet) John has forgotten how to work out a highest common factor, and chooses his number at random, what amount can Janet expect to win, on average?

LEARNING OUTCOMES

Now you have finished this chapter, you should be able to

➤ understand, interpret and construct pay-off matrices
➤ find play-safe strategies and the value of the game
➤ prove the existence or non-existence of a stable solution
➤ identify and make use of dominated strategies
➤ find optimal mixed strategies for a game, including use of graphical methods
➤ convert higher-order games to linear programming problems, and solve them.

KEY POINTS

1 In a zero-sum game between two players, if player 1 wins a certain amount, then player 2 loses that amount.
2 The pay-off matrix shows the possible gains from player 1's point of view.
3 A play-safe strategy is where a player chooses the option with the smallest downside.
4 A stable solution exists when it is in both players' interests to adopt the play-safe strategy. This occurs when the maximum of the row minima equals the minimum of the column maxima.
5 A pay-off matrix can be reduced if one strategy dominates another.
6 In a mixed strategy, the players select their options with a certain probability in such a way that their expected outcomes are optimised.
7 The value of a game is player 1's pay-off, where there is a stable solution; or their expected pay-off when a mixed strategy is employed.
8 A mixed strategy can be employed whenever the (reduced) pay-off matrix is of order $2 \times n$ or $n \times 2$.
9 In more complicated cases, the Simplex method may be employed.

Transportation problems

→ Andi is an artist who has five paintings for sale: three large paintings and two small paintings. Ben will buy four of the paintings and Chiara will buy the other one. They have no preference based on the artistic merits of the paintings. Including delivery costs, each large painting costs Ben £500 or Chiara £620 and each small painting costs Ben £200 or Chiara £310.

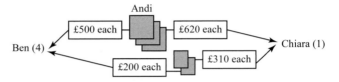

How many large paintings should Ben buy to minimise the total cost for Ben and Chiara?

1 Finding initial solutions

In many situations involving logistics, such as in industry and retailing, the cost of transporting goods can sometimes make a big difference to the profits that a company makes. Goods may be made in several different factories and need to be transported to warehouses and then transported from the warehouses to shops. The location of the various factories, warehouses and shops will affect the transportation costs.

The goods will be transported from **sources** (or suppliers) to **destinations**.

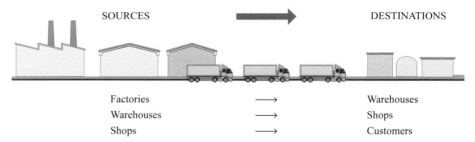

Factories	⟶	Warehouses
Warehouses	⟶	Shops
Shops	⟶	Customers

Figure 9.1

This can be modelled using a network in which the sources and destinations are represented as vertices and the possible routes between them as edges. The edge weights will show the transport costs.

For simplicity, the goods will be transported in whole numbers of units. A **unit** is any standard-sized container load. This may be a single item, a crate, a vanload, and so on.

The **unit cost** is the cost of transporting one unit from a given source to a given destination. The goods will all be transported at the same time, rather than there being a continuous flow of deliveries.

Note

Supply may be referred to as **availabilities** and the demand as **requirements**.

The amount (number of units) available at each source is called the **stock** or **supply** and the amount (number of units) required at each destination is called the **demand**. The total demand must not exceed the total stock. Often the total stock will equal the total demand and then there is no excess.

Example 9.1

A chain of furniture shops needs to supply beds to three of its showrooms. The beds are stored in four warehouses and are delivered to the showrooms in vans that carry ten beds each.

The cost (in £) of supplying a vanload of ten beds from each warehouse to each showroom is shown in the table below. The stock (in units of vanloads) at each warehouse and the demand (in units of vanloads) at each showroom are shown in the right-hand column and the bottom row of the table.

		Destination		
£	Showroom X	Showroom Y	Showroom Z	Stock or supply
Warehouse A	300	100	200	6
Warehouse B	200	400	300	4
Warehouse C	400	300	200	5
Warehouse D	300	200	100	4
Demand	6	5	5	

Source (label for the warehouse rows)

Table 9.1

(i) What is the cost of transporting 6 vanloads from warehouse A to showroom X?

(ii) What is the cheapest way to supply 5 vanloads to showroom Z?

(iii) How many more units (vanloads) are available than are required?

Note

There are 6 vanloads available at A and 6 required at X.

The cheapest unit cost to Z is 100 from D. But the stock at D is only 4 vanloads.

This is the excess stock.

Solution

(i) The unit cost is 300 so it costs £300 for each vanload. The cost is $6 \times £300 = £1800$.

(ii) 4 vanloads from D and 1 vanload from either A or C.

$(4 \times £100) + (1 \times £200) = £600$

(iii) Total stock = $6 + 4 + 5 + 4 = 19$ units (vanloads).

Total demand = $6 + 5 + 5 = 16$ units (vanloads).

There are 3 more units (vanloads) available than are required.

Note

Each cell in the table represents a transport route from a source to a destination. Multiple units may be transported along a route (subject to the supply and demand requirements).

The table in Example 9.1 is really a merge of two tables, one showing the unit costs (Table 9.2) and the other showing the stock at each source and the demand at each destination (Table 9.3).

£	X	Y	Z
A	300	100	200
B	200	400	300
C	400	300	200
D	300	200	100

Table 9.2

Units	X	Y	Z	Stock
A				6
B				4
C				5
D				4
Demand	6	5	5	

Table 9.3

Note

An extreme case is one where as many units as possible are allocated to one supplier at the start, and again at each stage, for a given destination, whilst satisfying the constraints.

It is important to be aware of whether an entry in a cell is the unit cost or the number of units being transported on that route.

A valid way to transport units from the sources to the destinations so that all the demand is met is called a **feasible solution**. An extreme case of a feasible solution is a **basic feasible solution**.

The transportation problem is about finding the least-cost basic feasible solution.

Example 9.2

For the problem in Example 9.1, find the cost of each of the following solutions.

(i)

Units	From	To
6	A	X
4	B	Y
1	C	Y
4	C	Z
1	D	Z

Table 9.4

(ii)

Units	From	To
5	A	Y
3	B	X
5	C	Z
3	D	X

Table 9.5

This is a solution because there is sufficient stock at the warehouses and it meets the demands at the showrooms.

This is a better solution because it costs less.

Solution

(i) $(6 \times £300) + (4 \times £400) + (1 \times £300) + (4 \times £200) + (1 \times £100)$
$= £4600$

(ii) $(5 \times £100) + (3 \times £200) + (5 \times £200) + (3 \times £300) = £3000$

The strategy for solving a transportation problem is described below.

Step 1 Find an initial basic feasible solution that satisfies all the demands and calculate the total cost of this solution.

Step 2 Check whether the total cost can be reduced by transporting some of the goods using a route that is not currently included. If no such improvement is possible, then the solution is optimal.

Step 3 If an improvement can be made, transfer as many units as possible to the new route to get an improved solution and calculate the total cost of this solution.

Step 4 Repeat from Step 2 until an optimal solution is achieved.

The north-west corner method

For a large problem it could be difficult to find an initial solution in Step 1, so a method is used for this step. This is called the north-west corner method.

Step 1	Make a table with the sources on the rows and the destinations on the columns. Record the stock or supply at each source at the end of its row and the demand at each destination at the bottom of its column. The cells in the table will be used to record the number of units transported on that route. Initially, all the cells are empty.
Step 2	Start with the cell in the first row and first column (the north-west corner) and allocate the maximum number of units that can be delivered using this route, without exceeding the stock or the demand.
Step 3	If there is stock remaining at the source on this row, move to the next column and continue the allocation. If all the stock is used at the source on this row, move to the next row down and continue the allocation. If the cell moved to has all its stock used and all its demand met, give it an entry of 0. It is important to realise that a zero is different from a blank entry.
Step 4	Stop when all the demands are met.

To avoid degenerate solutions (see page 148), movements are made in a zig-zag fashion, moving horizontally or vertically but never diagonally. An entry of 0 is used to avoid a diagonal movement.

Example 9.3

Use the north-west corner method to construct an initial basic feasible solution for the problem in Example 9.1.

Destination

		X	Y	Z	Stock
Source	**A**				6
	B				4
	C				5
	D				4
	Demand	6	5	5	

Table 9.6

Solution

Start in cell (A, X) and send 6 units from A to X. The stock at A is all used so move to row B.

	X	Y	Z	Stock
A	6			6
B				4
C				5
D				4
Demand	6	5	5	

Table 9.7

→

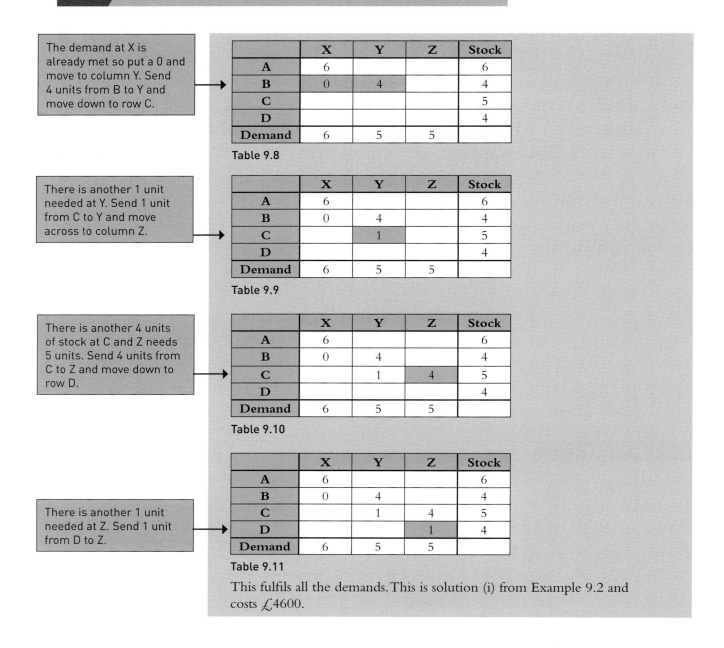

The demand at X is already met so put a 0 and move to column Y. Send 4 units from B to Y and move down to row C.

	X	Y	Z	Stock
A	6			6
B	0	4		4
C				5
D				4
Demand	6	5	5	

Table 9.8

There is another 1 unit needed at Y. Send 1 unit from C to Y and move across to column Z.

	X	Y	Z	Stock
A	6			6
B	0	4		4
C		1		5
D				4
Demand	6	5	5	

Table 9.9

There is another 4 units of stock at C and Z needs 5 units. Send 4 units from C to Z and move down to row D.

	X	Y	Z	Stock
A	6			6
B	0	4		4
C		1	4	5
D				4
Demand	6	5	5	

Table 9.10

There is another 1 unit needed at Z. Send 1 unit from D to Z.

	X	Y	Z	Stock
A	6			6
B	0	4		4
C		1	4	5
D			1	4
Demand	6	5	5	

Table 9.11

This fulfils all the demands. This is solution (i) from Example 9.2 and costs £4600.

Example 9.4

Use the north–west corner method to construct an initial basic feasible solution for the following transportation problem.

		Destination			
		X	Y	Z	Supply
Source	A				5
	B				6
	C				9
	Demand	6	4	10	

Table 9.12

Solution

Send 5 units from A to X. The supply at A is all used so move to row B.

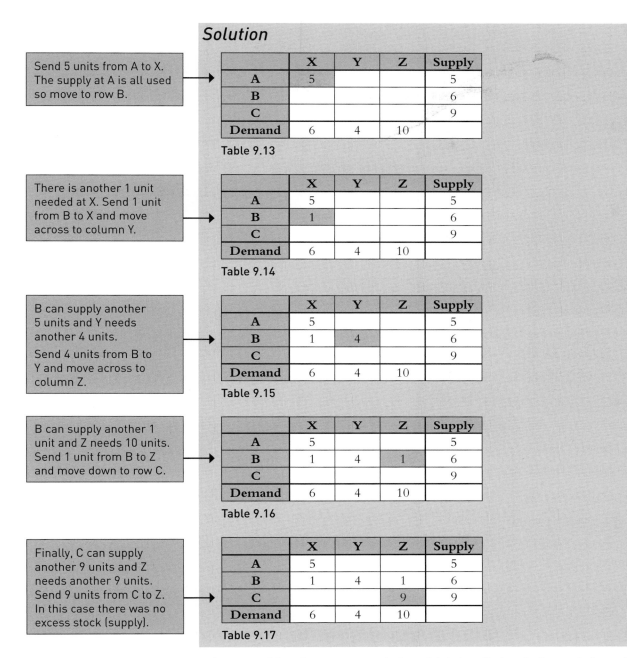

	X	Y	Z	Supply
A	5			5
B				6
C				9
Demand	6	4	10	

Table 9.13

There is another 1 unit needed at X. Send 1 unit from B to X and move across to column Y.

	X	Y	Z	Supply
A	5			5
B	1			6
C				9
Demand	6	4	10	

Table 9.14

B can supply another 5 units and Y needs another 4 units.

Send 4 units from B to Y and move across to column Z.

	X	Y	Z	Supply
A	5			5
B	1	4		6
C				9
Demand	6	4	10	

Table 9.15

B can supply another 1 unit and Z needs 10 units. Send 1 unit from B to Z and move down to row C.

	X	Y	Z	Supply
A	5			5
B	1	4	1	6
C				9
Demand	6	4	10	

Table 9.16

Finally, C can supply another 9 units and Z needs another 9 units. Send 9 units from C to Z. In this case there was no excess stock (supply).

	X	Y	Z	Supply
A	5			5
B	1	4	1	6
C			9	9
Demand	6	4	10	

Table 9.17

When a problem has excess stock (supply) it is called **unbalanced**. An unbalanced problem can be converted into a balanced problem by introducing a dummy destination with demand equalling the excess stock and with unit costs of £0.

Example 9.5

Convert the problem in Example 9.3 into a balanced problem and apply the north-west corner method to find an initial basic feasible solution.

	X	Y	Z	Stock
A				6
B				4
C				5
D				4
Demand	6	5	5	

Table 9.18

Solution

The total stock is 19 units and the total demand is 16 units, so the excess stock is 3 units. Introduce a dummy destination with demand = 3.

	X	Y	Z	Dummy	Stock
A					6
B					4
C					5
D					4
Demand	6	5	5	3	

Table 9.19

The zig-zag path will be the same as in Example 9.3 until the cell (D, Z) is completed. At this point all the original demand has been met. Now move across to the dummy column.

	X	Y	Z	Dummy	Stock
A	6				6
B	0	4			4
C		1	4		5
D			1		4
Demand	6	5	5	3	

Table 9.20

There are another 3 units of stock at D, which matches the demand at the dummy. Send 3 units from D to the dummy.

	X	Y	Z	Dummy	Stock
A	6				6
B	0	4			4
C		1	4		5
D			1	3	4
Demand	6	5	5	3	

Table 9.21

An unbalanced problem should always be made into a balanced problem by adding a dummy destination.

Provided 0s are used to avoid degenerate solutions, the cells used will always form a zig-zag from the north-west corner to the south-east corner. This path will pass through every column and every row.

The number of cells used (the number of routes used plus the number of 0s) for a balanced problem is given by:
number of sources + number of destinations − 1.

The cells used are the ones with numerical values in them.

An unbalanced problem will not satisfy this rule if any source remains unused.

If a feasible solution exists for which fewer than (number of rows + number of columns − 1) routes are used, then the problem is **degenerate** and 0s must be used to make up the shortfall. This will happen when a cell in the middle of the table uses all the stock and satisfies the demand at the same time.

It is always useful to check that for any solution the number of cells used equals number of rows + number of columns − 1.

ACTIVITY 9.1

Verify that the rule above holds for the solutions found in Example 9.4 and Example 9.5.

Exercise 9.1

① The table shows the cost (in £) of transporting 1 unit along routes from three factories to two warehouses.

Destination

£	Warehouse 1	Warehouse 2
Factory 1	56	19
Factory 2	29	64
Factory 3	43	37

Source

Table 9.22

(i) Calculate the cost of transporting 1 unit from factory 1 to warehouse 1 and 2 units from factory 2 to warehouse 2.

(ii) How much cheaper would it be to transport these units from factory 3 instead?

② A balanced transportation problem has two sources and four destinations. How many cells are used in the initial basic feasible solution given by the north–west corner method?

③ For the situation in question 1, each factory has 10 units in stock, the demand from warehouse 1 is for 8 units and the demand from warehouse 2 is for 22 units.

(i) Use the north-west corner method to find an initial basic feasible solution.

(ii) Find the cost of this solution.

④ A transportation problem has four sources, A, B, C, D, and three destinations, P, Q, R. The stock is 5 units at A, 6 units at B, 4 units at C and 2 units at D. The demand is 8 units at P 3 units at Q and 6 units at R.

(i) Use the north-west corner method to find an initial basic feasible solution for this problem.

(ii) Use this solution to explain what it means for a solution to be degenerate.

⑤ The unit costs, stock and demand for a transportation problem are shown in Table 9.23.

(i) Show that the problem is unbalanced and convert it into a balanced problem.

(ii) Use the north-west corner method to find an initial basic feasible solution.

(iii) Calculate the cost of this solution.

(iv) Verify that the number of cells used is given by:

number of sources + number of destinations − 1

Destination

£	Warehouse 1	Warehouse 2	Warehouse 3	Supply
Factory 1	56	24	19	8
Factory 2	29	38	64	10
Factory 3	43	16	37	12
Demand	12	10	4	

Source

Table 9.23

2 Finding an improved solution

The strategy for improving a solution in Steps 2 and 3 of the transportation problem is described below.

Step 1	Use the non-empty cells to calculate a shadow cost for each cell.
Step 2	Use the shadow costs to calculate an improvement index for each empty cell.
Step 3	Use the improvement indices and the stepping-stone method to find an improved solution.

The calculations involved are now explained.

Shadow costs

The unit cost of each route being used can be thought of as being the sum of two parts, one from its source and the other from its destination. These costs are the shadow costs at the sources and destinations. Shadow costs may be positive, zero or negative.

ACTIVITY 9.2

The table below shows the unit costs for a transportation problem.

Shadow costs		K_1	K_2
	$\pounds$	Warehouse 1	Warehouse 2
R_1	Factory 1	56	19
R_2	Factory 2	29	64
R_3	Factory 3	43	37

Table 9.24

Suppose the north-west corner method has been used to find an initial basic feasible solution for this transportation problem. The cells used in this solution are shaded in the table of unit costs.

The shadow costs are R_1, R_2, R_3, K_1 and K_2.

For each shaded cell, the unit cost is the sum of the shadow cost for its source and the shadow cost for its destination. For example, $56 = R_1 + K_1$.

(i) Use the shaded cells to write down four equations involving the five shadow costs.

(ii) Supposing that $R_1 = 0$, find the values of the other shadow costs.

Note

1 Cells that are empty in the basic feasible solution are not used in calculating shadow costs.

2 The table of unit costs is used to calculate the shadow costs (not the basic feasible solution showing how many units are transported).

3 The system of equations does not have a unique solution. Any suitable set of shadow costs can be used so, arbitrarily, you choose to set the shadow cost for the first source as zero.

Step 1	Start in the north-west corner and set the shadow cost for the source on row 1 as 0.
	For each non-empty cell in this row calculate a shadow cost for the destination in that column.
Step 2	Move to the next row and use the first non-empty cell in this row to calculate the shadow cost for the source on that row. Use the other non-empty cells in this row to find any further unknown shadow costs for destinations.
	For each cell used in the basic feasible solution:
	unit cost = shadow cost for source + shadow cost for destination
Step 3	Repeat Step 2 until all shadow costs are known.

A transportation problem involves transporting units of goods from three shops to three customers. The table shows the unit costs (in £), the supply at each shop and the demand from each customer.

		Destination			
£		**Customer P**	**Customer Q**	**Customer R**	**Supply**
Source	**Shop A**	26	54	13	8
	Shop B	9	29	104	9
	Shop C	33	36	7	12
	Demand	7	10	5	

Table 9.25

Calculate the shadow costs.

Solution

First add a dummy column, d, with demand = 29 – 22 = 7. Then use the north-west corner method to find an initial basic feasible solution.

	P	**Q**	**R**	**d**	**Supply**
A	7	1			8
B		9			9
C		0	5	7	12
Demand	7	10	5	7	

Table 9.26

Use the unit costs to calculate shadow costs.

$R_1 = 0$
$\Rightarrow K_1 = 26$ and $K_2 = 54$
$\Rightarrow R_2 = 29 - 54 = -25$
$R_3 = 36 - 54 = -18$
$\Rightarrow K_3 = 7 - (-18) = 25$
and $K_4 = 0 - (-18) = 18$

These are recorded above and to the left of the labels.

Shadow costs (£)		26	54	25	18
	Unit costs (£)	**P**	**Q**	**R**	**d**
0	**A**	26	54		
−25	**B**		29		
−18	**C**		36	7	0

Table 9.27

Improvement indices

For each cell that is empty in the basic feasible solution an **improvement index** is calculated. This shows the change in the cost when 1 unit is sent along the route represented by the cell.

Step 1 For each cell that is empty in the basic feasible solution calculate the improvement index given by:

unit cost − (shadow cost for source + shadow cost for destination).

Step 2 Choose the cell with the most negative improvement index. If there are two or more such cells, choose either. This cell will become part of the improved solution.

The cell with the most negative improvement index is called the **entering cell**.

If no cell has a negative improvement index then the basic feasible solution is optimal.

Example 9.7

(i) Calculate the improvement indices for the solution used in Example 9.6.

(ii) Hence identify the entering cell.

Solution

(i)

> The empty cells in the initial basic feasible solution are the unshaded cells. The improvement indices are listed: e.g. I_{13} is the index for cell (A, R).

Shadow costs (£)		26	54	25	18
	Unit costs (£)	P	Q	R	d
0	A	26	54	13	0
−25	B	9	29	104	0
−18	C	33	36	7	0

Table 9.28

$$I_{13} = 13 - (0 + 25) = -12, \qquad I_{14} = 0 - (0 + 18) = -18$$
$$I_{21} = 9 - (-25 + 26) = 8, \qquad I_{23} = 104 - (-25 + 25) = 104$$
$$I_{24} = 0 - (-25 + 18) = 7$$
$$I_{31} = 33 - (-18 + 26) = 25$$

> Each unit sent along this route will reduce the cost by £18.

(ii) The most negative improvement index is I_{14}, so the route from source A to the dummy destination enters the solutions and the cell from A to the dummy is the entering cell.

In Example 9.7, the route from A to the dummy enters the solution and for each unit re-routed £18 is saved.

The number of units that can be re-routed is found using the stepping–stone method.

Stepping-stone method

Step 1   Start from the entering cell.

Construct a cycle through cells where the path zig-zags, starting and ending at the entering cell, by adding or subtracting an unknown θ units so that the row and column totals still match the supply and the demand.

Step 2   Find the maximum possible value of θ such that, for each cell, the number of units being transported is not negative.

Step 3   Adjust the solution accordingly.

The cell for which the number of units becomes 0 leaves the solution and is called the **exiting cell**. The entry for this cell becomes blank.

Step 4　This solution can then be used as a new basic feasible solution. The zig-zag path may now start somewhere in the middle of the table and jump from the last row to the first row.

Check that the number of cells used equals

(number of rows + number of column) − 1.

The process is repeated to find new shadow costs and improvement indices.

Example 9.8

Use the stepping-stone method to improve the solution from Examples 9.6 and 9.7.

Solution

This table shows the unit costs and shadow costs.

Shadow costs (£)		26	54	25	18
Units	**Unit costs (£)**	**P**	**Q**	**R**	**d**
0	**A**	26	54	13	0
−25	**B**	9	29	104	0
−18	**C**	33	36	7	0

Table 9.29

This table shows the number of units being transported along each route in the current solution, with the supply and demand in the final column and bottom row. The cost of the current solution is £532.

Units	P	Q	R	d	Supply
A	7	1			8
B		9			9
C		0	5	7	12
Demand	7	10	5	7	

Table 9.30

The entering cell (entering route) is shaded in Table 9.30. This cell has improvement index −£18.

θ units are sent along the entering route (cell A, d).

Demand for the dummy = 7, so the entry in cell (C, d) is reduced to 7 − θ.

[B, d] is empty so cannot be used. [C, R] cannot be used as there are no other entries in column R to compensate for a change in the value in [C, R].

Units	P	Q	R	d	Supply
A	7	1		θ	8
B		9			9
C		0	5	7 − θ	12
Demand	7	10	5	7	

Table 9.31

The cycle then travels through (C, Q) and (A, Q) to return to (A, d).

The entry 1 − θ in cell (A, Q) becomes 0 and is then removed. (A, Q) is the exiting cell and the maximum increase is θ = 1.

Units	P	Q	R	d	Supply
A	7	1 − θ		θ	8
B		9			9
C		0 + θ	5	7 − θ	12
Demand	7	10	5	7	

Table 9.32

The solution is adjusted. Number of cells used = 6.

This is a new basic feasible solution.

Units	P	Q	R	d	Supply
A	7			1	8
B		9			9
C		1	5	6	12
Demand	7	10	5	7	

Table 9.33

The cost of this solution is £532 − 1 × £18 = £514.

This can be checked as $(7 \times 26) + (9 \times 29) + (1 \times 36) + (5 \times 7)$

This solution can now be used as the new basic feasible solution and new shadow costs and improvement indices calculated.

Units costs (£)	P	Q	R	d
A	26	54	13	0
B	9	29	104	0
C	33	36	7	0

Table 9.34

Note

1 The shadow costs are usually written above and to the left of the labels.

2 Similar to the way in which the initial information is often presented in a table showing unit costs, with the supply and demand values given in the final column and last row, the working of the solution may be presented in a table that shows the number of units transported. The shadow costs are written in the first row and first column.

Caution: Great care must be taken when the format described in note 2 is used, so that numbers of units and unit costs are not confused when calculating the shadow costs. It is probably safer to use separate tables until you are confident with using the method.

ACTIVITY 9.3

Use the unit costs to calculate the new shadow costs and improvement indices for the solution to Example 9.8. What can you conclude from the values calculated?

Example 9.9

The unit costs (in £), supply and demand for a transportation problem are shown in the table below.

£	P	Q	R	S	Supply
A	3	4	3	5	6
B	4	2	6	3	9
C	17	14	13	11	7
Demand	8	4	5	5	

Table 9.35

Find the least cost of transporting the goods.

Solution

The problem is balanced since total supply = total demand.

Use the north-west corner method to find an initial basic feasible solution.

Number of cells used = 6.

Units	P	Q	R	S	Supply
A	6				6
B	2	4	3		9
C			2	5	7
Demand	8	4	5	5	

Table 9.36

Calculate the cost of the initial basic feasible solution.

$$\text{Cost} = \pounds[(6 \times 3) + (2 \times 4) + (4 \times 2) + (3 \times 6) + (2 \times 13) + (5 \times 11)]$$
$$= \pounds 133$$

Shadow costs (£)		3	1	5	3
	£	P	Q	R	S
0	A	3	4	3	5
1	B	4	2	6	3
8	C	17	14	13	11

Table 9.37

Calculate shadow costs.

Calculate improvement indices.

$I_{12} = 3, I_{13} = -2, I_{14} = 2, I_{24} = -1, I_{31} = 6, I_{32} = 5$

So the entering cell is (A, R).

Units	P	Q	R	S	Supply
A	$6 - \theta$		θ		6
B	$2 + \theta$	4	$3 - \theta$		9
C			2	5	7
Demand	8	4	5	5	

Table 9.38

Cycle $(A, R) \rightarrow (B, R) \rightarrow (B, P) \rightarrow (A, P) \rightarrow (A, R)$
As θ increases, $3 - \theta = 0$ first.

So $\theta = 3$, and the exiting cell is (B, R).

Units	P	Q	R	S	Supply
A	3		3		6
B	5	4			9
C			2	5	7
Demand	8	4	5	5	

Table 9.39

Improved solution:
Number of cells used = 6
Cost = £133 + (3 × –£2)
= £127

Calculate new shadow costs. Be careful to change to the cost table to calculate the shadow costs.

Shadow costs (£)		3	1	3	1
	£	P	Q	R	S
0	A	3	4	3	5
1	B	4	2	6	3
10	C	17	14	13	11

Table 9.40

$I_{12} = 3, I_{14} = 4, I_{23} = 2, I_{24} = 1, I_{31} = 4, I_{32} = 3$

There are no negative improvement indices, so the current solution is optimal.

Improved solution:
A to P = 3, A to R = 3
B to P = 5, B to Q = 4
C to R = 2, C to S = 5

Least cost = £127

Using the single table formulation, the solution looks like this:

Solution

The problem is balanced since
total supply = total demand.

Use the north-west corner method to find an initial basic feasible solution.

Number of cells used = 6.

Units	P	Q	R	S	Supply
A	6				6
B	2	4	3		9
C			2	5	7
Demand	8	4	5	5	

Table 9.41

Cost = £[(6 × 3) + (2 × 4) + (4 × 2) + (3 × 6) + (2 × 13) + (5 × 11)]

= £133

Use *unit costs* for cells in the solution to calculate shadow costs. Calculate improvement indices for cells not in the solution and identify the entering cell.

Record the number of units in each cell and indicate the cycle. Find the maximum number of units that can be re-routed and identify the exiting cell.

Calculate the new cost.

Shadow costs (£)		3	1	5	3	
	Units	P	Q	R	S	Supply
0	A	$6 - \theta$		θ		6
1	B	$2 + \theta$	4	$3 - \theta$		9
8	C			2	5	7
	Demand	8	4	5	5	

Table 9.42

$I_{12} = 3, I_{13} = -2, I_{14} = 2, I_{14} = -1, I_{31} = 6, I_{32} = 5$

So the entering cell is (A, R).

$\theta = 3$, and the exiting cell is (B, R).

Cost = £133 − 3 × £2 = £127

Cells show improved solution.

Number of cells used = 6.

Use *unit costs* to calculate new shadow costs and improvement indices.

Shadow costs (£)		3	1	3	1	
	Units	P	Q	R	S	Supply
0	A	3		3		6
1	B	5	4			9
10	C			2	5	7
	Demand	8	4	5	5	

Table 9.43

$I_{12} = 3, I_{14} = 4, I_{23} = 2, I_{24} = 1, I_{31} = 4, I_{32} = 3$

There are no negative improvement indices, so the current solution is optimal.

Least cost = £127

Note

Only use this format when you are confident with doing the calculations.

① The problem at the start of the chapter is modelled as a transportation problem with unit costs (in £), stock and demands as shown in the table below.

£	B	C	Supply
A_1	500	620	3
A_2	200	310	2
Demand	4	1	

Table 9.44

Solve this transportation problem to find how many units should be transported from A_1 to B (how many large paintings Ben should buy to minimise the total cost).

② The unit costs (in £) for a transportation problem are given below. The shaded cells correspond to those that are used in the initial basic feasible solution.

£	P	Q
A	76	54
B	85	71
C	29	68

Table 9.45

(i) Calculate the shadow costs.

(ii) Calculate the improvement indices and identify the entering cell.

③ For the problem in question 2, each source can supply 10 units and each destination demands 15 units.

(i) Calculate the cost of the initial basic feasible solution.

(ii) Use the stepping-stone method to find an improved solution and give the cost of this improved solution.

(iii) Update the shadow costs and improvement indices to find a second improved solution. You do not need to check whether this solution is optimal or not.

④ (i) Explain why the shadow cost of the first source is set to be zero when shadow costs are calculated.

(ii) Describe what would happen to the shadow costs if the shadow cost for the first source were set to be some positive value, x.

(iii) Show what would happen to the values of the improvement indices if the shadow costs from part (ii) are used.

⑤ Complete the solution of Example 9.8, following the calculations done in Activity 9.3.

⑥ The unit costs (in £), stock and demand for a transportation problem are shown in the table below.

£	X	Y	Z	Supply
A	62	43	25	3
B	54	32	30	10
C	41	52	63	8
D	12	35	96	4
Demand	7	9	9	

Table 9.46

Find the least cost of transporting the goods.

3 Formulation as a linear programming problem

The idea of formulating linear programming problems and solving two-variable problems graphically is studied in AS Decision Mathematics 1. Using the Simplex algorithm to solve larger linear programming problems is studied in A level Decision Mathematics 1.

A transportation problem can be formulated as a linear programming problem with the routes corresponding to the variables. The value of each variable is then the number of units being transported along that route.

Example 9.10

Model the problem from Example 9.9 as a linear programming problem.

Solution

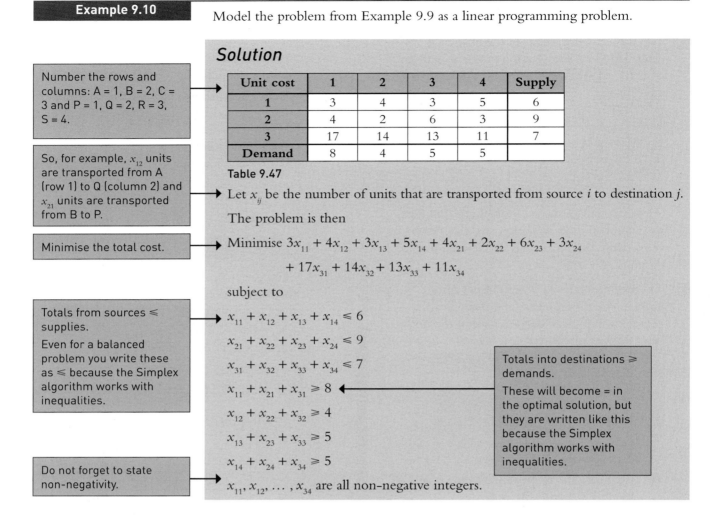

Number the rows and columns: A = 1, B = 2, C = 3 and P = 1, Q = 2, R = 3, S = 4.

Unit cost	1	2	3	4	Supply
1	3	4	3	5	6
2	4	2	6	3	9
3	17	14	13	11	7
Demand	8	4	5	5	

Table 9.47

So, for example, x_{12} units are transported from A (row 1) to Q (column 2) and x_{21} units are transported from B to P.

Let x_{ij} be the number of units that are transported from source i to destination j.

The problem is then

Minimise the total cost.

Minimise $3x_{11} + 4x_{12} + 3x_{13} + 5x_{14} + 4x_{21} + 2x_{22} + 6x_{23} + 3x_{24}$
$$+ 17x_{31} + 14x_{32} + 13x_{33} + 11x_{34}$$

subject to

Totals from sources ⩽ supplies.

Even for a balanced problem you write these as ⩽ because the Simplex algorithm works with inequalities.

$x_{11} + x_{12} + x_{13} + x_{14} \leqslant 6$

$x_{21} + x_{22} + x_{23} + x_{24} \leqslant 9$

$x_{31} + x_{32} + x_{33} + x_{34} \leqslant 7$

$x_{11} + x_{21} + x_{31} \geqslant 8$

$x_{12} + x_{22} + x_{32} \geqslant 4$

$x_{13} + x_{23} + x_{33} \geqslant 5$

$x_{14} + x_{24} + x_{34} \geqslant 5$

Totals into destinations ⩾ demands.

These will become = in the optimal solution, but they are written like this because the Simplex algorithm works with inequalities.

Do not forget to state non-negativity.

$x_{11}, x_{12}, \ldots, x_{34}$ are all non-negative integers.

The supply and demand constraints are written as inequalities because the Simplex algorithm works with inequalities. At the optimal solution, the demand constraints will all become equalities. For a balanced problem this will also be the case for the supply constraints.

This problem involves 12 variables $(x_{11}, x_{12}, \ldots, x_{34})$. In practice, any problem with more than about four variables would be solved using a computer package (rather than using the Simplex algorithm by hand). Some computer packages will accept equality constraints.

You need to be able to formulate a transportation problem as a linear programming problem that could be solved using the Simplex algorithm, but you would not be expected to solve it this way.

Step 1	Define the decision variables, $x_{11}, x_{12}, \ldots$
Step 2	Define the objective function and state that this is to be minimised.
Step 3	Use the stock at the sources to write a set of ⩽ constraints.
	Use the demands at the destinations to write a set of ⩾ constraints.
	Include non-negativity constraints.

In general, if the unit cost from i to j is c_{ij}, the stock for source i is S_i (for $i = 1, 2, \ldots, m$) and the demand at destination j is D_j (for $j = 1, 2, \ldots, n$), then the transportation problem is as follows.

$$\text{Minimise} \quad \sum_{i=1}^{m}\sum_{j=1}^{n} c_{ij}x_{ij}$$

$$\text{subject to} \quad \sum_{j=1}^{n} x_{ij} \leqslant S_i \quad \text{for each } i = 1, 2, \ldots, m$$

$$\sum_{i=1}^{m} x_{ij} \geqslant D_j \quad \text{for each } j = 1, 2, \ldots, n$$

and all the x_{ij} are non-negative integers.

Exercise 9.3

① Explain what would happen if, when a transportation problem was set up as a linear programming problem, the demand constraints were written with $\leqslant$ inequalities instead of $\geqslant$ inequalities.

② A transportation problem is formulated as the linear programming problem below.

Minimise $\quad x_{11} + 2x_{12} + 3x_{21} + x_{22} + 3x_{31} + 2x_{32}$

subject to $\quad x_{11} + x_{12} \leqslant 4$

$\qquad\qquad x_{21} + x_{22} \leqslant 7$

$\qquad\qquad x_{31} + x_{32} \leqslant 5$

$\qquad\qquad x_{11} + x_{21} + x_{31} \geqslant 10$

$\qquad\qquad x_{12} + x_{22} + x_{32} \geqslant 6$

$\qquad\qquad x_{11}, x_{12}, \ldots, x_{32}$ are all non-negative integers.

Write out a table showing the unit costs, the supplies and the demands.

③ (i) Formulate the problem from Exercise 9.2 question 1 as a linear programming problem.

£	B	C	Supply
A_1	500	620	3
A_2	200	310	2
Demand	4	1	

Table 9.48

(ii) The cost of cell A_1C is reduced. At what value does the solution change?

④ (i) Formulate this transportation problem as a linear programming problem.

£	X	Y	Z	Supply
A	62	43	25	3
B	54	32	30	10
C	41	52	63	8
D	12	35	96	4
Demand	7	9	9	

Table 9.49

Suppose that the Simplex algorithm is used to solve this problem.

(ii) Explain why, in the optimal solution, the slack variables will all be zero.

LEARNING OUTCOMES

When you have finished this chapter, you should be able to
➤ use the north-west corner method to find an initial basic feasible solution
➤ use the stepping-stone method to obtain an improved solution
➤ understand what improvement indices are
➤ formulate a transportation problem as a linear programming problem.

KEY POINTS

1 Goods are transported in multiples of units from sources to destinations.
2 The unit cost is the cost of transporting one unit from a given source to a given destination.
3 The number of units available at each source is called the stock or supply, and the number of units required at each destination is called the demand.
4 A valid solution is called a feasible solution. An extreme case of a feasible solution is a basic feasible solution. The transportation problem is about finding the least-cost basic feasible solution.
5 To solve a transportation problem, first find an initial basic feasible solution using the north-west corner method and then try to reduce the total cost of this solution using the stepping-stone method. When no further improvements can be made the solution is optimal.
6 To use the north-west corner method, set up a table with the sources on rows and the destinations on columns. Record the stock at the end of each row and the demand at the bottom of each column. Use the cells in the table to record the number of units transported on each route.

Start in the north-west corner and fulfil requirements by moving across if stock remains or down if not. Stop when all demands are met.

If necessary, use zeros to avoid diagonal movements (degenerate solutions).
7 When a problem has excess stock (supply) it is called unbalanced. An unbalanced problem should be converted into a balanced problem by introducing a dummy destination with demand equalling the excess stock and with unit costs of 0.
8 When the north-west corner method is used for a balanced problem, the number of cells used is given by:
number of sources + number of destinations − 1
9 For each cell that is used in the basic feasible solution:
unit cost = shadow cost for source + shadow cost for destination
The shadow cost for the source on the first row is set as 0.
10 The improvement index for each empty cell is the unit cost minus the shadow cost for the source and the shadow cost for the destination.
11 The entering cell is the cell with the most negative improvement index.
12 Use the stepping-stone method to construct a cycle through cells where the path zig-zags, starting and ending at the entering cell. Adjust the entries by the maximum number of units possible without any entry becoming negative. Recalculate the cost.
13 The exiting cell is the cell for which the entry becomes 0.
14 A transportation problem can be formulated as a linear programming problem.

Dynamic programming

➡ What is the route from A to D with least weight?

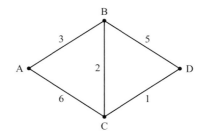

Introduction to dynamic programming

Dynamic programming is a technique for solving problems which are multi-stage decision-making questions. Such problems can often be represented by a directed network showing possible decisions at each stage. The term 'dynamic programming' was first coined by the mathematician Richard Bellman in the 1940s and specifically refers to the way that larger decisions can be made by considering and storing the answers to a sequence of smaller 'nested' decisions.

Discussion point
➡ Is this self-evident? How would you begin to prove it?

1 Principles of dynamic programming

Bellman's principle of optimality:

> Any part of an optimal path is itself optimal.

So, if the path through a network ACDFG is the least weight route from A to G then the least weight route between A and F is ACDF or between C and G is CDFG and so on.

Figure 10.1 shows an example of an optimal route from A to J on a given network.

Suppose the optimal path represents the least weight path from A to J.
The optimal path is ACEGJ.

ACTIVITY 10.1
Dijkstra's algorithm provides a shortest path from one node to each of the others. How many distinct optimal paths can you find using Dijkstra's algorithm on a network of six nodes? What if the network has n nodes?

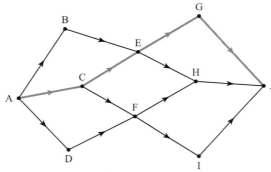

Figure 10.1

Here the least weight path from E to J must be EGJ rather than EHJ because if the weight of EHJ is less than the weight of EGJ then the optimal route from A to J would be ACEHJ rather than ACEGJ. This argument could be applied to any section of the optimal route.

Dynamic programming exploits this way that optimal paths are created, by working backwards from the final destination node, noting the best route to get to the end each time.

> **Note**
>
> Whilst the optimal path between two points on an established optimal route is known, the optimal path between one such point and a point not on the optimal route will not be known. For example, it is not known whether the least weight path from C to H is CEH or CFH.

The path from the starting node to the final destination is made up of a sequence of steps. Each step is referred to as a **stage**. The stage number tells you how many steps it will take to get to the destination.

The **state** is the node that you are considering at any one time. This could be a label or a number.

The **action** is the directed arc connecting one state to the next.

The **destination** is the node which you arrive at, having taken an action.

The **value** is the 'running total' of the set of arcs connecting to the final destination node.

Example 10.1

A commuter wants to minimise the number of traffic lights she goes through on the way to work, starting at A and finishing at K. There are a number of different routes she could take and Figure 10.2 shows those routes. The weights on each of the directed arcs represent the number of sets of traffic lights between each of the places.

> **Note**
>
> **Labelling procedure**
>
> You will notice that each of the nodes H, I and J are one 'step' from the final destination K. Therefore, they will have the stage value of 1.
>
> In the same way, E, F and G will have the stage value 2. B, C and D have the stage value of 3 and A has the stage value of 4.

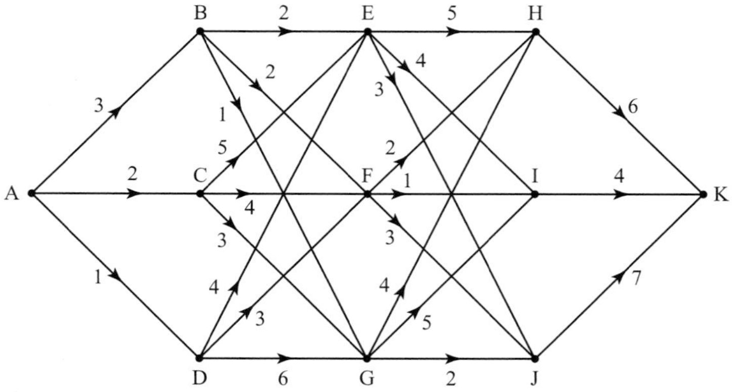

Figure 10.2

State the meaning of the stage, state and action for this problem and draw a table summarising the data.

Solution

The stage is the number of arcs away from K, the state is the place the commuter is currently at, and the action is the journey to the next place.

The table can be used to solve the problem.

Stage	State	Action	Destination
1	H	HK	K
	I	IK	K
	J	JK	K
2	E	EH	H
		EI	I
		EJ	J
	F	FH	H
		FI	I
		FJ	J
	G	GH	H
		GI	I
		GJ	J
3	B	BE	E
		BF	F
		BG	G
	C	CE	E
		CF	F
		CG	G
	D	DE	E
		DF	F
		DG	G
4	A	AB	B
		AC	C
		AD	D

Table 10.1

The destinations in stage 2 are the states in stage 1.

The destinations in stage 3 are the states in stage 2.

The destinations in stage 4 are the states in stage 3.

ACTIVITY 10.2

Try to find the best route for the commuter, passing the fewest sets of traffic lights, using *ad hoc* methods.

Dynamic programming problems can also be expressed in table form. These are often allocation or production planning problems, where a series of orders need to be filled or resources allocated. In these cases it is important to be very clear what you mean by the stage, state, action, destination and value.

Example 10.2

A manufacturer has an order book to deliver certain large components at the end of each month. They are able to make at most 5 of these components each month and can store up to 2 of them for the following month. They want to make sure that they have no components left at the end of August.

State the meaning of the stage, state and action for this problem and draw a table summarising the data.

By the end of each month they need the numbers of components shown in Table 10.2.

Month	May	June	July	August
Number required	3	4	6	5

Table 10.2

Solution

Here the state is used to represent how many components are stored at the beginning of the month and the action to represent how many components are created. The destination is how many will have been stored at the end of the month (and therefore at the start of the next one). The stage is how many months there are until the end of August, but for clarity it is useful to write the name of the month as well.

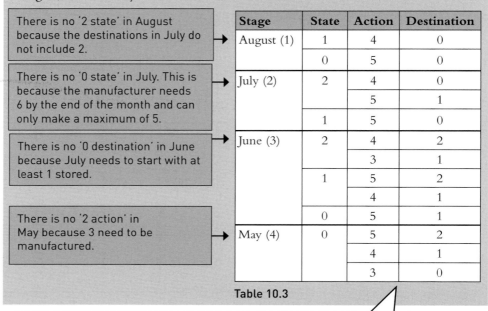

There is no '2 state' in August because the destinations in July do not include 2.

There is no '0 state' in July. This is because the manufacturer needs 6 by the end of the month and can only make a maximum of 5.

There is no '0 destination' in June because July needs to start with at least 1 stored.

There is no '2 action' in May because 3 need to be manufactured.

Stage	State	Action	Destination
August (1)	1	4	0
	0	5	0
July (2)	2	4	0
		5	1
	1	5	0
June (3)	2	4	2
		3	1
	1	5	2
		4	1
	0	5	1
May (4)	0	5	2
		4	1
		3	0

Table 10.3

Discussion point

→ How would a question like this differ if you were allowed storage at the beginning and end?

Exercise 10.1

① The optimal route from A to I is shown in Figure 10.3 and forms the path ACDHI.

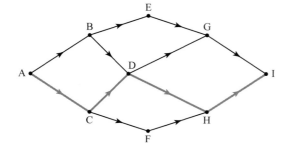

Figure 10.3

Find the optimal route between the following sets of nodes or state that the optimal route is unknown:

(i) C and I

(ii) A and G

(iii) B and I

(iv) C and I

(v) C and H.

② The optimal route on a network is given by ADFGIT. Find the optimal routes from:

(i)   D to G

(ii)   A to G

(iii) F to T

(iv)   D to I.

③ Table 10.4 gives the maximum weight route between sets of nodes on a network.

Start node	Destination node	Route	Weight
A	I	ACEGI	10
B	J	BDEGIJ	17
C	I	CEGI	8
D	J	DEGIJ	13
E	I	EGI	6

Table 10.4

Find the maximum weight route between the following sets of nodes and give the weight:

(i)   A and E

(ii)   C and E

(iii) B and D

(iv)   A and C.

④ Draw a table showing the stage, state, action and destination for the network in Figure 10.4.

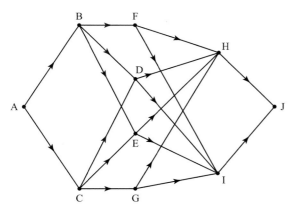

Figure 10.4

⑤ An artist has been commissioned to create a number of artistic pieces to install in airports around Europe. Table 10.5 shows how many finished pieces they need at the end of each month. The maximum the artist can create in a month is six pieces and they have storage for up to three pieces of art. They have one piece of artwork already in storage and want to finish with no pieces in storage.

Month	June	July	August
No. of pieces of art required	4	7	5

Table 10.5

Define the stage, state, action and destination for this problem and construct a table for this information.

⑥ Draw a table showing the stage, state, action and destination for the network in Figure 10.5.

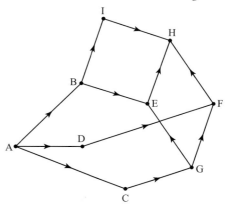

Figure 10.5

⑦ A postal service has to deliver parcels each day. Owing to the nature of their workforce, the number of vans they can send to deliver parcels varies each day. Each van can deliver 100 parcels. Table 10.6 shows how many parcels are estimated to arrive each day, to the nearest hundred, as well as how many vans are available. Up to 200 parcels can be stored at the end of a day, and it is necessary to start with no parcels in storage before day 1 and finish with no parcels in storage after day 5.

Day	1	2	3	4	5
Arriving (100s)	6	7	5	3	2
Maximum no. of vans	5	6	6	5	4

Table 10.6

Define the stage, state, action and destination for this problem and construct a table for this information.

2 Solving problems using dynamic programming

In order to use the tables to solve different types of dynamic programming problems, another column is added to the table, for the value.

Example 10.3

Use dynamic programming for the network in Figure 10.6 to find:

(i)   the minimum cost route from A to K

(ii)   the maximum cost route from A to K.

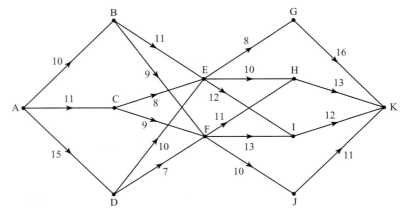

Figure 10.6

Solution

At each stage make sure you have a state representing each of the nodes.

Each of the states needs an action representing the arc connecting the state to its destination node.

The values are the sum of the weights of the arcs and the current 'best running total' of the destination node.

(i)

Stage	State	Action	Destination	Value
1	G	GK	K	16★
	H	HK	K	13★
	I	IK	K	12★
	J	JK	K	11★
2	E	EG	G	8 + 16 = 24
		EH	H	10 + 13 = 23★
		EI	I	12 + 12 = 24
	F	FH	H	11 + 13 = 24
		FI	I	13 + 12 = 25
		FJ	J	10 + 11 = 21★

For each **state** use a star to help you quickly identify the optimal (in this case minimum) route back to the final destination.

Stage	State	Action	Destination	Value
3	B	BE	E	11 + 23 = 34
		BF	F	9 + 21 = 30★
	C	CE	E	8 + 23 = 31
		CF	F	9 + 21 = 30★
	D	DE	E	10 + 23 = 33
		DF	F	7 + 21 = 28★
4	A	AB	B	10 + 30 = 40
		AC	C	15 + 30 = 45
		AD	D	11 + 28 = 39★

Table 10.7

The minimum cost route from A to K has a weight of 39. To find the route itself you work back up the table, choosing the value and destination you have identified with a star each time.

In this case, the minimum cost route is ADFJK.

(ii) Because you are using the same network to find the maximum cost route from A to K, the stage, state, action and destination columns will stay the same but you will have to recalculate the values after stage 1.

Stage	State	Action	Destination	Value
1	G	GK	K	16★
	H	HK	K	13★
	I	IK	K	12★
	J	JK	K	11★
2	E	EG	G	8 + 16 = 24★
		EH	H	10 + 13 = 23
		EI	I	12 + 12 = 24★
	F	FH	H	11 + 13 = 24
		FI	I	13 + 12 = 25★
		FJ	J	10 + 11 = 21
3	B	BE	E	11 + 24 = 35★
		BF	F	9 + 25 = 34
	C	CE	E	8 + 24 = 32
		CF	F	9 + 25 = 34★
	D	DE	E	10 + 24 = 34★
		DF	F	7 + 25 = 32
4	A	AB	B	10 + 35 = 45
		AC	C	11 + 34 = 45
		AD	D	15 + 34 = 49★

Notice here that either EG or EI could be chosen for the maximum value, so if the optimal route goes through E there will be multiple options.

Table 10.8

The maximum cost route from A to K has a value of 49; there are two routes, ADEGK and ADEIK.

Up to this point in Decision Mathematics you will only have seen algorithms that can minimise or maximise a total.

Dynamic programming can be used to solve two other types of problem:

■ **Minimax problem:** This is a problem in which you want to minimise the maximum weight of an arc in the route. In other words, make the largest arc as small as possible.

■ **Maximin problem:** This is a problem in which you want to maximise the minimum weight of an arc in the route, in other words to make the smallest arc as large as possible.

Example 10.4

For the network in Figure 10.7, find

(i)   the minimax route

(ii)   the maximin route.

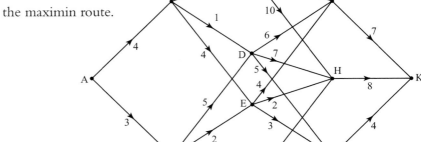
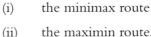

Figure 10.7

Solution

(i)   For a minimax route write Max(a, b), where a is the weight of the current action and b is the starred value for the destination state. This will be equal to the larger value of a or b. For each state you will then star the minimum value.

It's helpful to be consistent about this throughout, as it makes the route easier to follow.

Stage	State	Action	Destination	Value
1	I	IK	K	7★
	H	HK	K	8★
	J	JK	K	4★
2	F	FI	I	Max(9, 7) = 9★
		FH	H	Max(10, 8) = 10
	D	DI	I	Max(6, 7) = 7
		DH	H	Max(7, 8) = 8
		DJ	J	Max(5, 4) = 5★
	E	EI	I	Max(4, 7) = 7
		EH	H	Max(2, 8) = 8
		EJ	J	Max(3, 4) = 4★
	G	GH	H	Max(7, 8) = 8★
		GJ	J	Max(8, 4) = 8★

Notice that Max(9, 7) returns the largest value of 9 and 7 and Max(10, 8) returns the largest value of 10 and 8 but the smallest of these numbers is starred in a minimax problem.

Stage	State	Action	Destination	Value
3	B	BF	F	Max(6, 9) = 9
		BD	D	Max(1, 5) = 5
		BE	E	Max(4, 4) = 4★
	C	CD	D	Max(5, 5) = 5
		CE	E	Max(2, 4) = 4★
		CG	G	Max(7, 8) = 8
4	A	AB	B	Max(4, 4) = 4★
		AC	C	Max(3, 4) = 4★

Table 10.9

The minimax route is either ABEJK, or ACEJK, both of which have a maximum arc weight of 4.

(ii) For a maximin route write Min(a, b), where a is the weight of the current action and b is the starred value for the destination state. This will be equal to the smaller value of a or b. For each state you will then star the maximum value.

Again, whilst it is possible to put the numbers in either order, it's helpful to be consistent about this throughout, as it makes the route easier to follow.

Stage	State	Action	Destination	Value
1	I	IK	K	7★
	H	HK	K	8★
	J	JK	K	4★
2	F	FI	I	Min(9, 7) = 7
		FH	H	Min(10, 8) = 8★
	D	DI	I	Min(6, 7) = 6
		DH	H	Min(7, 8) = 7★
		DJ	J	Min(5, 4) = 4
	E	EI	I	Min(4, 7)= 4★
		EH	H	Min(2, 8) = 2
		EJ	J	Min(3, 4) = 3
	G	GH	H	Min(7, 8) = 7★
		GJ	J	Min(8, 4) = 4
3	B	BF	F	Min(6, 8) = 6★
		BD	D	Min(1, 7) = 1
		BE	E	Min(4, 4) = 4
	C	CD	D	Min(5, 7) = 5
		CE	E	Min(2, 4) = 2
		CG	G	Min(7, 7) = 7★
4	A	AB	B	Min(4, 6) = 4★
		AC	C	Min(3, 7) = 3

Table 10.10

So the maximin route for this network is ABFHK, in which the least weight arc is 4.

You will also need to be able to solve dynamic programming problems in table form.

Example 10.5

A company builds large container ships. The order book over the next four months is shown in Table 10.11.

Month	April	May	June	July
Number	2	4	5	3

Table 10.11

The ships are delivered to customers at the end of each month. Up to four ships can be made in any month, but if more than three are made then an additional dock and equipment will need to be hired at £25 000 per month. Up to two ships can be held in dry docks at a cost of £15 000 per ship per month. The overhead costs of completing any work during a month are £40 000.

There are no ships held at the beginning of April and there must be no ships left in dock at the end of July after delivery.

Use dynamic programming to determine the production schedule that minimises the costs.

Solution

First define the stage, state, action and destination.

Stage – the number of months remaining

State – the number of ships in storage at the beginning of the month

Action – the number of ships made in that month

Destination – the number of ships stored at the end of the month

The value will be the running total of the costs. This value will include the cost of the stored ships from the beginning of the month.

Although it isn't necessary, it can be helpful to put some of these definitions into the headings of your table.

Each value is the sum of overhead costs, additional equipment and storage, in that order.

The last number in each addition is for the destination.

Stage (month)	State (ships stored)	Action (ships made)	Destination (ships stored)	Value (£1000)
1 (July)	1	2	0	$40 + 15 = 55\star$
	0	3	0	$40\star$
2 (June)	2	4	1	$40 + 25 + 30 + 55 = 150$
		3	0	$40 + 30 + 40 = 110\star$
	1	4	0	$40 + 25 + 15 + 40 = 120\star$
3 (May)	2	4	2	$40 + 25 + 30 + 110 = 205$
		3	1	$40 + 30 + 120 = 190\star$
	1	4	1	$40 + 25 + 15 + 120 = 200\star$
4 (April)	0	4	2	$40 + 25 + 190 = 255$
		3	1	$40 + 200 = 240\star$

Table 10.12

So the ship builder should make the following numbers of ships in each month:

Month	April	May	June	July
Number of ships	3	4	4	3

Table 10.13

Example 10.6

A market stall trader will go to three different market towns over the next three days. He will need to travel from his home to one of the markets and then travel between each of the markets and then back to home.

There are seven different market towns he could go to in the next three days and he must decide which of the towns he should take his stall to.

Table 10.14 gives the days in which the towns are holding markets, Table 10.15, gives the expected profits in hundreds of pounds and Table 10.16 gives the travel costs in hundreds of pounds.

(i)   Define the stage, state and action.

(ii) Use dynamic programming to find the maximum profit the trader can make from his stall in the next three days.

Day	1	2	3
Towns	A, B	C, D, E	F, G

Table 10.14

Town	A	B	C	D	E	F	G
Profit (£100)	5	4	7	9	12	17	13

Table 10.15

Costs (£100)	A	B	C	D	E	F	G
Home	5	4	–	–	–	10	7
A	–	–	5	3	2	–	–
B	–	–	1	4	4	–	–
C	–	–	–	–	–	6	6
D	–	–	–	–	–	7	3
E	–	–	–	–	–	2	2

Table 10.16

Solution

(i)   The stage is the number of days remaining.

The state is the town that the trader is in during the day.

The action is the journey that the trader makes at the end of the day.

The destination is where the trader's market stall will be the following day.

The value is the cumulative profit.

(ii) When you calculate the value, you will find the expected profit minus the costs. This means that in stage 4 there will only be costs.

→

> Each calculation is worked out as 'expected profit minus costs plus value at destination'.

Stage (day)	State (current location)	Action (journey)	Destination	Value
1 (day 3)	F	F–Home	Home	$17 - 10 = 7\star$
	G	G–Home	Home	$13 - 7 = 6\star$
2 (day 2)	C	CF	F	$7 - 6 + 7 = 8\star$
		CG	G	$7 - 6 + 6 = 7$
	D	DF	F	$9 - 7 + 7 = 9$
		DG	G	$9 - 3 + 6 = 12\star$
	E	EF	F	$12 - 2 + 7 = 17\star$
		EG	G	$12 - 2 + 6 = 16$
3 (day 1)	A	AC	C	$5 - 5 + 8 = 8$
		AD	D	$5 - 3 + 12 = 14$
		AE	E	$5 - 2 + 17 = 20\star$
	B	BC	C	$4 - 1 + 8 = 11$
		BD	D	$4 - 4 + 12 = 12$
		BE	E	$4 - 4 + 17 = 17\star$
4	Home	Home–A	A	$-5 + 20 = 15\star$
		Home–B	B	$-4 + 17 = 13$

Table 10.17

So the market trader should attend the markets at A, E and F to make a profit of £1500.

Exercise 10.2

① For each of the following scenarios state whether it is a maximise, minimise, maximin or minimax problem and state the meaning of the stage and state variables.

(i) A group of walkers are planning a hike from Land's End to John O'Groats. They want to make sure that they stop each night in a village or a town and don't walk too far on any one day.

(ii) A large company has a variety of marketing strategies to use each year and wants to find one that makes the largest profit over the course of 5 years.

(iii) A forestry organisation wants to plant a large number of trees over the course of the next 4 years. At the end of 4 years they want to have covered the entire area in trees but want to employ staff such that they don't have to work for too long in any one year, in order to reduce overtime costs.

(iv) A lorry driver driving between two locations has to cross rivers on a number of bridges. They want to make sure that each bridge they cross is able to take the heaviest load.

(v) A traveller journeying from London to Edinburgh via a number of other locations wants to ensure that the cost of their journey is as small as possible.

② For each of the following four networks find the route from S to T with

(a) the maximum cost

(b) the minimum cost.

(i)

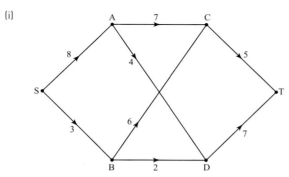

Figure 10.8

(ii)

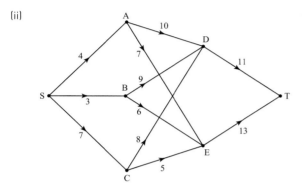

Figure 10.9

(iii)

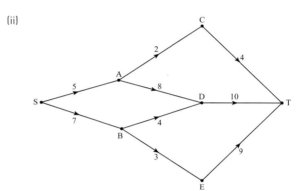

Figure 10.10

(iv)

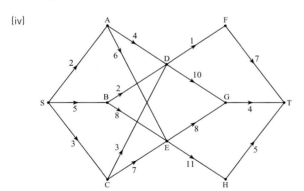

Figure 10.11

(i)

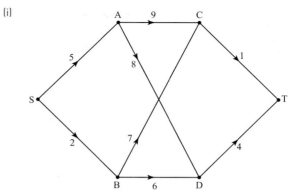

Figure 10.12

(ii)

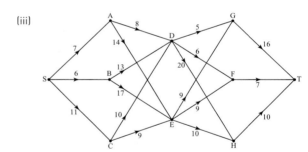

Figure 10.13

(iii)

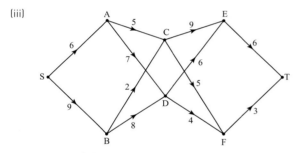

Figure 10.14

(iv)

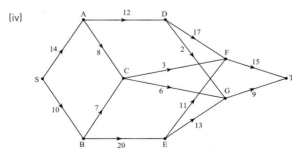

Figure 10.15

③ For each of the following four networks, find
  (a) the minimax
  (b) the maximin route from S to T.

Solving problems using dynamic programming

④ Complete Table 10.18 to find the solution to the maximin problem.

Stage	State	Action	Destination	Value
1	F	FT	T	6
	G	GT	T	3
2	D	DF	F	Min(5
		DG	G	Min(8
	E	EF	F	Min(6
		EG	G	Min(9
3	A	AD	D	Min(10
		AE	E	Min(6
	B	BD	D	Min(7
		BE	E	Min(3
	C	CD	D	Min(8
		CE	E	Min(9
4	S	SA	A	Min(10
		SB	B	Min(2
		SC	C	Min(8

Table 10.18

⑤ Complete Table 10.19, to find the solution to the minimax problem.

Stage	State	Action	Destination	Value
1	G	GT	T	11
	H	HT	T	8
	I	IT	T	13
2	E	EG	G	Max(9
		EH	H	Max(14
		EI	I	Max(12
	F	FG	G	Max(7
		FH	H	Max(3
		FI	I	Max(6
3	C	CE	E	Max(11
		CF	F	Max(15
	D	DE	E	Max(8
		DF	F	Max(7
4	A	AC	C	Max(15
		AD	D	Max(14
	B	BC	C	Max(17
		BD	D	Max(8
5	S	SA	A	Max(9
		SB	B	Max(2

Table 10.19

⑥ At the beginning of a big project the number of components needed at the end of each phase is worked out and outlined in Table 10.20.

Phase	1	2	3	4	5
Components needed	4	6	7	5	3

Table 10.20

During each phase, up to three components can be made at a cost of £200 per component and three further components can be made at the cost of £300 per component (the additional cost is for the overtime and extra workers). Up to two components can be stored between phases at a cost of £50 per component. The running costs for the process are £100 per phase. There are no components in storage before Phase 1.

(i) State the meaning of the stage, state and action in this context.

(ii) Use dynamic programming to determine the production schedule that minimises costs.

⑦ A media company is created to provide news and current affairs. They want to start a service in three different ways and decide to introduce one new type of service in each of the next three years. The costs of starting up a new service will be reduced as each service is added. The estimates of annual costs for each of the services are given in Table 10.21 (in hundreds of pounds).

Media service already running	Internet (A)	Television (B)	Print (C)
None	50	100	65
A	–	70	50
B	30	–	60
C	40	90	–
A and B	–	–	40
A and C	–	60	–
B and C	25	–	–

Table 10.21

The company wants to choose the order in which the media services are introduced and wants to keep the annual cost as low as possible for tax purposes.

Use dynamic programming to determine the order in which the services are introduced.

⑧ A piano maker makes pianos between the months of February and June each year. The order book for pianos over these months is shown in Table 10.22.

Month	February	March	April	May	June
Number of pianos	2	4	5	3	1

Table 10.22

The pianos are delivered to customers at the end of each month.

The piano maker can make up to two pianos himself each month but can hire extra help at the additional cost of £400 a month if he wants to make more than two. With the extra help, the maximum number he can make is four.

He can put two pianos into storage at the end of a month at a cost of £100 per piano.

The overhead costs of running the piano-making workshop are £200 each month.

There are no pianos in storage at the beginning of February and there should be no pianos in storage at the end of June.

(i) Explain the meaning of stage, state and action in this context.

(ii) Use dynamic programming to determine the production schedule that minimises costs to the piano maker.

⑨ The diagram in Figure 10.16 shows the effect on a technology company's profits, in £1000s, of taking various advertising decisions. The company wishes to devise a three-year marketing strategy that will maximise its total profits.

Each year the company must decide whether to advertise on the internet, the television or both.

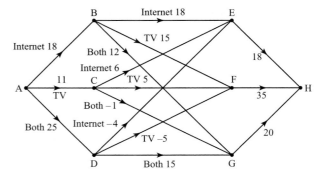

Figure 10.16

Use dynamic programming to find the optimal strategy for the company to take if they want to maximise their total profit over the two-year period.

⑩ A biscuit manufacturer can make plain, chocolate or jam flavoured biscuits. Up to four units of biscuits can be processed and the profits (in £000s) from the various allocations are shown in Table 10.23.

Number of units	1	2	3	4
Plain	17	19	22	23
Chocolate	10	15	20	25
Jam	8	13	20	27

Table 10.23

The manufacturer wants to maximise their profit.

Use dynamic programming to find an optimal solution and state the profit.

LEARNING OUTCOMES

Now that you have finished this chapter, you should be able to

➤ understand Bellman's principle of optimality
➤ understand the principles of dynamic programming
➤ understand the terminology used in dynamic programming
➤ use dynamic programming to solve maximise, minimise, minimax and maximin problems
➤ use dynamic programming to solve problems presented in table form.

KEY POINTS

1 The **stage** number tells you how many steps it will take to get to your destination.
2 The **state** is the node that you are considering at any one time.
3 The **action** is the directed arc connecting one state to the next.
4 The **destination** is the node which you arrive at having taken an action.
5 The **value** is the 'running total' of the set of arcs connecting to the final destination node.
6 A **minimax** is a problem in which you want to minimise the maximum weight of an arc in the route.
7 A **maximin** is a problem in which want to maximise the minimum weight of an arc in the route.
8 Any part of an optimal route is in itself an optimal route. This is **Bellman's principle of optimality**.
9 Remember to work backwards from the end when solving dynamic programming problems.

11

Decision analysis

→ You pay the banker £5 to flip two coins. For two heads you win £5 (and get your £5 stake back), for a head and a tail you win £2 (and get your stake back), and for two tails your £5 stake is forfeit.

Should you play this game?

1 Decision analysis

ACTIVITY 11.1
Play the game in the opening problem several times – without using real money, of course!

Analysis of the game

You can tabulate the profit to the player for each outcome as shown in the table.

Result	HH	HT or TH	TT
Probability	$\frac{1}{4}$	$\frac{1}{2}$	$\frac{1}{4}$
Profit (£)	+5	+2	−5

Table 11.1

The player's average profit per game (or the expected profit) is therefore

$$\left(\frac{1}{4} \times £5\right) + \left(\frac{1}{2} \times £2\right) + \left(\frac{1}{4} \times -£5\right) = £1$$

So the game is in the player's favour and he or she can expect to gain £1 per game on average in the long run. The name given to the average gain in the long run is the **expected monetary value** (EMV for short). Hence, in this game, the player's EMV is £1 per game.

An alternative method of analysing this game is to use a tree diagram as in Figure 11.1. A triangle symbol is used to represent the outcomes and the EMV of +1 is written in a circle or **chance node**.

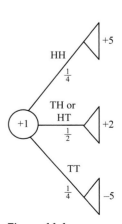

Figure 11.1

You could extend the diagram as shown in Figure 11.2.

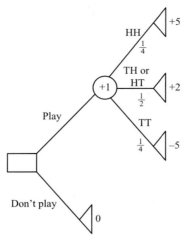

Figure 11.2

Figure 11.2 shows that the player can decide whether to play or not. There are now three types of node in the diagram:

■ **triangles** to denote end pay-offs to the player – **end nodes**

■ **rectangles** to denote stages at which the player makes a decision – **decision nodes**

■ **circles** to denote stages where chance determines the outcome – **chance nodes**.

This kind of diagram is called a **decision tree**. To use it to analyse the problem you work from the right-hand side by labelling the pay-off boxes, and then you calculate the EMV of +1 as you did above and insert this in the chance node.

You now move back to the rectangular decision node and see that 'Play' has an EMV of +1, and 'Don't play' an EMV of 0. On this basis, you would decide to choose 'Play' and a double line is put through 'Don't play' to show that this is an inferior option. This is shown in Figure 11.3. You again, of course, conclude that the game is in the player's favour with an EMV of £1 per game.

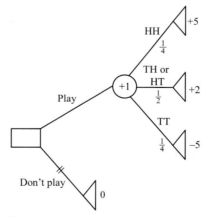

Figure 11.3

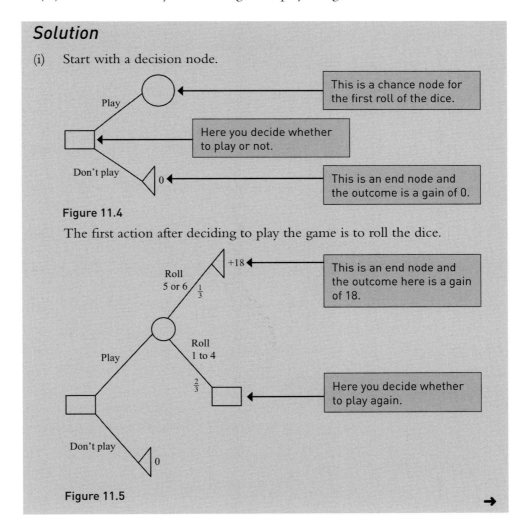

ACTIVITY 11.2

A game involves throwing a dice. If a 5 or 6 shows the banker pays you £18, for any other number you lose £6. However, in the latter case, you may if you wish throw the dice again.

This time if you throw a 6 you win £36 but otherwise you lose a further £6.

Obviously, play without using real money.

Example 11.1

For the game in Activity 11.2

(i)   construct a decision tree diagram

(ii)   calculate the expected monetary values (EMVs)

(iii) decide whether you should agree to play this game.

Solution

(i)   Start with a decision node.

> This is a chance node for the first roll of the dice.

> Here you decide whether to play or not.

> This is an end node and the outcome is a gain of 0.

Figure 11.4

The first action after deciding to play the game is to roll the dice.

> This is an end node and the outcome here is a gain of 18.

> Here you decide whether to play again.

Figure 11.5

→

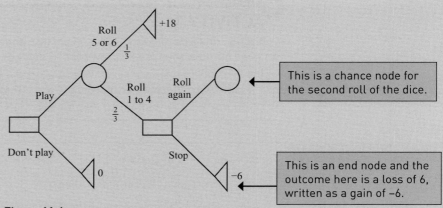

Figure 11.6

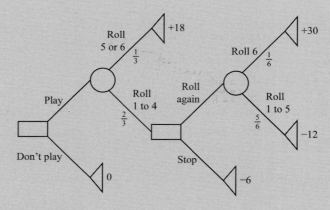

Figure 11.7

(ii) Work through the diagram in Figure 11.7 from the right.

The EMV for the chance node on the right is

$$\frac{1}{6} \times 30 + \frac{5}{6} \times (-12) = -5.$$

Label this chance node with '–5'.

Moving back to the decision node in the middle of the diagram, you see that 'Roll again' has an EMV of –5 and 'Stop' has an EMV of –6.
The double line is therefore placed across the 'Stop' option to denote that this is the inferior option.

To complete the diagram, the EMV for the chance node on the left of the diagram must be found. This is

$$\left(\frac{1}{3} \times 18 \right) + \left(\frac{2}{3} \times -5 \right) = \frac{8}{3} = 2\frac{2}{3}$$

The final diagram is shown in Figure 11.8.

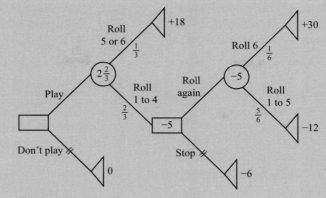

Figure 11.8

(iii) The analysis suggests the following strategy:

'Play the game, and if you roll a 1, 2, 3 or 4 on the first throw then roll again.'

With this strategy the player's EMV is £$2\frac{2}{3}$ per game.

The procedure developed in Example 11.1 is usually referred to as the **EMV algorithm**. At each stage, you take the decision which maximises your EMV.

Utility

There is an important assumption implicit in using EMV to measure the worth of alternative courses of action: namely, that £1 is worth the same to everybody. You might argue that it is obviously worth the same since it will buy the same. But others might argue that a rich person would not regard £1 as being worth very much. To model this decision, analysts often use the concept of utility to measure the relative worth of alternative actions. The analyst has to investigate the decision–maker's **utility function**. This gives the value of an extra £1 as a function of the wealth held by the decision–maker. It is always an increasing function of the wealth, but the slope is usually decreasing.

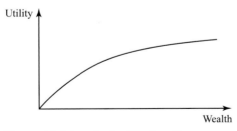

Figure 11.9 A typical utility function

Determining a decision–maker's utility function is an exercise in psychology rather than in mathematics but, having determined it, the function can be applied and the course of action which maximises utility can be chosen. For example, consider the possibility of playing a game in which you win £10 with probability 0.05, or lose £1 with probability 0.95. Would you choose to play?

One possible analysis, using the EMV algorithm, is represented by the tree diagram in Figure 11.10. This shows the EMV of playing a game, but it does not analyse the decision (although the decision is obvious – do not play!).

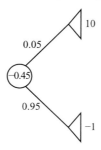

Figure 11.10

The decision analysis might be represented by the tree diagram in Figure 11.11, in which it is assumed that you have £100 in your pocket. This says exactly the same thing: either keep your £100 in your pocket or play, in which case the expected value will drop by £0.45 to £99.55.

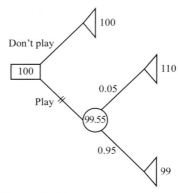

Figure 11.11

Discussion point

→ Is it helpful to use utilities when trying to make a decision? Is it worth the extra work?

If, however, you wish to consider expected utilities, then since your utility function will be non-linear, you must use the decision analysis approach. Using utilities, the analysis is not independent of your wealth. For instance, suppose that your utility function is given by utility $= \sqrt[4]{\text{wealth}^3}$. Then the analysis is shown in the tree diagram in Figure 11.12 (note that $\sqrt[4]{100^3} \approx 31.62$). In this case, the decision is the same: do not play. It is almost always the case for this particular utility function that, no matter what the wealth, prize or probability of winning, the decision using the EMV criterion will be the same as the decision using the utility criterion. A more complex utility function might explain why people buy lottery tickets!

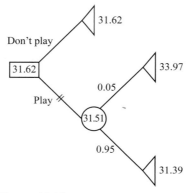

Figure 11.12

① (i) In a simple game, the player chooses a playing card from a normal pack of 52. For an ace he wins £20, for a king or queen £15, and for a jack he pays the banker £50. If any other card is chosen he neither wins nor loses. What is the EMV of the game?

(ii) A roulette wheel has 37 numbers into which the ball can drop. Eighteen of these are coloured red, eighteen are coloured black and the number 0 is not coloured. A player bets £1 on red. If the ball lands in a red number then he wins £1 and gets his £1 stake back, but for any other number his £1 stake is forfeited. Find the EMV of the game.

② (i) You play a game in which you will win £15 if you throw a total score of 11 or 12 with two dice, otherwise you will lose £2. What is the EMV of the game?

(ii) What would your winnings need to be in part (i) instead of £15 to make your EMV zero?

(iii) You have just £2. Your utility function is given by utility $= \sqrt[4]{\text{wealth}^3}$. What would your winnings need to be to tempt you to risk your last £2 on a game?

③ (i) Three normal unbiased dice are thrown. Explain why P(three 6s) $= \frac{1}{216}$ and find P(no 6s), P(one 6) and P(two 6s).

(ii) In the game 'Crown and Anchor' a player pays £1 to throw three normal unbiased dice. If three 6s turn up he wins £3 and gets his £1 stake back, if two 6s turn up he wins £2 and gets his £1 stake back, and if one 6 turns up he wins £1 and gets his £1 stake back. If no 6s turn up his £1 stake is forfeit. Find the EMV of the game.

④ The organiser of a tennis tournament has to decide whether to take out pluvius insurance (that is, insurance against rain on the day of the tournament). She estimates that on a fine day the tournament will make a profit of £5000 but on a wet day it will make a loss of £10000. The pluvius insurance will cost £1500 and pay out £6000 if it rains on the day of the tournament. The probability of rain is estimated to be $\frac{1}{5}$.

(i) Construct a decision tree to work out the organiser's best policy.

(ii) The day before the tournament, a weather forecaster now estimates the probability of rain to be be $\frac{1}{3}$. If the organiser had used this probability would she have made the same decision?

⑤ A company has just developed a new product and now a decision must be taken as to whether to launch the product without delay, to run a market test or to abandon the product. If the product is launched without delay, then market research suggests that a strong market will occur with probability 0.3 and a weak market will occur with probability 0.7. A strong market will bring a profit of £200000, while a weak market will bring a profit of £50000. To run a market test will cost £5000, which will have to be deducted from profits, and this will give favourable or unfavourable indications. The probability of a favourable indication is calculated to be $\frac{1}{6}$.

If the result of the market test is favourable, then the probability of a strong market is now 80%, but if the market test is unfavourable, then the probability of a weak market is 80%.

The product may be abandoned at any stage, either now or after the market test, and the technology developed may be sold to a rival company for a net profit of £90000.

(i) Draw and label a decision tree to describe the above situation.

(ii) Use the decision tree to say what decision should be taken and find the EMV associated with this plan.

(iii) What is the maximum amount (instead of £5000) that the company should be prepared to pay to run the market test?

⑥ You are fortunate enough to hold the winning ticket in a raffle in which the first prize is £100000. As you go to claim your prize you are offered the following deal: you may either take your £100000 prize or forgo this for a second bet. In this second bet, you have a 0.1 chance of winning £1500000 and a 0.9 chance of winning nothing.

(i) Draw a decision tree to represent this situation and use the EMV algorithm to determine your optimal decision.

(ii) Do you think you would really follow the decision in part (i)? What if your utility function is given by utility = $\sqrt{\text{wealth}}$ and you are currently broke?

⑦ A government has to decide how to dispose of nuclear waste material. One possibility is to build a long-term store immediately. This will cost £2500 million.

Alternatively, the material can be put into temporary storage for 50 years, after which time the long-term store will be built. The total cost of this alternative depends on the general level of growth in the economy, and is shown in the table.

Growth of economy	Total cost
Low growth	£6100 million
Medium growth	£2400 million
High growth	£1760 million

Table 11.2

It is estimated that the probability of low growth is 30%, the probability of medium growth is 50% and the probability of high growth is 20%.

(i) Construct a decision tree for this situation, marking on outcomes and probabilities, and use it to find which is the best decision for the government to take. Give the cost advantage of that decision compared to the alternative.

In reviewing the decision, the government's economic spokesman expresses the opinion that low growth will not occur. He estimates that the probabilities of medium growth and high growth are each 50%.

(ii) Find the best decision, and the cost advantage of it, under these assumptions.

(You are not required to draw another decision tree.)

In the debate leading to a decision, the opposition party calls for an independent inquiry to be set up. The government has to decide whether or not to agree to do this. If an inquiry is set up, then a decision will have to be made about whether or not to accept its recommendations.

(iii) Draw a modified decision tree to show all of the alternatives:

- whether or not the government sets up an inquiry

- whether such an inquiry recommends building now or storing first

- whether the government decides to build now or to store first

- the economic conditions (assuming that high, medium and low growth are all possible).

You are not required to show outcomes or probabilities, but you are required to show the correct structure of the decision tree. Only those nodes representing decisions that are within the control of the government should be shown as decision nodes. [MEI]

⑧ A fairground game offers three outcomes: £10, £1 or £0. A player has just been offered £1. She can accept or 'go again', in which case the offer of £1 will be withdrawn and she will be offered £10, £1 or £0 with probabilities p, q and $1 - p - q$ respectively.

(i) Draw a decision tree for this game.

(ii) If q is 0.5, what value must p exceed to tempt her to go again?

In a similar game, the player has again been offered £1, but gets two chances to go again. If she elects not to take the £1 and is subsequently offered £10, she will accept it. However, if the subsequent offer is £0, she will go again for the second and last time. If the offer is £1, then she must decide whether to accept it this time or to go again for the last time.

(iii) Draw a decision tree for this game.

(iv) If $p = 0.02$ and $q = 0.5$, compute the EMV at each node and give the player's best strategy. [MEI]

⑨ A decision has to be made regarding a project. It can be allowed to proceed (A), or it can be cancelled (~A). Outcomes, pay-offs and probabilities are summarised in the decision tree.

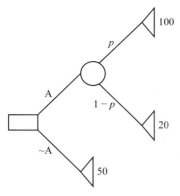

Figure 11.13

(i) If the EMV of proceeding is equal to the EMV of cancelling, show that $p = 0.375$.

(ii) In fact, $p = 0.25$. Advice can be sought on whether or not to proceed. If advice is sought, then there is a probability of 0.2 that the advice will be to proceed, in which case the resultant probabilities will be more favourable. If the advice is to cancel, then the probabilities are less favourable. The values are summarised in the decision tree.

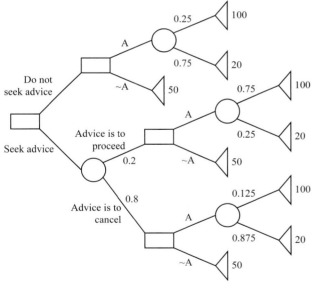

Figure 11.14

(a) Copy and complete the second decision tree, showing the EMVs.

(b) What is the value of the advice?

(c) To what value would the cancellation pay-off of 50 have to increase to make it not worth seeking advice? [MEI adapted]

⑩ Despina can invest her savings of £1000 in bonds or in equities. Bonds are generally reckoned to be safer than equities. Equities have potentially higher returns (measured in % per annum), but may suffer losses (again measured in % per annum).

From past history the probability of equity returns being +15% is 0.6, but the probability of equity returns being −10% is 0.4. For bonds, the probability of a 5% increase is 0.8 and the probability of a 3% increase is 0.2.

(i) What will be the value of Despina's savings after one year under each of the four possible scenarios, i.e.

- if she invests in equities and they increase in value by 15%

- if she invests in equities and they decrease in value by 10%

- if she invests in bonds and they increase in value by 5%

- if she invests in bonds and they increase in value by 3%?

(ii) Draw a decision tree for Despina. Use the EMV algorithm, to advise her where to invest her money?

Despina's utility function for her savings is given by

$$\text{utility} = (\text{monetary value})^p,$$

where $p < 1$.

(iii) Using expected utility, show that the value of p which will make Despina indifferent between investing in equities and investing in bonds is 0.5 (correct to 1 d.p.). [MEI]

LEARNING OUTCOMES

Now you have finished this chapter, you should be able to

➤ construct a decision tree to analyse a more complicated decision situation

➤ understand that decision trees have three types of node: end nodes, chance nodes and decision nodes

➤ calculate the average profit per game in a simple game of chance

➤ use the EMV algorithm to evaluate the EMV from a decision tree.

➤ calculate utilities to compare alternative courses of action.

KEY POINTS

1 When the outcomes of events are uncertain, and where probabilities can be assigned to those outcomes, the expected monetary values (EMVs) of courses of action can be calculated.

2 Decisions can be taken that maximise the EMV or the utility of the outcomes.

3 A decision tree can be constructed using three types of node:
   - end nodes, denoted by a triangle
   - decision nodes, denoted by a rectangle
   - chance nodes, denoted by a circle.

4 The appropriate pay-offs are written at each end node.

5 When the tree has been constructed the EMV algorithm is used, working from right to left, to work out the EMVs (or utilities) at chance nodes.

6 The best courses of action are selected at the decision nodes and the EMVs (or utilities) of that course of action are included at those nodes.

Chapter 1

Opening activity (page 1)

2098

Activity 1.1 (page 1)

Answer will depend on student's birth date.

Activity 1.2 (page 3)

Step	N	A	B	Comments	Passes
1	2				
2		1		$A = \frac{1}{2} \times 2$	
3			1.5	$B = \frac{1}{2}(1 + (2 \div 1))$	First pass
4				$(A - B)^2 = (1 - 1.5)^2 = 0.25$	
5		1.5		(new) A = (old) B	
3			1.41667	$B = \frac{1}{2}(1.5 + (2 \div 1.5))$	Second pass
4				$(1.5 - 1.41667)^2 = 0.00694$	
5		1.41667			
3			1.41422	$(1.41667 - 1.41422)^2 < 0.001$	Third pass
6				DISPLAY 1.41422	

Activity 1.3 (page 4)

Russian algorithm		Euclidean algorithm	
13	37	x	y
~~26~~	~~18~~	6	15
52	9	6	9
~~104~~	~~4~~	6	3
~~208~~	~~2~~	3	3
416	1	Output value 3	
481			

Discussion point (page 4)

You can check it does what if it is supposed to, and correct it if necessary.

Exercise 1.1 (page 6)

1

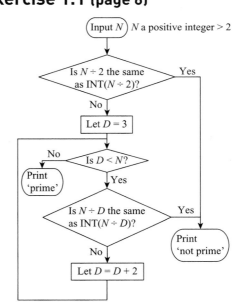

2 (i) e.g. sixty-two 8 eight 5 five 4 four 4

(ii) $\{1, 2, 6, 10\}$ → 3, 5, 4

$\{4, 5, 9\}$ → 4

$\{3, 7, 8\}$ → 5, 4

$\{11, 12\}$ → 6, 3, 5, 4

3 (i) 0.12 seconds   (ii) 54 minutes

(iii) 0.2 nanoseconds

4 (i) $r = 41, q = 0; r = 38, q = 1; \ldots ; r = 2, q = 13$

(ii) Division by repeated subtraction

(iii) $r = 4, q_1 = 0; r = 1, q_1 = 1; r = 11, q_2 = 0;$
$r = 8, q_2 = 1; r = 5, q_2 = 2; r = 2, q_2 = 3$

(iv) Second algorithm is a form of long division. It is more efficient but less transparent.

5 (i) e.g.

Step 1   Input N, the number of symbols in the Roman numeral

Step 2   Let $A = 1, R = 1$ and $T = 0$

Step 3   Read the symbol in position A of the Roman numeral, call this S

Step 4   Read the cell in row R and the column labelled S. Increase T by the first number in the cell and change R to the second number in the cell.

Step 5   Increase A by 1

Step 6   If $A > N$, display T and stop

Step 7   Otherwise go to Step 3

(ii) Roman numeral must be less than 5000.

(iii) e.g.

Step 1   Input N {N a positive integer < 5000}

Step 2 $U = N - 10 \times INT(N \div 10)$

Step 3   If $U < 5$ let $I = U$
If $U > 5$ let $V = 1$ and $I = U - 5$

Step 4 $N = (N - U) \div 10$

Step 5 $T = N - 10 \times INT(N \div 10)$

Step 6   If $T < 5$ let $X = T$
If $T > 5$ let $L = 1$ and $X = T - 5$

Step 7 $N = (N - T) \div 10$

Step 8 $H = N - 10 \times INT(N \div 10)$

Step 9   If $H < 5$ let $C = H$
If $H > 5$ let $D = 1$ and $C = H - 5$

Step 10 $N = (N - H) \div 10$

Step 11 $M = N - 10 \times INT(N \div 10)$

Step 12   Display M copies of the symbol "M"

Step 13   If $C = 4$ and $D = 0$ display "CD"
If $C = 4$ and $D = 1$ display "CM"
Otherwise display D copies "D" followed by C copies of "C"

Step 14   If $X = 4$ and $L = 0$ display "XL"
If $X = 4$ and $L = 1$ display "XC"
Otherwise display L copies of "L" followed by X copies of "X"

Step 15   If $I = 4$ and $V = 0$ display "IV"
If $I = 4$ and $V = 1$ display "IX"
Otherwise display V copies of "V" followed by I copies of "I"

6 (i) 592

(iii) A uses 30 592 additions, 0 subtractions and 10 000 comparisons
B uses 10 592 additions, 1110 subtractions and 10 000 comparisons
B is more efficient than A.

7 $O(n^2)$

8 (i) HCF = 180

(ii) One extra iteration in which A and B are swapped

(iii) 12 iterations, formula gives $12.0001\ldots$

Discussion points (page 10)

Optimal here means using the least number of bins.

Depending on the context other criteria may be more appropriate, for example it may be better to aim for an even balance of weights rather than having some full bins and other nearly empty bins, or other factors may need to be considered, such as the size of the boxes or (for food) their use by dates.

Using a complete enumeration will be very time consuming, a good solution that can be found quickly may be more useful than a best solution that cannot be found quickly.

Discussion point (page 13)

Replace 'greater' with 'less' and 'less' with 'greater' in the algorithm.

Exercise 1.2 (page 14)

1 Sum of sizes is 63.2 GB < 4 × 16 GB, so potentially this is possible.
First-fit decreasing, for example, gives:
P(8) + J(5.6) + C(2.4)
L(4.8) + Q(4.8) + E(4.4) + G(2)
A(4) + N(4) + I(3.6) + B(3.2) + F(1)
K(3) + M(3) + O(2.8) + D(2.6) + H(2.4) + R(1.6)
So it is possible to fit the programs onto four 16 GB discs.

2 Sum of lengths is 82 m so at least 5 lanes are needed.
First-fit decreasing, for example, gives
14 + 5; 12 + 8; 11 + 4 + 4; 10 + 4 + 4; 3 + 3
So five lanes are sufficient.

3   (i) and (ii) 2 4 5 5 6 9 – obviously

4   (i) blue, green, orange, pink, purple, red, yellow – obviously

     (ii) 14

5   3.5, 2; 3.5, 2; 3, 2, 1; 1.5, 1.5, 1.5, 1.5; 1 so 5 pipes needed

6   (i) 2 + 1 + 6; 3 + 3; 5 uses 3 bags.

     (ii) 6 + 3 + 1; 5 + 3 + 2 uses 2 bags (no spare).

7   0.18 seconds

8   (i) (a) 15   (b) 21   (c) $\frac{1}{2}n(n-1)$

     (ii) Each item in a list of n items is compared with $n-1$ items on the first pass, then $n-2$ on the next pass and so on until just 1 on the final pass. Total = $n-1+n-2+\ldots+2+1$ $=\frac{1}{2}n(n-1)=\frac{1}{2}n^2-\frac{1}{2}n$. The dominant term here is the one in n^2 so the order is quadratic.

9   (i) (a) Session 1   F H H I A

           Session 2   B B B E E C D

           Session 3   C C G G G A A D D

      (b) Session 1   F H I B E

           Session 2   H B E C

           Session 3   B C

      (c) Each session must have A, B, C, D and G, leaving 36 minutes. But there are four 20-minute activities, so one session must have two of these. As there are only 36 minutes available there will not be a fit.

     (ii) (a) 9 + 8 + 7 + 6 + 5 + 4 + 3 = 42 comparisons

      (b) B A C E F G H I J D

           92 81 76 82 45 51 93 71 62 43

           B A E C G H I J F D

           92 81 82 76 51 93 71 62 45 43

           B E A C H I J G F D

           92 82 81 76 93 71 62 51 45 43

           9 + 8 + 7 = 24 comparisons

Discussion point (page 17)

The smallest number of edges occurs when the graph is a tree, when the number of edges will be $n-1$.

Activity 1.5 (page 18)

Every edge contributes two to the sum of the degrees of the vertices, so that this sum must be even. As the sum of the degrees of the even vertices is even, the sum of the degrees of the odd vertices must also be even, in order to give an even sum overall. So the number of odd vertices must be even.

Exercise 1.3 (page 21)

1   (i) ABCA, ABCDEA, ACEA, ACDEA, ABCEA

     (ii) ABCEDCA is not a cycle since vertex C is repeated.

     (iii) A (closed) trail. It is a walk too, but since no edge is repeated it is best described as a trail.

2   Graph 1 – (ii)

     Graph 2 – (i)

     Graph 3 – (iii)

     Graph 4 – (ii)

3   For example,

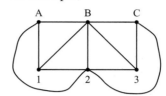

4   (2) and (6); (1), (3), (4) and (5)

5   Possible examples are:

6   It is Eulerian when it has an odd number of vertices, as that makes each vertex even. It can only be semi-Eulerian when there are two odd vertices.

7   (i) For example A↔1; D↔2; E↔3; B↔5; C↔6; F↔4

     (ii)

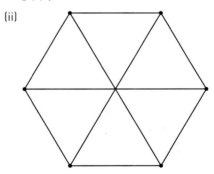

8   B is a 4-node and connects to C which is a 2-node in the first graph. The only 2-node in the second graph, U, does not connect with the only 4-node, which is Q and so they cannot be isomorphic.

9 (i)

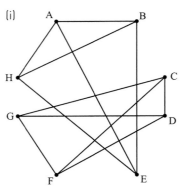

(ii) $^8C_2 = 28$

10 (i) AB; ACB; ADB; ACDB; ADCB

(ii) 1 direct, AB

3 through one other point

$^3P_2 = 6$ through 2 other points

$3! = 6$ through 3 other points

$1 + 3 + 6 + 6 = 16$

Activity 1.6 (page 22)

Penzance

Exercise 1.4 (page 24)

1 Yes, no, yes, yes

2 Yes, no, yes

3 (i)

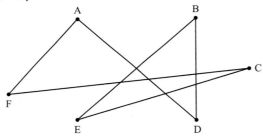

(ii)

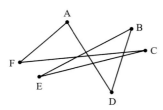

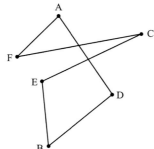

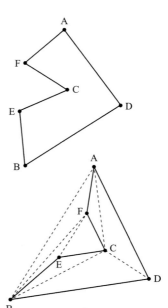

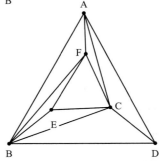

4 (i) For example, DCBAFED

(ii) The answer depends on the Hamiltonian cycle found in (i).

5 (i) EFGABDCE

(ii)

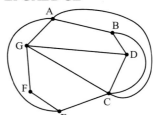

6 (i)

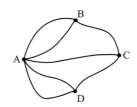

(ii) The four vertices of the graph are all odd, so that the graph is neither Eulerian nor semi-Eulerian.

7 24

Chapter 2

Opening activity (page 28)

For example, ABCDCBA: 14

Exercise 2.1 (page 34)

1   Bod–Tru 26; Tru–Pen 27; Bod–Bud 30;
    Bud–Oke 30; Oke–Exe 23; Exe–Tor 22;
    Bod–Ply 31 (or could choose any other of the
    31 weight arcs from Plymouth);
    Oke–Bar 31; Exe–Tau 35; Tau–Min 24

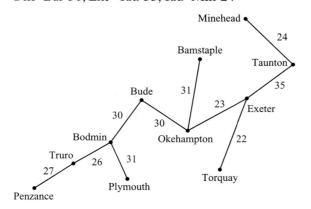

Total weight = 279

2

	A	B	C	D	E	F	G	H
A	–	4	–	2	6	–	–	–
B	4	–	1	–	–	–	–	–
C	–	1	–	5	–	–	–	2
D	2	–	5	–	3	–	–	8
E	6	–	–	3	–	2	5	–
F	–	–	–	–	2	–	2	–
G	–	–	–	–	5	2	–	17
H	–	–	2	8	–	–	17	–

3

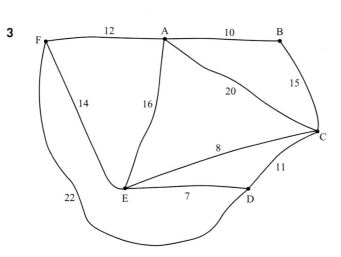

4   AB 10
    AF 12
    FE 14
    ED 7
    EC 8
    Total weight = 51

5   ED 7
    EC 8
    AB 10
    CD 11 (exclude)
    AF 12
    FE 14

6   MST has length 82.

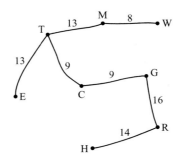

7   MST has length 66.

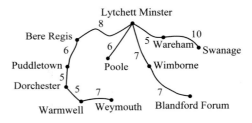

Activity 2.1 (page 36)

A possible route is ABCBFBDFEDCA.
In order to ensure that the arcs CB and BF are repeated,
a useful device is to repeat each one straightaway: thus
CB comes after BC and FB comes after BF.

Activity 2.2 (page 37)

A possible route is: ACABFEFDBCDEA
(which repeats AC and EF).

Activity 2.3 (page 38)

A is an odd node, so you are happy to start there, if you don't need to finish there. B is an even node, so if you are to finish there then you need to turn it into an odd node by repeating a suitable path. Thus, the problem is the same as for category C(i), but with the four nodes to be dealt with being B, C, E and F (instead of A, C, E and F).

Activity 2.4 (page 38)

The relevant pairings are

BC   4
BE   14 (BDE)
BF   7
CE   15 (CDE)
CF   11 (CBF)
EF   10

The possible ways of pairing up the nodes are

BC EF   4 + 10 = 14
BE CF   14 + 11 = 25
BF CE   7 + 15 = 22

The combination that gives the shortest total distance is thus BC EF, and the shortest route becomes 74 + 14 = 88.

Discussion point (page 38)

You can select two of the odd nodes to be the start and end points, so that the path between them no longer has to be repeated. As AC is the shortest path between any pair of odd nodes, this is the one that you want to repeat, and so you choose E and F as the start and end nodes (or the other way round).

Exercise 2.2 (page 40)

1   (i) e.g. 1, 3, 1, 2, 3, 4, 1 (length = 87)
     (ii) e.g. 1, 2, 3, 4, 1, 3 (length = 76)
2   For example, OYCYBLBOLCO, 1190 miles
3   For example, OYCYBLBOLCOL, 1247 miles
4   For example, YBOYCOLCLB, 979 miles
5   For example, Okehampton, Barnstaple, Bude, Okehampton, Bodmin, Truro, Plymouth, Exeter, Torquay, Plymouth, Bodmin, Bude, Barnstaple, Minehead, Taunton, Barnstaple, Exeter, Taunton, Exeter, Okehampton; 655 miles
6   For example, Taunton, Exeter, Okehampton, Barnstaple, Bude, Okehampton, Bodmin, Truro, Plymouth, Exeter, Torquay, Plymouth, Bodmin, Bude, Barnstaple, Minehead, Taunton, Barnstaple, Exeter; 620 miles

7   (i) 83 + 18
     (ii) e.g. D → I → H → F → D → H → G → F → C → B → F → C → E → G → H → I → A → B → A → D
     (iii) 3 times

Discussion point (page 43)

The shortest distances are from S, so that you are effectively being guided back to S. Were you to work forwards from S, there would be no way of knowing whether your route was going to be the shortest one to T.

Discussion point (page 43)

You could reverse the process, and find the shortest route from T to one of S_1, S_2, ...

Exercise 2.3 (page 43)

1   (i) SPQRT or SUVWT; 15
     (ii) SABFEDT; 8
     (iii) SBFJT; 12
2   (i) L.A.–San Fran–Salt Lake–Omaha–Chicago; 42
     (ii) New Orleans–Chicago–Omaha–Denver; 34
     (iii) L.A–Santa Fe–Denver–Omaha–Chicago; 42 (no better)
     New Orleans–El Paso–Santa Fe–Denver; 31 (better)
3   C: 3 + 4 + 2 + 2 + 3 = 14

Exercise 2.4 (page 49)

1   (i)

D(0)

	1	2	3	4
1	–	9	–	3
2	9	–	2	–
3	–	2	–	2
4	3	–	2	–

R(0)

	1	2	3	4
1	1	2	3	4
2	1	2	3	4
3	1	2	3	4
4	1	2	3	4

D(1)

	1	2	3	4
1	–	9	–	3
2	9	–	2	–
3	–	2	–	2
4	3	–	2	–

R(1)

	1	2	3	4
1	1	2	3	4
2	1	1	3	1
3	1	2	3	4
4	1	1	3	1

D(2)

	1	2	3	4
1	18	9	11	3
2	9	18	2	12
3	11	2	4	2
4	3	12	2	6

R(2)

	1	2	3	4
1	2	2	2	4
2	1	1	3	1
3	2	2	2	4
4	1	1	3	1

D(3)

	1	2	3	4
1	18	9	11	3
2	9	4	2	4
3	11	2	4	2
4	3	4	2	4

R(3)

	1	2	3	4
1	2	2	2	4
2	1	3	3	3
3	2	2	2	4
4	1	3	3	3

D(4)

	1	2	3	4
1	6	7	5	3
2	7	4	2	4
3	5	2	4	2
4	3	4	2	4

R(4)

	1	2	3	4
1	4	4	4	4
2	3	3	3	3
3	4	2	2	4
4	1	3	3	3

(ii) Final matrices

D(8)

	1	2	3	4	5	6	7	8
1	6	7	5	3	9	13	8	18
2	7	4	2	4	6	10	8	15
3	5	2	4	2	4	8	6	13
4	3	4	2	4	6	10	5	15
5	9	6	4	6	8	10	10	9
6	13	10	8	10	10	14	7	12
7	8	8	6	5	10	7	10	10
8	18	15	13	15	9	12	10	18

R(8)

	1	2	3	4	5	6	7	8
1	4	4	4	4	4	4	4	4
2	3	3	3	3	3	3	3	3
3	4	2	2	4	5	6	7	5
4	1	3	3	3	3	3	7	3
5	3	3	3	3	3	6	3	8
6	3	3	3	3	5	7	7	8
7	4	3	3	4	3	6	4	8
8	5	5	5	5	5	6	7	5

2 (i)

D(0)

	A	B	C	D
A	–	7	9	–
B	7	–	18	6
C	9	18	–	3
D	–	6	3	–

R(0)

	A	B	C	D
A	1	2	3	4
B	1	2	3	4
C	1	2	3	4
D	1	2	3	4

D(1)

	1	2	3	4
1	–	7	9	–
2	7	14	16	6
3	9	16	18	3
4	–	6	3	–

R(1)

	1	2	3	4
1	1	2	3	4
2	1	1	1	4
3	1	1	1	4
4	1	2	3	4

D(2)

	1	2	3	4
1	14	7	9	13
2	7	14	16	6
3	19	16	18	3
4	13	6	3	12

R(2)

	1	2	3	4
1	2	2	3	2
2	1	1	1	4
3	1	1	1	4
4	2	2	3	2

D(3)

	1	2	3	4
1	14	7	9	12
2	7	14	16	6
3	9	16	18	3
4	12	6	3	6

R(3)

	1	2	3	4
1	2	2	3	3
2	1	1	1	4
3	1	1	1	4
4	3	2	3	3

D(4)

	1	2	3	4
1	14	7	9	12
2	7	12	9	6
3	9	9	6	3
4	12	6	3	6

R(4)

	1	2	3	4
1	2	2	3	3
2	1	4	4	4
3	1	4	4	4
4	3	2	3	3

(ii)

D(0)

	1	2	3	4	5
1	–	7	9	–	–
2	7	–	18	6	–
3	9	18	–	3	1
4	–	6	3	–	1
5	–	–	1	1	–

R(0)

	1	2	3	4	5
1	1	2	3	4	5
2	1	2	3	4	5
3	1	2	3	4	5
4	1	2	3	4	5
5	1	2	3	4	5

D(1)

	1	2	3	4	5
1	–	7	9	–	–
2	7	14	16	6	–
3	9	16	18	3	1
4	–	6	3	–	1
5	–	–	1	1	–

R(1)

	1	2	3	4	5
1	1	2	3	4	5
2	1	1	1	4	5
3	1	1	1	4	5
4	1	2	3	4	5
5	1	2	3	4	5

D(2)

	1	2	3	4	5
1	14	7	9	13	–
2	7	14	16	6	–
3	19	16	18	3	1
4	13	6	3	12	1
5	–	–	1	1	–

R(2)

	1	2	3	4	5
1	2	2	3	2	5
2	1	1	1	4	5
3	1	1	1	4	5
4	2	2	3	2	5
5	1	2	3	4	5

D(3)

	1	2	3	4	5
1	14	7	9	12	10
2	7	14	16	6	17
3	9	16	18	3	1
4	12	6	3	6	1
5	10	17	1	1	2

R(3)

	1	2	3	4	5
1	2	2	3	3	3
2	1	1	1	4	1
3	1	1	1	4	5
4	3	2	3	3	5
5	3	3	3	4	3

D(4)

	1	2	3	4	5
1	14	7	9	12	10
2	7	12	9	6	7
3	9	9	6	3	1
4	12	6	3	6	1
5	10	7	1	1	2

R(4)

	1	2	3	4	5
1	2	2	3	3	3
2	1	4	4	4	4
3	1	4	4	4	5
4	3	2	3	3	5
5	3	4	3	4	3

D(5)

	1	2	3	4	5
1	14	7	9	11	10
2	7	12	8	6	7
3	9	8	2	2	1
4	11	6	2	2	1
5	10	7	1	1	2

R(5)

	1	2	3	4	5
1	2	2	3	3	3
2	1	4	4	4	4
3	1	5	5	5	5
4	5	2	5	5	5
5	3	4	3	4	3

(iii) Final matrices

D(7)

	A	B	C	D	E	F	G
A	14	7	9	17	12	14	17
B	7	10	9	10	5	7	10
C	9	9	8	9	4	6	9
D	17	10	9	6	5	3	6
E	12	5	4	6	4	2	5
F	14	7	6	3	2	4	3
G	17	10	9	6	5	3	6

R(7)

	A	B	C	D	E	F	G
A	2	2	3	2	2	2	2
B	1	5	5	5	5	5	5
C	1	5	5	5	5	5	5
D	6	6	6	6	6	6	6
E	2	2	3	6	6	6	6
F	5	5	5	4	5	5	7
G	6	6	6	6	6	6	6

Discussion point (page 53)

Prim's algorithm joins the nearest new node to **any** existing node, whereas the nearest neighbour algorithm joins it to the last node obtained. Also, Prim's algorithm is designed to produce a tree and you don't return to the start node.

Activity 2.7 (page 54)

Arcs are added in the following order:

Tau–Min 24
Min–Bar 38
Bar–Oke 31
Oke–Exe 23
Exe–Tor 22
Tor–Ply 31
Ply–Bod 31
Bod–Tru 26

Unfortunately, you are now stranded, and so the algorithm breaks down for this particular starting point. The algorithm is completed by taking each of the other nodes to be the starting point, in turn.

Exercise 2.5 (page 55)

1   Remove A, 21; remove B, 21; remove C, 24; remove D, 22; remove E, 33; remove F, 21; remove G, 21; remove H, 24. The lower bound is 33.
2   Starting with A, 33; starting with B, can't return; starting with C, 33; starting with D, 33; starting with E, 33; starting with F, 33; starting with G, 33; starting with H, 33. The upper bound is 33.
3   Remove A, 66; remove B, 66; remove C, 62; remove D, 62; remove E, 63; remove F, 66. The lower bound is 66.
4   Starting with A, 74; starting with B, 69; starting with C, 74; starting with D, 74; starting with E, 69; starting with F, 74. The upper bound is 69.

5

	A	B	C	D	E	F
A	–	3	7	13	6	5
B	3	–	4	10	3	2
C	7	4	–	6	5	6
D	13	10	6	–	11	12
E	6	3	5	11	–	1
F	5	2	6	12	1	–

6   (i)   Weston → Burnham → Bridgwater → Glastonbury → Wells → Bath → Cheddar → Weston; 95
    (ii) Weston → Burnham → Bridgwater → Glastonbury → Wells → Cheddar → Bath → Weston; 103
7   (i)   Birmingham → Gloucester → Hereford → Shrewsbury → Stoke → Sheffield → Nottingham → Northampton → Birmingham; 357
    (ii) The roads may be slower so the time is longer than an alternative. It may not provide appropriate stopping or refuelling points.

Chapter 3

Opening activity (page 58)

3 minutes

Activity 3.1 (page 59)

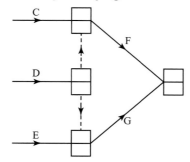

Exercise 3.1 (page 61)

1

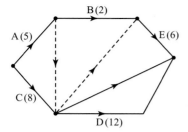

2

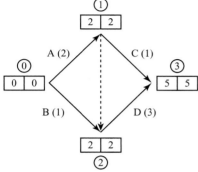

Minimum completion time 5 days.
A dummy is needed to show that D must follow A and B, and C must only follow A.

3

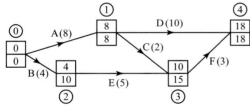

18 days

4

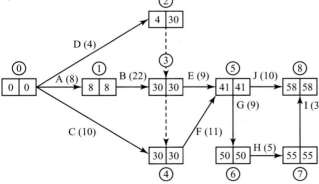

Minimum completion time: 58 weeks

5

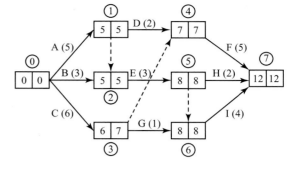

Minimum completion time is 12 days.

Activity 3.2 (page 62)

17 hours

Exercise 3.2 (page 65)

1 (i)   Reduce A by 2 days.

(ii)   Reduce A by 2 days, D by 5 days and F by 1 day.

2   A = 0, B = 1, C = 2, D = 0

3 (i)

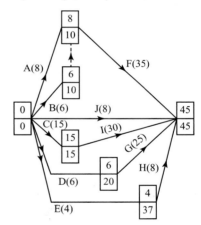

(ii)   45 minutes

(iii)   C and I

4 (i)

Activity	Immediate predecessors
A	–
B	–
C	–
D	A, B
E	B
F	B, C
G	D
H	D, E, F
I	F

(ii)

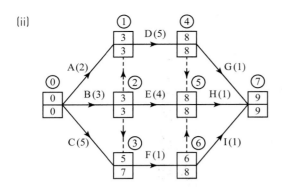

(iii)

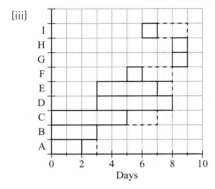

Activity 3.3 (page 66)

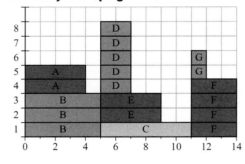

Exercise 3.3 (page 68)

1 (i)

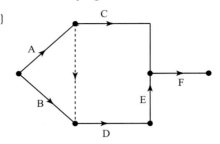

(ii) e.g.

Day	Harry	Nisha
1	A1	B1
2	D1	A2
3	E1	C1 B2
4	F1	D2
5	A3	B3 C2
6	D3	C3
7	E3	E2
8	F3	F2

2 (i) 44 days, A, B, C, G, I, L, N

(ii) D = 19 days
E = 20 days
F = 20 days
H and K = 1 day
J and M = 2 days

(iii)

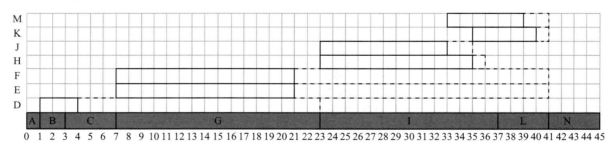

(iv) Delay J by 12 days to extend the project
completion time to 54 days.

3 (i)

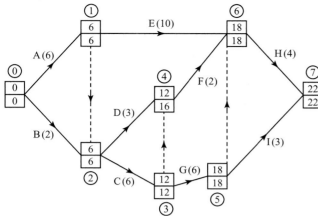

(ii) Minimum time to completion = 22 days.
   Critical activities are A, C, G and H.

(iii) Latest start time for D is 13 (16 − 3).
   Earliest finish time for C is 12.
   So the project can be completed in 22 days.

4 (i)

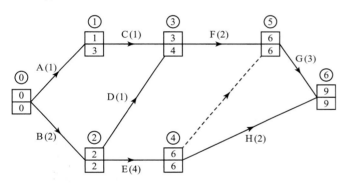

(ii) 9 days: B; E; G.

(iii)

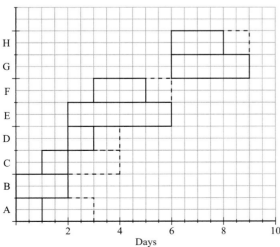

Days

(iv) Start C at beginning of day 4.
   Start F at beginning of day 5.

Chapter 4

Opening activity (page 71)

Cost of materials, How much people are prepared to pay, Number of potential customers, etc.

Activity 4.1 (page 74)

At A, $3x + 4y = 24$ and $y = 3x \Rightarrow 15x = 24 \Rightarrow x = \frac{8}{5}$

so that A is (1.6, 4.8), with $P = 8$.

Exercise 4.1 (page 74)

1 $x = 3\frac{1}{7}, y = 2\frac{6}{7}, P = 8\frac{6}{7}$

2 $x = 4\frac{1}{4}, y = 3\frac{1}{6}, P = 55\frac{1}{12}$

3 Let x be the number of minutes spent walking.
   Let y be the number of minutes spent running.
   Maximise $D = 90x + 240y$
   subject to $90x + 720y \leqslant 9000$
   $\qquad\qquad\quad x + y \leqslant 30$
   Answer: $x = 20, y = 10, D = 4200$

4 13 luxury and 17 standard, giving a profit of
   £335 000

5 $x = 1; y = 2; z = 3$

6 (i) $x + y \leqslant 4$
   $x \geqslant 2$
   $y \geqslant 0.6$
   $y \geqslant 0.25x$

(ii)

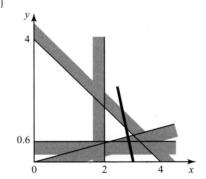

(iii) £3.2 million

(iv) 2.3

(v) See heavy line on graph in part (ii).
   Points of equal (fan) satisfaction

(vi) £3 382 000 in total; £618 000 less
   £2 706 000 on the playing squad;
   £206 000 more

7 (i) Let x be the number of units of X produced and y be the number of units of Y produced.
Maximise $x + y$
subject to $15x + 5y \leqslant 600$
$\qquad\qquad 10x + 7y \leqslant 560$
$\qquad\qquad 8x + 12y \leqslant 768$

(ii)

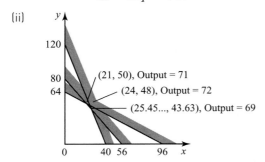

(21, 50), Output = 71
(24, 48), Output = 72
(25.45..., 43.63), Output = 69

(iii) The second constraint becomes
$10x + 7y \leqslant 576$, making (24, 48) feasible.

(iv) Any further increase in availability of B is irrelevant since the constraint is now not active.

8 Let x be the number of tonnes of deep-mined and y the number of tonnes of opencast.
Maximise $10x + 15y$ (or minimise $10x + 5y$)
subject to $x + y = 20\,000$
$2x + y \leqslant 34\,000$ (chlorine)
$3x + y \leqslant 40\,000$ (sulphur)
$35x + 10y \leqslant 400\,000$ (ash)
$5x + 12y \leqslant 200\,000$ (water)
Gives $x \approx 5700$; $y \approx 14\,300$, with water constraint critical and the others redundant.

9 12 tables and 30 chairs; profit = £390
It is likely that the demand for chairs will be greater than the supply.

10 (i) Let x be the number of the cheaper jacket and y be the number of the more expensive jacket.
Maximise $P = 10x + 20y$
subject to $x + y \geqslant 200$
$10x + 30y \leqslant 2700$
$20x + 10y \leqslant 4000$.

(ii) $x = 186$; $y = 28$; $P = 2420$

(iii) The purchase constraint exceeds the maximum order allowed by the other constraints ($220 > 214$).

Exercise 4.2 (page 81)

1

P	x	y	z	s_1	s_2	Value
1	−9	−10	−6	0	0	0
0	2	3	4	1	0	3
0	6	6	2	0	1	8
1	$-\frac{7}{3}$	0	$\frac{22}{3}$	$\frac{10}{3}$	0	10
0	$\frac{2}{3}$	1	$\frac{4}{3}$	$\frac{1}{3}$	0	1
0	2	0	−6	−2	1	2
1	0	0	$\frac{1}{3}$	1	$\frac{7}{6}$	$\frac{37}{3}$
0	0	1	$\frac{10}{3}$	1	$-\frac{1}{3}$	$\frac{1}{3}$
0	1	0	−3	−1	$\frac{1}{2}$	1

Solution: $x = 1, y = \frac{1}{3}, z = 0, P = 12\frac{1}{3}$

2

P	w	x	y	z	s_1	s_2	Value
1	−3	−2	0	0	0	0	0
0	1	1	1	1	1	0	150
0	2	1	3	4	0	1	200
1	0	−0.5	4.5	6	0	1.5	300
0	0	0.5	−0.5	−1	1	−0.5	50
0	1	0.5	1.5	2	0	0.5	100
1	0	0	4	5	1	1	350
0	0	1	−1	−2	2	−1	100
0	1	0	2	3	−1	1	50

Solution: $w = 50, x = 100, y = 0, z = 0, P = 350$

3

P	w	x	y	z	s_1	s_2	s_3	Value
1	−3	−2	0	0	0	0	0	0
0	1	1	1	1	1	0	0	150
0	2	1	3	4	0	1	0	200
0	−1	1	0	0	0	0	1	0
1	0	−0.5	4.5	6	0	1.5	0	300
0	0	0.5	−0.5	−1	1	−0.5	0	50
0	1	0.5	1.5	2	0	0.5	0	100
0	0	1.5	1.5	2	0	0.5	1	100
1	0	0	5	$\frac{20}{3}$	0	$\frac{5}{3}$	$\frac{1}{3}$	$\frac{1000}{3}$
0	0	0	−1	$-\frac{5}{3}$	1	$-\frac{2}{3}$	$-\frac{1}{3}$	$\frac{50}{3}$
0	1	0	1	$\frac{4}{3}$	0	$\frac{1}{3}$	$-\frac{1}{3}$	$\frac{200}{3}$
0	0	1	1	$\frac{4}{3}$	0	$\frac{1}{3}$	$\frac{2}{3}$	$\frac{200}{3}$

Solution: $w = 66\frac{2}{3}, x = 66\frac{2}{3}, y = 0, z = 0, P = 333\frac{1}{3}$

4   (i) a is the number of aardvarks, etc.

First inequality models the furry material constraint.

Second inequality models the woolly material constraint.

Third inequality models the glass eyes constraint. That would model a 'pairs of glass eyes' constraint.

(ii) The problem is an IP, so the number of eyes used will be integer anyway.

(iii) e.g.

P	a	b	c	s_1	s_2	s_3	Value
1	−3	−5	−2	0	0	0	0
0	0.5	1	1	1	0	0	11
0	2	1.5	1	0	1	0	24
0	2	2	2	0	0	1	30
1	−0.5	0	3	5	0	0	55
0	0.5	1	1	1	0	0	11
0	1.25	0	−0.5	−1.5	1	0	7.5
0	1	0	0	−2	0	1	8
1	0	0	2.8	4.4	0.4	0	58
0	0	1	1.2	1.6	−0.4	0	8
0	1	0	−0.4	−1.2	0.8	0	6
0	0	0	0.4	−0.8	−0.8	1	2

Make 6 aardvarks and 8 bears giving £58 profit. 2 eyes are left over.

5   (i) Let x be the number of maths books produced.

Line 1 $\Leftrightarrow$ max $6x + 3y + 7z$ $(10 − 4 = 6,$ etc.)

Line 2 $\Leftrightarrow 2x + 1.5y + 2.5z \leqslant 10\,000$

(printing time)

Line 3 $\Leftrightarrow x + 0.5y + 1.5z \leqslant 7500$

(packing time)

Line 4 $\Leftrightarrow 300x + 200y + 400z \leqslant 2\,000\,000$

(storage space)

(ii)

P	x	y	z	s_1	s_2	s_3	Value
1	−6	−3	−7	0	0	0	0
0	2	1.5	2.5	1	0	0	10000
0	1	0.5	1.5	0	1	0	7500
0	300	200	400	0	0	1	2000000
1	−0.4	1.2	0	2.8	0	0	28000
0	0.8	0.6	1	0.4	0	0	4000
0	−0.2	−0.4	0	−0.6	1	0	1500
0	−20	−40	0	−160	0	1	400000
1	0	1.5	0.5	3	0	0	30000
0	1	0.75	1.25	0.5	0	0	5000
0	0	−0.25	0.25	−0.5	1	0	2500
0	0	−25	25	−150	0	1	500000

Produce 5000 maths books at a profit of £30000 (2500 packing minutes spare and 0.5 m³ storage space spare.)

(iii) £1.50 and 50p respectively.

Exercise 4.3 (page 85)

1

Q	P	x	y	s_1	s_2	s_3	s_4	a	Value
1	0	0	1	0	0	0	−1	0	2
0	1	−16	−24	0	0	0	0	0	0
0	0	2	3	1	0	0	0	0	24
0	0	2	1	0	1	0	0	0	16
0	0	0	1	0	0	1	0	0	6
0	0	0	1	0	0	0	−1	1	2
1	0	0	0	0	0	0	0	−1	0
0	1	−16	0	0	0	0	−24	24	48
0	0	2	0	1	0	0	3	−3	18
0	0	2	0	0	1	0	1	−1	14
0	0	0	0	0	0	1	1	−1	4
0	0	0	1	0	0	0	−1	1	2
	1	−16	0	0	0	24	0		144
	0	2	0	1	0	−3	0		6
	0	2	0	0	1	−1	0		10
	0	0	0	0	0	1	1		4
	0	0	1	0	0	1	0		6
	1	0	0	8	0	0	0		192
	0	1	0	0.5	0	−1.5	0		3
	0	0	0	−1	1	2	0		4
	0	0	0	0	0	1	1		4
	0	0	1	0	0	1	0		6

Solution: $x = 3$, $y = 6$, $P = 192$.

2

Q	P	x	y	s_1	s_2	s_3	s_4	a	Value
1	0	1	1	1	0	0	−1	0	1
0	1	−9	−10	−6	0	0	0	0	0
0	0	2	3	4	1	0	0	0	3
0	0	6	6	2	0	1	0	0	8
0	0	1	1	1	0	0	−1	1	1
1	0	0	0	0	0	0	0	−1	0
0	1	0	−1	3	0	0	−9	9	9
0	0	0	1	2	1	0	2	−2	1
0	0	0	0	−4	0	1	6	−6	2
0	0	1	1	1	0	0	−1	1	1
	1	0	0	5	1	0	−7		10
	0	0	1	2	1	0	2		1
	0	0	0	−4	0	1	6		2
	0	1	0	−1	−1	0	−3		0
	1	0	0	$\frac{1}{3}$	1	$\frac{7}{6}$	0		$\frac{37}{3}$
	0	0	1	$\frac{10}{3}$	1	$-\frac{1}{3}$	0		$\frac{1}{3}$
	0	0	0	$-\frac{2}{3}$	0	$\frac{1}{6}$	1		$\frac{1}{3}$
	0	1	0	−3	−1	0.5	0		1

Solution: $x = 1$, $y = \frac{1}{3}$, $P = 12\frac{1}{3}$.

3

Q	P	w	x	y	z	s_1	s_2	s_3	a	Value
1	0	0	0	1	1	0	0	−1	0	1
0	1	−3	−2	0	0	0	0	0	0	0
0	0	1	1	1	1	1	0	0	0	150
0	0	2	1	3	4	0	1	0	0	200
0	0	0	0	1	1	0	0	−1	1	50
1	0	0	0	0	0	0	0	0	−1	0
0	1	−3	−2	0	0	0	0	0	0	0
0	0	1	1	0	0	1	0	1	−1	100
0	0	2	1	0	1	0	1	3	−3	50
0	0	0	0	1	1	0	0	1	1	50
	1	0	−0.5	0	1.5	0	1.5	4.5		75
	0	0	0.5	0	−0.5	1	−0.5	−0.5		75
	0	1	0.5	0	0.5	0	0.5	1.5		25
	0	0	0	1	−1	0	0	−1		50
	1	1	0	0	2	0	2	6		100
	0	−1	0	0	−1	1	−1	−2		50
	0	2	1	0	1	0	1	3		50
	0	0	0	1	1	0	0	−1		50

Solution: $w = 0$, $x = 50$, $y = 50$, $z = 0$, $P = 100$.

4

Q	P	w	x	y	z	s_1	s_2	s_3	s_4	a	Value
1	0	0	0	1	1	0	0	−1	0	0	50
0	1	−3	−2	0	0	0	0	0	0	0	0
0	0	1	1	1	1	1	0	0	0	0	150
0	0	2	1	3	4	0	1	0	0	0	200
0	0	−1	1	0	0	0	0	0	1	0	0
0	0	0	0	1	1	0	0	−1	0	1	50
1	0	0	0	0	0	0	0	0	0	−1	0
0	1	−3	−2	0	0	0	0	0	0	0	0
0	0	1	1	0	0	1	0	1	0	−1	100
0	0	2	1	0	1	0	1	3	0	−3	50
0	0	−1	1	0	0	0	0	0	1	0	0
0	0	0	0	1	1	0	0	1	0	1	50
	1	0	−0.5	0	1.5	0	1.5	4.5	0		75
	0	0	0.5	0	−0.5	1	−0.5	−0.5	0		75
	0	1	0.5	0	0.5	0	0.5	1.5	0		25
	0	0	1.5	0	0.5	0	0.5	1.5	1		25
	0	0	0	1	−1	0	0	−1	0		50
	1	0	0	0	$\frac{5}{3}$	0	$\frac{5}{3}$	5	$\frac{1}{3}$		$\frac{250}{3}$
	0	0	0	0	$-\frac{2}{3}$	1	$-\frac{2}{3}$	−1	$-\frac{1}{3}$		$\frac{200}{3}$
	0	1	0	0	$\frac{1}{3}$	0	$\frac{1}{3}$	1	$-\frac{1}{3}$		$\frac{50}{3}$
	0	0	1	0	$\frac{1}{3}$	0	$\frac{1}{3}$	1	$\frac{2}{3}$		$\frac{50}{3}$
	0	0	0	1	1	0	0	−1	0		50

Solution: $w = 16\frac{2}{3}$, $x = 16\frac{2}{3}$, $y = 50$, $z = 0$, $P = 83\frac{1}{3}$.

5

P	x	y	s_1	s_2	s_3	s_4	a	Value
1	−16	−(24 + M)	0	0	0	M	0	−2M
0	2	3	1	0	0	0	0	24
0	2	1	0	1	0	0	0	16
0	0	1	0	0	1	0	0	6
0	0	1	0	0	0	−1	1	2
1	−16	0	0	0	0	−24	24 + M	48
0	2	0	1	0	0	3	−3	18
0	2	0	0	1	0	1	−1	14
0	0	0	0	0	1	1	−1	4
0	0	1	0	0	0	−1	1	2
1	−16	0	0	0	24	0	M	144
0	2	0	1	0	−3	0	0	6
0	2	0	0	1	−1	0	0	10
0	0	0	0	0	1	1	−1	4
0	0	1	0	0	1	0	0	6
1	0	0	8	0	0	0	M	192
0	1	0	0.5	0	−1.5	0	0	3
0	0	0	−1	1	2	0	0	4
0	0	0	0	0	1	1	−1	4
0	0	1	0	0	1	0	0	6

Solution: $x = 3$, $y = 6$, $P = 192$.

6

P	x	y	z	s_1	s_2	s_3	a	Value
1	−(9 + M)	−(10 + M)	−(6 + M)	0	0	M	0	−M
0	2	3	4	1	0	0	0	3
0	6	6	2	0	1	0	0	8
0	1	1	1	0	0	−1	1	1
1	1	0	4	0	0	−10	10 + M	10
0	−1	0	1	1	0	3	−3	0
0	0	0	−4	0	1	6	−6	2
0	1	1	1	0	0	−1	1	1
1	$-\frac{7}{3}$	0	$\frac{22}{3}$	$\frac{10}{3}$	0	0	M	10
0	$-\frac{1}{3}$	0	$\frac{1}{3}$	$\frac{1}{3}$	0	1	−1	0
0	2	0	−6	−2	1	0	0	2
0	$\frac{2}{3}$	1	$\frac{4}{3}$	$\frac{1}{3}$	0	0	0	1
1	0	0	$\frac{1}{3}$	1	$\frac{7}{6}$	0	M	$\frac{37}{3}$
0	0	0	$-\frac{2}{3}$	0	$\frac{1}{6}$	1	−1	$\frac{1}{3}$
0	1	0	−3	−1	0.5	0	0	1
0	0	1	$\frac{10}{3}$	1	$-\frac{1}{3}$	0	0	$\frac{1}{3}$

Solution: $x = 1$, $y = \frac{1}{3}$, $P = 12\frac{1}{3}$.

7

P	w	x	y	z	s_1	s_2	s_3	a	Value
1	−3	−2	−M	−M	0	0	M	0	−50M
0	1	1	1	1	1	0	0	0	150
0	2	1	3	4	0	1	0	0	200
0	0	0	1	1	0	0	−1	1	50
1	−3	−2	0	0	0	0	0	M	0
0	1	1	0	0	1	0	1	−1	100
0	2	1	0	1	0	1	3	−3	50
0	0	0	1	1	0	0	−1	1	50
1	0	−0.5	0	1.5	0	1.5	4.5	M − 4.5	75
0	0	0.5	0	−0.5	1	−0.5	−0.5	0.5	75
0	1	0.5	0	0.5	0	0.5	1.5	−1.5	25
0	0	0	1	0	0	0	−1	1	50
1	1	0	0	2	0	2	6	M − 6	100
0	−1	0	0	−1	1	−1	−2	2	50
0	2	1	0	1	0	1	3	−3	50
0	0	0	1	1	0	0	−1	1	50

Solution: $w = 0$, $x = 50$, $y = 50$, $z = 0$, $P = 100$.

8

P	w	x	y	z	s_1	s_2	s_3	s_4	a	Value
1	−3	−2	−M	−M	0	0	M	0	0	−50M
0	1	1	1	1	1	0	0	0	0	150
0	2	1	3	4	0	1	0	0	0	200
0	−1	1	0	0	0	0	0	1	0	0
0	0	0	1	1	0	0	−1	0	1	50
1	−3	−2	0	0	0	0	0	0	M	0
0	1	1	0	0	1	0	1	0	−1	100
0	2	1	0	1	0	1	3	0	−3	50
0	−1	1	0	0	0	0	0	1	0	0
0	0	0	1	1	0	0	1	0	1	50
1	0	−0.5	0	1.5	0	1.5	4.5	0		75
0	0	0.5	0	−0.5	1	−0.5	−0.5	0		75
0	1	0.5	0	0.5	0	0.5	1.5	0		25
0	0	1.5	0	0.5	0	0.5	1.5	1		25
0	0	0	1	−1	0	0	−1	0		50
1	0	0	0	$\frac{5}{3}$	0	$\frac{5}{3}$	5	$\frac{1}{3}$		$\frac{250}{3}$
0	0	0	0	$-\frac{2}{3}$	1	$-\frac{2}{3}$	−1	$-\frac{1}{3}$		$\frac{200}{3}$
0	1	0	0	$\frac{1}{3}$	0	$\frac{1}{3}$	1	$-\frac{1}{3}$		$\frac{50}{3}$
0	0	1	0	$\frac{1}{3}$	0	$\frac{1}{3}$	1	$\frac{2}{3}$		$\frac{50}{3}$
0	0	0	1	1	0	0	−1	0		50

Solution: $w = 16\frac{2}{3}$, $x = 16\frac{2}{3}$, $y = 50$, $z = 0$, $P = 83\frac{1}{3}$.

Chapter 5

Opening activity (page 87)

AS, BQ, CP, DR (5 + 3 + 4 + 7 = 19)
or AS, BQ, CR, DP (5 + 3 + 6 + 5 = 19)

Activity 5.1 (page 88)

AP, BR and CQ – time taken is 9 + 7 + 8 = 24;

AR, BQ and CP – time taken is 6 + 8 + 10 = 24.

Discussion point (page 88)

The total of the (optimum) allocations can be retrieved by adding back the reductions that were made when creating the corresponding zeros. The allocations will involve all of the rows, so that each row reduction will have affected (just) one of the allocations. After the row reductions, some of the columns will have contained zeros. Any columns that didn't contain a zero will have had a column reduction applied, and each of these reductions will have affected (just) one of the allocations, because the allocations involve all of the columns. So each row or column reduction affects (just) one of the allocations, and the total of the allocations is the total of the row and column reductions.

Activity 5.3 (page 89)

AP(3) + BR(1) + CQ(4) = 8,
or AQ(5) + BR(1) + CP(2) = 8

Exercise 5.1 (page 89)

1 AP, BR, CQ (3 + 2 + 5 = 10)
   or AQ, BR, CP (7 + 2 + 1 = 10)
2 AP, BQ, CR, DS (5 + 2 + 2 + 2 = 11)
   or AQ, BP, CR, DS (3 + 4 + 2 + 2 = 11)
3 (i) Reduced matrix is

	P	Q	R	S
A	0	4	0	3
B	0	0	3	1
C	1	0	2	2
D	3	0	0	0

AR, BP, CQ, DS (2 + 4 + 4 + 7 = 17)

(ii) Reduced matrix is

	P	Q	R	S
A	0	4	0	2
B	0	0	3	0
C	1	0	2	1
D	4	1	1	0

AR, BP, CQ, DS (2 + 4 + 4 + 7 = 17)

4 AR, BP, CQ (150 + 190 + 200 = 540)
5 OS, EF, TZ, BM, PC (1 + 9 + 1 + 4 + 2 = 17)

Exercise 5.2 (page 93)

1 6; for example:

	P	Q	R	S	T	U	V	W
A	3	2	0	2	1	0	4	2
B	4	1	5	0	3	2	1	1
C	2	4	0	3	0	4	0	3
D	2	3	1	0	1	0	2	6
E	0	5	4	2	0	1	5	4
F	3	0	1	0	2	2	3	0
G	2	1	0	6	3	0	4	4
H	3	2	1	0	4	3	1	6

2 AP, BQ, CR (9 + 8 + 6 = 23)
3 AR, BQ, CP (90 + 40 + 50 = 180)
4 AP, BQ, CR, DS (4 + 3 + 4 + 6 = 17)
   or AS, BQ, CR, DP (5 + 3 + 4 + 5 = 17)
5 AT, BP, CR, DS, EQ (3 + 3 + 1 + 5 + 5 = 17)
   or AR, BP, CQ, DT, ES (3 + 3 + 4 + 4 + 3 = 17)
   or AS, BP, CR, DT, EQ (4 + 3 + 1 + 4 + 5 = 17)

Activity 5.4 (page 94)

Were you to reduce the matrix by columns, this would convert the column of 9s to a column of zeros, and it would not be possible to then reduce the matrix by rows, because each row would already contain a zero. It is then quite likely that fewer than 4 rows and/or columns would be needed to cover the zeros.

Exercise 5.3 (page 94)

1 BP, CR, DQ (6 + 3 + 3 = 12)
   or BR, CP, DQ (4 + 5 + 3 = 12)
2 AP, BQ, CR (4 + 7 + 5 = 16)
   or AR, BQ, CP (3 + 7 + 6 = 16)
3 AP, BS, CQ, DR (5 + 2 + 4 + 4 = 15)
   or AS, BQ, CR, DP (4 + 3 + 5 + 3 = 15)
4 A3, B1, C5, D2, E4; check: total of scores
   = 7 + 9 + 6 + 7 + 8 = 37; had each score been
   9, then no reductions would have been necessary
   after subtracting from 9; total of row reductions
   = 8, so total of scores should be 5 × 9 – 8 = 37.
5 AR, BQ, CS (20 + 22 + 16 = 58)

Exercise 5.4 (page 95)

1   Minimise $3AX + 6AY + 4AZ + 7BX + 4BY + 6BZ + 6CX + 4CY + 5CZ$

   subject to $AX + AY + AZ = 1$
                $BX + BY + BZ = 1$
                $CX + CY + CZ = 1$
                $AX + BX + CX = 1$
                $AY + BY + CY = 1$
                $AZ + BZ + CZ = 1$

   with all variables as indicator variables.

2   Minimise $6A_1 + 5A_2 + 3A_3 + A_5 + 2A_6 + B_1 + 2B_2 + 5B_3 + 3B_5 + 10C_1 + 7C_2 + 2C_4 + 3C_6 + 4D_4 + D_5 + 5D_6 + 6E_1 + 3E_2 + 2E_3 + 5E_5 + 4E_6 + 3F_1 + 7F_2 + 3F_4 + 2F_5 + F_6$

   subject to

   $A_1 + A_2 + A_3 + A_4 + A_5 + A_6 = 1$
   $B_1 + B_2 + B_3 + B_4 + B_5 + B_6 = 1$
   $C_1 + C_2 + C_3 + C_4 + C_5 + C_6 = 1$
   $D_1 + D_2 + D_3 + D_4 + D_5 + D_6 = 1$
   $E_1 + E_2 + E_3 + E_4 + E_5 + E_6 = 1$
   $F_1 + F_2 + F_3 + F_4 + F_5 + F_6 = 1$
   $A_1 + B_1 + C_1 + D_1 + E_1 + F_1 = 1$
   $A_2 + B_2 + C_2 + D_2 + E_2 + F_2 = 1$
   $A_3 + B_3 + C_3 + D_3 + E_3 + F_3 = 1$
   $A_4 + B_4 + C_4 + D_4 + E_4 + F_4 = 1$
   $A_5 + B_5 + C_5 + D_5 + E_5 + F_5 = 1$
   $A_6 + B_6 + C_6 + D_6 + E_6 + F_6 = 1$

   with all variables as indicator variables.

3   Minimise $5AP + 7AR + 4AS + 3BQ + 5BR + 2BS + 6CP + 4CQ + 5CR + 3DP + 4DR + 6DS$,

   subject to

   $AP + AR + AS = 1$
   $BQ + BR + BS = 1$
   $CP + CQ + CR = 1$
   $DP + DR + DS = 1$
   $AP + CP + DP = 1$
   $BQ + CQ = 1$
   $AR + BR + CR + DR = 1$
   $AS + BS + DS = 1$,

   where the variables take the values 0 or 1.

4   Maximise $14AQ + 20AR + 18AS + 15BP + 22BQ + 12BS + 13CP + 17CR + 16CS$,

   subject to

   $AQ + AR + AS = 1$
   $BP + BQ + BS = 1$
   $CP + CR + CS = 1$
   $BP + CP = 1$
   $AQ + BQ = 1$
   $AR + CR = 1$
   $AS + BS + CS = 1$,

   where the variables take the values 0 or 1.

Chapter 6

Opening activity (page 97)

It always ends in four. For example, in French it loops through quatre, six, trois, cinq. In German it always ends in vier.

Activity 6.1 (page 98)

It finds the square root of 25. Changing x_0 makes no difference.

Exercise 6.1 (page 102)

1   (i) $u_n = 7 \times 4^n$

   (ii) $u_n = 0.5^n$

   (iii) $9u_n = 26 \times 10^n - 8$

   (iv) $u_n = 30 \times 2^n - 5n - 10$

2   (i) $u_n = \left(c + \dfrac{b}{a-1}\right)a^n - \dfrac{b}{a-1}$ or $a^n c + b\dfrac{(a^n - 1)}{(a-1)}$

   (ii)
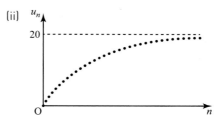

3   (i)   The initial population
   (ii) How much the population reduces by each year, so deaths.
   (iii) $u_n = 25 \times 1.2^n + 75$
   (iv) Yes, both terms of the solution are increasing.

4   £1490.29

5   $u_{n+1} = u_n + (10 \times 2^n)$ $u_0 = 7$

   $u_n = (10 \times 2^n) - 3$ $n \geqslant 0$

6   (i) $L(3, 2, 1)\ M(-)\ R(-) \to L(3, 2)\ M(-)\ R(1)$
            $\to L(3)\ M(2)\ R(1) \to L(3)\ M(2, 1)\ R(-)$
            $\to L(-)M(2, 1)\ R(3) \to L(1)\ M(2)\ R(3)$
            $\to L(1)\ M(-)\ R(3, 2)$
            $\to L(-)\ M(-)\ R(3, 2, 1)$
   (ii) $2^{64} - 1 \approx 18\,400\,000\,000\,000\,000\,000$ days

7   (i) $v_k = 0.99v_{k-1} + 0.1$
            Divide through by 10 to get concentrations, and use $c_k = v_k/10$.

   (ii) $c_k = 1 + 0.99^k(c_0 - 1)$
            $c_4 \approx 0.294$. It is 10 weeks before the concentration reaches 0.5.

8 (i) $u_{n+1} = 400 + 0.8u_n$
(ii) $u_n = 2000(1 - (0.8)^n)$ or $2000 - 1600(0.8)^{n-1}$
(iii) (a) $u_{12} = £1862.56$
(b) $£2000$

Activity 6.2 (page 106)

The terms oscillate between positive and negative values. The magnitude of the terms increases, though not uniformly.

Exercise 6.2 (page 107)

1 (i) $u_n = A2^n + Bn2^n$
(ii) $u_n = A3^n + Bn3^n$

2 $u_n = 3^{n-2} + 2n3^{n-2}$

3 $u_n = \dfrac{(6 \times 4^n) + (-3)^n}{7}$

4 $u_n = \dfrac{1}{\sqrt{5}}\left[\left(\dfrac{1 + \sqrt{5}}{2}\right)^{n+1} - \left(\dfrac{1 - \sqrt{5}}{2}\right)^{n+1}\right]$

5 $10\,946$ ways (the 20th Fibonacci number)
(You can form a path of length n by adding a 'sideways-on' slab to a path of length $n - 1$, or by adding two 'end-on' slabs to a path of length $n - 2$.)

6 $u_n = (-9 \times 2^n) + (3 \times 3^n) + 0.5n^2 + 3.5n + 8$

7 (i) (a) $£2520$
(b) $£3045.20$
(ii) (a) $0.25 \times £2520$
(b) $£761.30$
(iii) 1.01 to add on interest
0.25 for withdrawal
$£1000$ income
(iv) $\dfrac{1000}{0.24} = £4166.67$
$£1041.67$
(v) $\dfrac{1000}{0.49} = £2040.82$
$£1020.41$

8 (i) $u_3 = 12$
(ii) u_n = existing number
u_{n-1} = number at least one year old, and therefore number of new branches
(iii) (a) $u_n = \dfrac{4}{\sqrt{5}}\left[\left(\dfrac{1 + \sqrt{5}}{2}\right)^{n+1} - \left(\dfrac{1 - \sqrt{5}}{2}\right)^{n+1}\right]$
(b) $u_2 = \dfrac{4}{\sqrt{5}}\left[\left(\dfrac{1 + \sqrt{5}}{2}\right)^{3} - \left(\dfrac{1 - \sqrt{5}}{2}\right)^{3}\right]$

$= \dfrac{1}{2\sqrt{5}}\left[1 + 3\sqrt{5} + 15 + 5\sqrt{5} - \left(1 - 3\sqrt{5} + 15 - 5\sqrt{5}\right)\right]$

$= 8$

(iv) (a) $u_5 = 32; u_4 = 20$
(b) 9
(c) $239, 29\,411$
(d) 23 are old and 11 are new. Removing 14 leads to 127; removing 15 leads to 119.

Discussion point (page 109)

The function $u(x) - xu(x) - 6x^2u(x)$ is derived from the recurrence relation $u_{n+2} - u_{n+1} - 6u_n = 0$, so when all 3 terms are present they cancel out.

Activity 6.3 (page 109)

$u_4 = 13, u_5 = 55;$
$13x^4 - 7x^4 - 6x^4 = 0; 55x^5 - 13x^5 - 6 \times 7x^5 = 0$

Activity 6.4 (page 110)

$u_0 = 1, u_1 = 1, u_2 = 6, u_3 = 11, u_4 = 26$

Exercise 6.3 (page 111)

1 (i) $1, 2, 7, 20, 61$
(ii) $0, 1, 7, 27, 115$

2 (i) $1 + 2x + 7x^2 + 20x^3 + 61x^4$
(ii) $x + 7x^2 + 27x^3 + 115x^4$

3 (i) $\dfrac{3}{4(1 - 3x)} + \dfrac{1}{4(1 + x)}$
(ii) $\dfrac{4}{9(1 - 4x)} + \dfrac{1}{9(1 + 2x)} - \dfrac{5}{9(1 - x)}$

4 $u_n = 2 \times (-2)^n - 3 \times 5^n$

5 (i) $u_n = \dfrac{3}{4} \times 3^n + \dfrac{1}{4} \times (-1)^n$
(ii) $u_n = \dfrac{1}{9}\left(4^{n+1} + (-2)^n - 5\right)$

6 $u_n = -2^n + 3$

7 $u_n = \dfrac{1}{24}\left(11 \times 5^n + 22 \times (-1)^n - 9\right)$

8 $u_n = \dfrac{1}{4}\left(5 \times 3^n - 8 \times 2^n + 2n + 7\right)$

Chapter 7

Opening activity (page 113)

ABD, ABCD, ACD, ACBD

Exercise 7.1 (page 116)

1. (i) Source is B; sink is E.
   (ii) 27

2. (i) (a) {S, A, B, C, E}/{D, T}, capacity = 15
   (b) {S, A, B, C}/{D, E, T}, capacity = 14
   (ii) (a) SA = 2; SB = 6; SC = 7; AD = 2;
       AB = 0; BD = 5; BE = 1; CB = 0;
       CE = 7; DT = 7; ET = 8
   (b) SA = 2; SB = 5; SC = 7; AD = 2; AB = 0;
       BD = 5; BE = 0; CB = 0; CE = 7;
       DT = 7; ET = 7

3. {S}/{A, B, C, T}, capacity = 22;
   {S, A}/{B, C, T}, capacity = 20;
   {S, C}/{A, B, T}, capacity = 39;
   {S, A, B}/{C T}, capacity = 25;
   {S, A, C}/{B, T}, capacity = 27;
   {S, A, B, C}/{T}, capacity = 22

   Maximum flow = 20, with flow pattern, for example:

Route	Flow
SABT	10
SCT	7
SCBT	3

4. (i) B is the source, E is the sink.
   (ii) {A,B,G}/{C,D,E,F,H} has capacity 19;
       {B,C,H}/{A,D,E,F,G} has capacity 34.
   (iii) It is at most 19.

5. $a = 17; b = 2; c = 5; d = 18; e = 7$

6. (i) {S}/{A,B,C,T} has capacity 14; {S,A}/
       {B,C,T} has capacity 11; {S,B}/{A,C,T} has
       capacity 15; {S,A,B}/{C,T} has capacity 8;
       {S,B,C}/{A,T} has capacity 29; {S,A,B,C}/
       {T} has capacity 13.
   (ii) Minimum cut is 8 so maximum flow is 8.
   (iii) Flow is SAT = 3; SBCT = 5, so total flow of 8.

Exercise 7.2 (page 120)

1. (i) For example: BA = 8; BC = 7; BE = 12;
       AD = 8; CD = 2; CF = 5; DH = 10; FH = 0;
       FG = 2; FE = 3; HG = 10; GE = 12
   (ii) Total flow (for example BA+BC+BE) = 27
       This is the same as the capacity of the cut in
       Exercise 7.1 question 1 (ii), so it must be a
       maximal flow.

2. For example:

Route	Flow
SABT	10
SCT	7
SCBT	3

Route	Flow
SABT	10
SCT	5
SCBT	5

3. (i) Maximum total flow = 19
       e.g. SA = 10; SB = 9; AC = 14; DA = 4;
       BD = 9; CT = 14; DT = 5
   (ii) S | ABCDT; capacity of cut = 19 so flow must
       be a maximum.

4. (i) SABD | CT, capacity = 22
   (ii) Flow = 19 < 22
   (iii) S → A → D → B → C → T (augmentation
       of 3 possible)
       SA = 10; AD = 5; BD = 4; BC = 8; CT = 13;
       others unchanged

5. (i) Maximum flow is 43: BA = 25; BC = 18;
       AH = 12; AE = 13; HC = 0; CD = 18;
       HG = 12; DG = 8; DE = 10; GE = 5; GF = 15;
       EF = 28
   (ii) The value of the cut is 43 so, by the
       maximum flow–minimum cut theorem, the
       flow must be a maximum.

Activity 7.1 (page 123)

Route	Flow
SABCT	2
SAT	13
SBCT	6
Total	21

The flows along each of the arcs are shown overleaf.

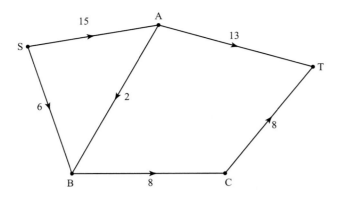

Activity 7.2 (page 123)

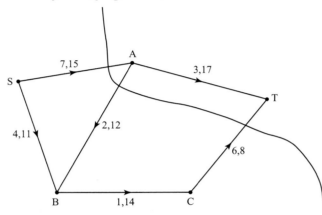

The cut in the diagram has value $15 - 2 + 8 = 21$. Hence the maximum possible flow is 21, as it cannot exceed the cut of 21.

Activity 7.3 (page 123)

A flow of 2 is possible along SBAT, to give the following revised network of potential changes.

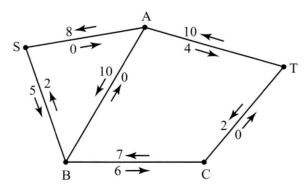

Although it is possible to have a flow along SB, and then a flow along BC, you come to a dead-end at C (as there is no scope for a flow along CT), unless you return to B. At B, the only other route is along BS, which is also a dead-end (as there is no scope for a flow along SA). Therefore you have reached the end of

the process. The combined effect of the initial flow and the augmentation is shown in the table below.

Route	Flow
SABCT	4
SAT	11
SBCT	4
SBAT	2
Total	21

The flows along each of the arcs are those already obtained in Activity 7.1.

Exercise 7.3 (page 123)

1 Maximum flow = 50

Route	Flow
SAB_1B_2T	20
SCDT	30

2 (i)

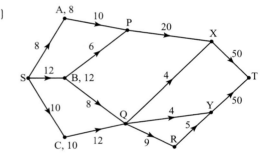

(ii) 27; SA = 8; SB = 12; SC = 7; AP = 8; BP = 6; BQ = 6; CQ = 7; PX = 14; QX = 4; QY = 4; QR = 5; RY = 5; XT = 18; YT = 9

(iii) {S, B, C, Q, R}/{A, P, X, Y, T} has value 27.

(iv) Augmentation of 3 available to give a new maximum of 30.

(v) Introduce an arc with large capacity from R to the sink T.

3 Maximum flow = 21

Route	Flow
SABCAT	1
SAT	11
SBCAT	3
SBCT	6

4 (i) Needs SS_1 with capacity 20 and SS_2 with capacity 30.

(ii) Needs T_1T with capacity 25 or more, T_2T with capacity 25 or more, and T_3T with capacity 20 or more.

(iii) Cut $\{S, S_1, S_2, A\}/\{B, C, D, T_1, T_2, T_3, T\}$ has capacity 47. There are many ways of achieving a flow of 47, e.g. $T_1T = 25, T_2T = 12, T_3T = 10$.

5 (i)

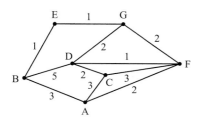

(ii) $BE = 0; BD = 5; BA = 3; EG = 0; DG = 2;$
$DF = 1; DC = 2; AC = 1; AF = 2; GF = 2;$
$CF = 3$
Cut $\{B, E, D, A, G, C\}/\{F\}$ has capacity 8, so the flow must be a maximum.

6 (i)

Route	Flow
SABT	9
SCABT	5
SCBT	5
SCT	8
Total	27

(ii) $\{S, C\}/\{A, B, T\}$ has capacity 27 units so that is the maximum flow.

(iii) 20, with $SC = 11$

7 (i) $\{S, B, D\}/\{A, B, T\}$ with capacity 24
The established flow is $18 < 24$.
Maximum flow is given by:

Route	Flow
SACT	12
SBDT	12
Total	24

(ii) Previous minimum cut now has capacity of 30 as the flow between A and D is from S to T now. New minimum cut $\{S, B\}/\{A, C, D, T\}$ has capacity 26. Maximum flow is given by:

Route	Flow
SACT	12
SBDT	12
SBDACT	2
Total	26

Chapter 8

Exercise 8.1 (page 129)

1 (i) $\begin{pmatrix} -2 & 1 \\ 0 & -3 \\ -1 & 4 \end{pmatrix}$

(ii) 4

(iii) 3

2 (i) Player 1 wins 1

(ii) Player 1 wins 0

(iii) Player 1 wins 2

3 Player 1 chooses option A; player 2 chooses option B, value is -1

4 (i) Player 1 chooses option B; player 2 chooses option B

(ii) Player 1 chooses option A; player 2 chooses option C

(iii) Not stable

(iv) Not stable

5 (i) Stable; value is 0

(ii) Stable; value is 0

(iii) Not stable

(iv) Not stable

6 The maximum of the row minima is c.
The minimum of the column maxima is also c.

Exercise 8.2 (page 130)

1 (i) B and C

(ii) A and D

2 (i) e.g. 1st column dominated; then 1st row; reduced matrix: (0) [B,B]

(ii) e.g. 2nd row dominated; then columns A, B and D are dominated; reduced matrix: (0) [A,C]

(iii) No dominated strategies

(iv) No dominated strategies

3 (i) Player 1 chooses option B; player 2 chooses option C; value is 0

(ii) The reduced matrix is (0).

4

	A	B	D	Row minima
A	2	–1	4	–1
B	0	6	2	0
C	4	0	1	0
Column maxima	4	6	4	

5 $x \geqslant 1$

Exercise 8.3 (page 136)

1 (ii) The value is 2.5.

2 (i) Player 1 should never choose option C.

(ii) The value is 1.5.

3 (i) 3.4

(ii) 4

(iii) $3\frac{2}{3}$

4   Player 1's strategy: choose A with prob. $\frac{1}{3}$

Player 2's strategy: choose A with prob. $\frac{5}{6}$

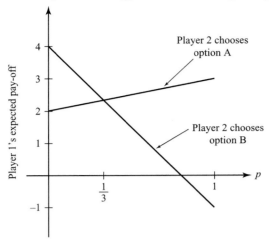

5   The value is 1.8.

6   Row C dominates row B, then col. B dominates col. A.

Player 1's strategy: choose A with prob. 0.8
Player 2's strategy: choose A with prob. 0.6
The value is 2.6.

Exercise 8.4 (page 140)

1   Maximise $P = v - 2$, subject to the constraints
$v \leqslant 3p_1 + 4p_2 + 6p_3$,
$v \leqslant 5p_1 + 2p_2 + p_3$,
$p_1 + p_2 + p_3 \leqslant 1$
$(p_1, p_2, p_3 \geqslant 0, v > 0)$.

2   The value is 2.5.

3   (i)   3.4
   (ii)   4
   (iii) $3\frac{2}{3}$

4   Maximise $P = v - 4$, subject to the constraints
$v \leqslant 2p_1 + p_2 + 5p_3$,
$v \leqslant 3p_1 + 4p_2 + 2p_3$,
$p_1 + p_2 + p_3 \leqslant 1$
$(p_1, p_2, p_3 \geqslant 0, v > 0)$.
Simplex equations:
$P - v = -4$
$v - 2p_1 - p_2 - 5p_3 + s_1 = 0$
$v - 3p_1 - 4p_2 - 2p_3 + s_2 = 0$
$p_1 + p_2 + p_3 + s_3 = 1$

5

P	v	p	q	s_1	s_2	s_3	Value	
1	−1	0	0	0	0	0	−4	①
0	1	−8	−3	1	0	0	0	②
0	1	−1	−6	0	1	0	0	③
0	0	1	1	0	0	1	1	④

6 $x \geqslant 2$

7   (i)   Janet should choose 30 and John should choose 24. Janet wins 6.
   (ii)   17

Chapter 9

Opening activity (page 142)

3

Activity 9.1 (page 148)

In Example 9.4 there are 3 sources and 3 destinations, $3 + 3 - 1 = 5$ cells used.

In Example 9.5 there are 4 sources and 4 destinations, $4 + 4 - 1 = 7$ cells used.

Exercise 9.1 (page 149)

1   (i)   £184
   (ii)   £67

2   5

3   (i)

Units	Warehouse 1	Warehouse 2	Stock or supply
Factory 1	8	2	10
Factory 2		10	10
Factory 3		10	10
Demand	8	22	

   (ii)   £1496

4   (i)   The problem is balanced so there is no need for a dummy destination.

Units	P	Q	R	Stock or supply
A	5			5
B	3	3		6
C		0	4	4
D			2	2
Demand	8	3	6	

   (ii)   Although 6 cells are used, one of them contains a 0. This happens because the supply from A and B equals the demand at P and Q. The 0 is needed to enable a zig-zag path rather than a diagonal movement and so that number of cells used = number of sources + number of destinations − 1.

5 (i) Total stock = 30 units, total demand = 26 units, so excess = 4 units.

	Warehouse 1	Warehouse 2	Warehouse 3	Dummy	Stock
Factory 1					8
Factory 2					10
Factory 3					12
Demand	12	10	4	4	

(ii)

Units	Warehouse 1	Warehouse 2	Warehouse 3	Dummy	Stock
Factory 1	8				8
Factory 2	4	6			10
Factory 3		4	4	4	12
Demand	12	10	4	4	

(iii) £1004

(iv) 6 cells used, 3 sources and 4 destinations, $3 + 4 - 1 = 6$

Activity 9.2 (page 150)

(i) $56 = R_1 + K_1$, $19 = R_1 + K_2$, $64 = R_2 + K_2$ and $37 = R_3 + K_2$.

(ii) $K_1 = 56$, $K_2 = 19$, $R_2 = 45$, $R_3 = 18$

Activity 9.3 (page 154)

$R_1 = 0$, $R_2 = -7$, $R_3 = 0$, $K_1 = 26$, $K_2 = 36$, $K_3 = 7$, $K_4 = 0$

$I_{12} = 18$, $I_{13} = 6$, $I_{21} = -10$, $I_{23} = 104$, $I_{24} = 7$, $I_{31} = 7$

The next entering cell will be BP with a saving of £10 for each unit re-routed.

Exercise 9.2 (page 157)

1 $(A_1, B) = 3$, $(A_2, B) = 1$, $(A_2, C) = 1$;
$R_1 = 0$, $R_2 = -300$, $K_1 = 500$, $K_2 = 610$;
$I_{22} = 10 > 0$ so optimal. A_1 to B = 3.

2 (i) $R_1 = 0$, $R_2 = 9$, $R_3 = 6$, $K_1 = 76$, $K_2 = 62$.

(ii) $I_{12} = -8$, $I_{31} = -53$, entering cell is (C, P).

3 (i) $(A, P) = 10$, $(B, P) = 5$, $(B, Q) = 5$, $(C, Q) = 10$, cost = £2220.

(ii) $(C, P) = \theta$, $(B, P) = 5 - \theta$, $(B, Q) = 5 + \theta$, $(C, Q) = 10 - \theta$; $\theta = 5$, exiting cell is (B, P). $(A, P) = 10$, $(B, Q) = 10$, $(C, P) = 5$, $(C, Q) = 5$, £2220 − 5 × £53 = £1955.

(iii) $R_1 = 0$, $R_2 = -44$, $R_3 = -47$, $K_1 = 76$, $K_2 = 115$; $I_{12} = -61$, $I_{21} = 53$, entering cell is (A, Q). $(A, Q) = \theta$, $(C, Q) = 5 - \theta$, $(C, P) = 5 + \theta$, $(A, P) = 10 - \theta$; $\theta = 5$, exiting cell is (C, Q). $(A, P) = 5$, $(A, Q) = 5$, $(B, Q) = 10$, $(C, P) = 10$, £1955 − 5 × £61 = £1650.

4 (i) The number of shadow costs is 1 more than the number of cells used so there are fewer equations than unknowns. There are many solutions for the shadow costs, one of which has the shadow cost of the first source = 0.

(ii) The shadow cost for every source increases by x and the shadow cost for every destination decreases by x.

(iii) For every cell the sum of the shadow cost for the source and the shadow cost for the destination is unchanged, so the improvement indices are unchanged and still represent the improvement in the cost for every unit that is transported on the route.

5 $(B, P) = \theta$, $(B, Q) = 9 - \theta$, $(C, Q) = 1 + \theta$, $(C, d) = 6 - \theta$, $(A, d) = 1 + \theta$, $(A, P) = 7 - \theta$; $\theta = 6$, exiting cell is (C, d). $(A, P) = 1$, $(A, d) = 7$, $(B, P) = 6$, $(B, Q) = 3$, $(C, Q) = 7$, $(C, R) = 5$. £514 − 6 × £10 = £454. $R_1 = 0$, $R_2 = -17$, $R_3 = -10$, $K_1 = 26$, $K_2 = 46$, $K_3 = 17$, $K_4 = 0$; $I_{12} = 8$, $I_{13} = -4$, $I_{23} = 104$, $I_{24} = 17$, $I_{31} = 17$, $I_{34} = 10$; entering cell is (A, R). $(A, R) = \theta$, $(A, P) = 1 - \theta$, $(B, P) = 6 + \theta$, $(B, Q) = 3 - \theta$, $(C, Q) = 7 + \theta$, $(C, R) = 5 - \theta$; $\theta = 1$, exiting cell is (A, P). $(A, R) = 1$, $(A, d) = 7$, $(B, P) = 7$, $(B, Q) = 2$, $(C, Q) = 8$, $(C, R) = 4$. £454 − 1 × £4 = £450. $R_1 = 0$, $R_2 = -13$, $R_3 = -6$, $K_1 = 22$, $K_2 = 42$, $K_3 = 13$, $K_4 = 0$; $I_{11} = 4$, $I_{12} = 12$, $I_{23} = 104$, $I_{24} = 13$, $I_{34} = 6$. No further improvements, solution is optimal.

6 $(A, X) = 3, (B, X) = 4, (B, Y) = 6,$
$(C, Y) = 3, (C, Z) = 5, (D, Z) = 4;$ cost $= £1449.$
$R_1 = 0, R_2 = -8, R_3 = 12, R_4 = 45, K_1 = 62, K_2 = 40,$
$K_3 = 51;$
$I_{12} = 3, I_{13} = -26, I_{23} = -13, I_{33} = -33, I_{41} = -95,$
$I_{42} = -50;$ entering cell is $(D, X).$
$(D, X) = \theta, (D, Z) = 4 - \theta, (C, Z) = 5 + \theta,$
$(C, Y) = 3 - \theta, (B, Y) = 6 + \theta, (B, X) = 4 - \theta;$
$\theta = 3;$ exiting cell is $(C, Y).$

$(A, X) = 3, (B, X) = 1, (B, Y) = 9, (C, Z) = 8,$
$(D, X) = 3, (D, Z) = 1; £1449 - 3 \times £95 = £1164.$
$R_1 = 0, R_2 = -8, R_3 = -83, R_4 = -50, K_1 = 62,$
$K_2 = 40, K_3 = 146;$
$I_{12} = 3, I_{13} = -121, I_{23} = -108, I_{31} = 62, I_{32} = 95,$
$I_{42} = 45;$ entering cell is $(A, Z).$
$(A, Z) = \theta, (D, Z) = 1 - \theta, (D, X) = 3 + \theta,$
$(A, X) = 3 - \theta; \theta = 1;$ exiting cell is $(D, Z).$

$(A, X) = 2, (A, Z) = 1, (B, X) = 1, (B, Y) = 9,$
$(C, Z) = 8, (D, X) = 4; £1164 - 1 \times £121 = £1043.$
$R_1 = 0, R_2 = -8, R_3 = 38, R_4 = -50, K_1 = 62,$
$K_2 = 40, K_3 = 25;$
$I_{12} = 3, I_{23} = 13, I_{31} = -59, I_{32} = -26, I_{42} = 45,$
$I_{43} = 121;$ entering cell is $(C, X).$
$(C, X) = \theta, (C, Z) = 8 - \theta, (A, Z) = 1 + \theta,$
$(A, X) = 2 - \theta; \theta = 2;$ exiting cell is $(A, X).$

$(A, Z) = 3, (B, X) = 1, (B, Y) = 9, (C, X) = 2,$
$(C, Z) = 6, (D, X) = 4; £1043 - 2 \times £59 = £925.$
$R_1 = 0, R_2 = 51, R_3 = 38, R_4 = 9, K_1 = 3,$
$K_2 = -19, K_3 = 25;$
$I_{11} = 59, I_{12} = 62, I_{23} = -46, I_{32} = 33, I_{42} = 45,$
$I_{43} = 62;$ entering cell is $(B, Z).$
$(B, Z) = \theta, (C, Z) = 6 - \theta, (C, X) = 2 + \theta, (B, X)$
$= 1 - \theta; \theta = 1;$ exiting cell is $(B, X).$

$(A, Z) = 3, (B, Y) = 9, (B, Z) = 1, (C, X) = 3,$
$(C, Z) = 5, (D, X) = 4; £925 - 1 \times £46 = £879.$
$R_1 = 0, R_2 = 5, R_3 = 38, R_4 = 9, K_1 = 3, K_2 = 27,$
$K_3 = 25;$
$I_{11} = 59, I_{12} = 16, I_{21} = 46, I_{32} = -13, I_{42} = -1,$
$I_{43} = 62;$ entering cell is $(C, Y).$
$(C, Y) = \theta, (B, Y) = 9 - \theta, (B, Z) = 1 + \theta,$
$(C, Z) = 5 - \theta; \theta = 5;$ exiting cell is $(C, Z).$
$(A, Z) = 3, (B, Y) = 4, (B, Z) = 6, (C, X) = 3,$
$(C, Y) = 5, (D, X) = 4; £879 - 5 \times £13 = £814.$
$R_1 = 0, R_2 = 5, R_3 = 25, R_4 = -4, K_1 = 16, K_2 = 27,$
$K_3 = 25;$
$I_{11} = 46, I_{12} = 16, I_{21} = 33, I_{33} = 13, I_{42} = 12,$
$I_{43} = 75;$ solution is optimal.

Exercise 9.3 (page 159)

1 The minimum cost would occur when each of the x_{ij} equals 0.

2

Unit cost	1	2	Supply
1	1	2	4
2	3	1	7
3	3	2	5
Demand	10	6	

3 (i) Minimise $500x_{11} + 620x_{12} + 200x_{21} + 310x_{22}$, subject to $x_{11} + x_{12} \leqslant 3, x_{21} + x_{22} \leqslant 2$, $x_{11} + x_{21} \geqslant 4, x_{12} + x_{22} \geqslant 1$ and $x_{11}, x_{12}, x_{21}, x_{22} \geqslant 0$ and integers.

(ii) 610

4 (i) Minimise $62x_{11} + 43x_{12} + 25x_{13} + 54x_{21} + 32x_{22} + 30x_{23} + 41x_{31} + 52x_{32} + 63x_{33} + 12x_{41} + 35x_{42} + 96x_{43}$, subject to
$x_{11} + x_{12} + x_{13} \leqslant 3, x_{21} + x_{22} + x_{23} \leqslant 10,$
$x_{31} + x_{32} + x_{33} \leqslant 8, x_{41} + x_{42} + x_{43} \leqslant 4, x_{11} + x_{21} + x_{31} + x_{41} \geqslant 7,$
$x_{12} + x_{22} + x_{32} + x_{42} \geqslant 9,$
$x_{13} + x_{23} + x_{33} + x_{43} \geqslant 9$ and $x_{11}, x_{12}, \ldots, x_{43}$ are all non-negative integers.

(ii) The slack variables will all be zero because the problem is balanced, and so the supply constraints are equalities. And at the optimal solution all the demand constraints are equalities as well.

Chapter 10

Opening activity (page 161)
ABCD with weight 6.

Discussion point (page 161)
Assume it is not true. Then the path between two of the nodes on the path is not optimal. Thus there is some other path between those two nodes that is optimal. So the original path cannot be optimal. So this is true by contradiction.

Activity 10.1 (page 161)
15, $\frac{1}{2}n(n - 1)$

Activity 10.2 (page 163)
ADFIK, with 9 sets of lights

Discussion point (page 164)
There would be more states at each stage.

Exercise 10.1 (page 164)

1   (i)   CDHI
     (ii)   Unknown
     (iii)   Unknown
     (iv)   CDHI
     (v)   CDH

2   (i)   DFG
     (ii)   ADFG
     (iii)   FGIT
     (iv)   DFGI

3   (i)   ACE weight 4
     (ii)   CE weight 2
     (iii)   BD weight 4
     (iv)   AC weight 2

4

Stage	State	Action	Destination
1	H	HJ	J
	I	IJ	J
2	F	FH	H
		FI	I
	D	DH	H
		DI	I
	E	EH	H
		EI	I
	G	GH	H
		GI	I
3	B	BF	F
		BD	D
		BE	E
	C	CD	D
		CE	E
		CG	G
4	A	AB	B
		AC	C

5   Stage – number of months to end of August
State – number of artworks in store at the beginning of the month
Action – number of artworks created
Destination – number of artworks stored at the end of the month

Stage	State	Action	Destination
1 (August)	2	3	0
	1	4	0
	0	5	0
2 (July)	3	6	2
		5	1
		4	0
	2	6	1
		5	0
	1	6	0
3 (June)	1	6	3
		5	2
		4	1

6

Stage	State	Action	Destination
1	I	IH	H
	E	EH	H
	G	GH	H
2	F	FG	G
		FE	E
	B	BE	E
		BI	I
	D	DG	G
3	A	AB	B
		AD	D
		AC	C

7   Stage – number of days before the end of day 5
State – number of parcels in storage at the beginning of the day (in hundreds)
Action – number of parcels delivered (in hundreds)
Destination – number of parcels in storage at the end of the day (in hundreds)

Stage	State	Action	Destination
1 (day 5)	2	4	0
	1	3	0
	0	2	0
2 (day 4)	2	3	2
		4	1
		5	0
	1	2	2
		3	1
		4	0
	0	1	2
		2	1
		3	0
3 (day 3)	2	5	2
		6	1
	1	4	2
		5	1
		6	0
	0	3	2
		4	1
		5	0
4 (day 2)	1	6	1
		5	2
5 (day 1)	0	5	1

Exercise 10.2 (page 172)

1 (i) Minimax: stage – number of days walking still to go to get to John O'Groats, state – the stopping place for the night, value – the distance walked each day.

(ii) Maximise: stage – the number of years left before the end of 5 years, state – the end of each year, value – the profit made by the company each year.

(iii) Minimax: stage – the number of years left before planting is complete, state – the number of trees planted (or left to plant) at the end of the year, value – the costs incurred from paying the workers.

(iv) Maximin: stage – the number of bridges still to cross, state – an area between two bridges, value – the weight that a bridge will take.

(v) Minimise: stage – the number of stages of the journey still to complete, state – the locations that are possible on the journey, value – the cost of the journey.

2 (i) (a)

Stage	State	Action	Destination	Value
1	C	CT	T	5★
	D	DT	T	7★
2	A	AC	C	7 + 5 = 12★
		AD	D	4 + 7 = 11
	B	BC	C	6 + 5 = 11★
		BD	D	2 + 7 = 9
3	S	SA	A	8 + 12 = 20★
		SB	B	3 + 11 = 14

So maximum route is SACT, of weight 20.

(b)

Stage	State	Action	Destination	Value
1	C	CT	T	5★
	D	DT	T	7★
2	A	AC	C	7 + 5 = 12
		AD	D	4 + 7 = 11★
	B	BC	C	6 + 5 = 11
		BD	D	2 + 7 = 9★
3	S	SA	A	8 + 11 = 19
		SB	B	3 + 9 = 12★

So minimum route is SBDT, of weight 12.

(ii) (a)

Stage	State	Action	Destination	Value
1	D	DT	T	11★
	E	ET	T	13★
2	A	AD	D	10 + 11 = 21★
		AE	E	7 + 13 = 20
	B	BD	D	9 + 11 = 20★
		BE	E	6 + 13 = 19
	C	CD	D	8 + 11 = 19★
		CE	E	5 + 13 = 18
3	S	SA	A	4 + 21 = 25
		SB	B	3 + 20 = 23
		SC	C	7 + 19 = 26★

So maximum route is SCDT, of weight 26.

(b)

Stage	State	Action	Destination	Value
1	D	DT	T	11★
	E	ET	T	13★
2	A	AD	D	10 + 11 = 21
		AE	E	7 + 13 = 20★
	B	BD	D	9 + 11 = 20
		BE	E	6 + 13 = 19★
	C	CD	D	8 + 11 = 19
		CE	E	5 + 13 = 18★
3	S	SA	A	4 + 20 = 24
		SB	B	3 + 19 = 22★
		SC	C	7 + 18 = 25

So minimum route is SBET, of weight 22.

(iii)　(a)

Stage	State	Action	Destination	Value
1	E	ET	T	6★
	F	FT	T	3★
2	C	CE	E	9 + 6 = 15★
		CF	F	5 + 3 = 8
	D	DE	E	6 + 6 = 12★
		DF	F	4 + 3 = 7
3	A	AC	C	5 + 15 = 20★
		AD	D	7 + 12 = 19★
	B	BC	C	2 + 15 = 17
		BD	D	8 + 12 = 20★
4	S	SA	A	6 + 20 = 26
		SB	B	9 + 20 = 29★

So maximum route is SBDET, of weight 29.

(b)

Stage	State	Action	Destination	Value
1	E	ET	T	6
	F	FT	T	3
2	C	CE	E	9 + 6 = 15
		CF	F	5 + 3 = 8★
	D	DE	E	6 + 6 = 12
		DF	F	4 + 3 = 7★
3	A	AC	C	5 + 8 = 13★
		AD	D	7 + 7 = 14
	B	BC	C	2 + 8 = 10★
		BD	D	8 + 7 = 15
4	S	SA	A	6 + 13 = 19★
		SB	B	9 + 10 = 19★

So there are two minimum routes, SACFT and SBCFT, both of which have weight 19.

(iv)　(a)

Stage	State	Action	Destination	Value
1	F	FT	T	7★
	G	GT	T	4★
	H	HT	T	5★
2	D	DF	F	1 + 7 = 8
		DG	G	10 + 4 = 14★
	E	EG	G	8 + 4 = 12
		EH	H	11 + 5 = 16★
3	A	AD	D	4 + 14 = 18
		AE	E	6 + 16 = 22★
	B	BD	D	2 + 14 = 16
		BE	E	8 + 16 = 24★
	C	CD	D	3 + 14 = 17★
		CE	E	7 + 16 = 23★
4	S	SA	A	2 + 22 = 24
		SB	B	5 + 24 = 29★
		SC	C	3 + 23 = 26

So maximum route is SBEHT, of weight 29.

(b)

Stage	State	Action	Destination	Value
1	F	FT	T	7★
	G	GT	T	4★
	H	HT	T	5★
2	D	DF	F	1 + 7 = 8★
		DG	G	10 + 4 = 14
	E	EG	G	8 + 4 = 12★
		EH	H	11 + 5 = 16★
3	A	AD	D	4 + 8 = 12★
		AE	E	6 + 12 = 18
	B	BD	D	2 + 8 = 10★
		BE	E	8 + 12 = 20
	C	CD	D	3 + 8 = 11★
		CE	E	7 + 12 = 19
4	S	SA	A	2 + 12 = 14★
		SB	B	5 + 10 = 15
		SC	C	3 + 11 = 14★

So the minimum routes are SADFT or SCDFT, both of which have weight 14.

3 (i) (a) Minimax

Stage	State	Action	Destination	Value
1	C	CT	T	1★
	D	DT	T	4★
2	A	AC	C	Max(9, 1) = 9
		AD	D	Max(8, 4) = 8★
	B	BC	C	Max(7,1) = 7
		BD	D	Max(6, 4) = 6★
3	S	SA	A	Max(5, 8) = 8
		SB	B	Max(2, 6) = 6★

So minimax route is SBDT, with maximum arc of 6.

(b) Maximin

Stage	State	Action	Destination	Value
1	C	CT	T	1★
	D	DT	T	4★
2	A	AC	C	Min(9, 1) = 1
		AD	D	Min(8, 4) = 4★
	B	BC	C	Min(7, 1) = 1
		BD	D	Min(6, 4) = 4★
3	S	SA	A	Min(5, 4) = 4★
		SB	B	Min(2, 4) = 2

So maximin route is SADT, with minimum arc of 4.

(ii) (a) Minimax

Stage	State	Action	Destination	Value
1	C	CT	T	4★
	D	DT	T	10★
	E	ET	T	9★
2	A	AC	C	Max(2, 4) = 4★
		AD	D	Max(8, 10) = 10
	B	BD	D	Max(4, 10) = 10
		BE	E	Max(3, 9) = 9★
3	S	SA	A	Max(5, 4) = 5★
		SB	B	Max(7, 9) = 9

So minimax route is SACT, with maximum weight arc of 5.

(b) Maximin

Stage	State	Action	Destination	Value
1	C	CT	T	4★
	D	DT	T	10★
	E	ET	T	9★
2	A	AC	C	Min(2, 4) = 2
		AD	D	Min(8, 10) = 8★
	B	BD	D	Min(4, 10) = 4★
		BE	E	Min(3, 9) = 3
3	S	SA	A	Min(5, 8) = 5★
		SB	B	Min(7, 4) = 4

So maximin route is SADT, with minimum arc of 5.

(iii) (a) Minimax

Stage	State	Action	Destination	Value
1	G	GT	T	16★
	F	FT	T	7★
	H	HT	T	10★
2	D	DG	G	Max(5, 16) = 16
		DF	F	Max(6, 7) = 7★
		DH	H	Max(20, 10) = 20
	E	EG	G	Max(9, 16) = 16
		EF	F	Max(9, 7) = 9★
		EH	H	Max(10, 10) = 10
3	A	AD	D	Max(8, 7) = 8★
		AE	E	Max(14, 9) = 14
	B	BD	D	Max(13, 7) = 13★
		BE	E	Max(17, 9) = 17
	C	CD	D	Max(10, 7) = 10
		CE	E	Max(9, 9) = 9★
4	S	SA	A	Max(7, 8) = 8★
		SB	B	Max(6, 13) = 15
		SC	C	Max(11, 9) = 11

So minimax route is SADFT, with maximum arc of 8.

(b) Maximin

Stage	State	Action	Destination	Value
1	G	GT	T	16★
	F	FT	T	7★
	H	HT	T	10★
2	D	DG	G	Min(5, 16) = 5
		DF	F	Min(6, 7) = 6
		DH	H	Min(20, 10) = 10★
	E	EG	G	Min(9, 16) = 9
		EF	F	Min(9, 7) = 7
		EH	H	Min(10, 10) = 10★
3	A	AD	D	Min(8, 10) = 8
		AE	E	Min(14, 10) = 10★
	B	BD	D	Min(13, 10) = 10★
		BE	E	Min(17, 10) 10★
	C	CD	D	Min(10, 10) = 10★
		CE	E	Min(9, 10) = 9
4	S	SA	A	Min(7, 10) = 7
		SB	B	Min(6, 10) = 6
		SC	C	Min(11, 10) = 10★

So maximin route is SCDHT, with minimum arc of 10.

(iv) (a) Minimax

Stage	State	Action	Destination	Value
1	F	FT	T	15★
	G	GT	T	9★
2	C	CF	F	Max(3, 15) = 15
		CG	G	Max(6, 9) = 9★
	D	DF	F	Max(17, 15) = 17
		DG	G	Max(2, 9) = 9★
	E	EF	F	Max(11, 15) = 15
		EG	G	Max(13, 9) = 13★
3	A	AD	D	Max(12, 9) = 12
		AC	C	Max(8, 9) = 9★
	B	BC	C	Max(7, 9) = 9★
		BE	E	Max(20, 13) = 20
4	S	SA	A	Max(14, 9) = 14
		SB	B	Max(10, 9) = 10★

So minimax route is SBCGT, with maximum arc of 10.

(b) Maximin

Stage	Stage	Action	Destination	Value
1	F	FT	T	15★
	G	GT	T	9★
2	C	CF	F	Min(3,15) = 3
		CG	G	Min(6, 9) = 6★
	D	DF	F	Min(17, 15) = 15★
		DG	G	Min(2, 9) = 2
	E	EF	F	Min(11, 15) = 11★
		EG	G	Min(13, 9) = 9
3	A	AD	D	Min(12, 15) = 12★
		AC	C	Min(8, 6) = 6
	B	BC	C	Min(7, 6) = 6
		BE	E	Min(20, 11) = 11★
4	S	SA	A	Min(14, 12) = 12★
		SB	B	Min(10, 11) = 10

So maximin route is SADFT, with minimum arc of 12.

4

Stage	State	Action	Destination	Value
1	F	FT	T	6★
	G	GT	T	3★
2	D	DF	F	Min(5, 6) = 5★
		DG	G	Min(8, 3) = 3
	E	EF	F	Min(6, 6) = 6★
		EG	G	Min(9, 3) = 3
3	A	AD	D	Min(10, 5) = 5
		AE	E	Min(6, 6) = 6★
	B	BD	D	Min(7, 5) = 5★
		BE	E	Min(3, 6) = 3
	C	CD	D	Min(8, 5) = 5
		CE	E	Min(9, 6) = 6★
4	S	SA	A	Min(10, 6) = 6★
		SB	B	Min(2, 5) = 2
		SC	C	Min(8, 6) = 6★

So there are two maximin routes: SCEFT and SAEFT, both with minimum arc of 6.

5

Stage	State	Action	Destination	Value
1	G	GT	T	11★
	H	HT	T	8★
	I	IT	T	13★
2	E	EG	G	Max(9, 11) = 11★
		EH	H	Max(14, 8) = 14
		EI	I	Max(12, 13) = 13
	F	FG	G	Max(7, 11) = 11
		FH	H	Max(3, 8) = 8★
		FI	I	Max(6, 13) = 13
3	C	CE	E	Max(11, 11) = 11★
		CF	F	Max(15, 8) = 15
	D	DE	E	Max(8, 11) = 11
		DF	F	Max(7, 8) = 8★
4	A	AC	C	Max(15, 11) = 15
		AD	D	Max(14, 8) = 14★
	B	BC	C	Max(17, 11) = 17
		BD	D	Max(8, 8) = 8★
5	S	SA	A	Max(9, 14) = 14
		SB	B	Max(2, 8) = 8★

So minimax route is SBDFHT, with maximum arc of 8.

6 (i) Stage is the beginning of each phase; state is the number of components in storage at the end of each phase; action is the number of components made during each phase.

(ii)

Stage	State	Action	Destination	Value
1 (phase 5)	2	1	0	$100 + 2 \times 50 + 1 \times 200 = £400\star$
	1	2	0	$100 + 1 \times 50 + 2 \times 200 = £550\star$
	0	3	0	$100 + 0 \times 50 + 3 \times 200 = £700\star$
2 (phase 4)	1	6	2	$100 + 1 \times 50 + 3 \times 200 + 3 \times 300 + 400 = £2050$
		5	1	$100 + 1 \times 50 + 3 \times 200 + 2 \times 300 + 550 = £1900$
		4	0	$100 + 1 \times 50 + 3 \times 200 + 1 \times 300 + 700 = £1750\star$
	0	6	1	$100 + 0 \times 50 + 3 \times 200 + 3 \times 300 + 550 = £2150$
		5	0	$100 + 0 \times 50 + 3 \times 200 + 2 \times 300 + 700 = £2000\star$
3 (phase 3)	2	6	1	$100 + 2 \times 50 + 3 \times 200 + 3 \times 300 + 1750 = £3450$
		5	0	$100 + 2 \times 50 + 3 \times 200 + 2 \times 300 + 2000 = £3400\star$
	1	6	0	$100 + 1 \times 50 + 3 \times 200 + 3 \times 300 + 2000 = £3650\star$
4 (phase 2)	2	6	2	$100 + 2 \times 50 + 3 \times 200 + 3 \times 300 + 3400 = £5100$
		5	1	$100 + 2 \times 50 + 3 \times 200 + 2 \times 300 + 3650 = £5050\star$
	1	6	1	$100 + 1 \times 50 + 3 \times 200 + 3 \times 300 + 3650 = £5300\star$
5 (phase 1)	0	6	2	$100 + 0 \times 50 + 3 \times 200 + 3 \times 300 + 5050 = £6650$
		5	1	$100 + 0 \times 50 + 3 \times 200 + 2 \times 300 + 5300 = £6600\star$

Minimum cost of £6600 by making 5 components in phase 1, 6 in phase 2, 6 in phase 3, 5 in phase 4 and 3 in phase 5.

7 Minimax problem
Stage is the time in years remaining.
State is the services already running.
Action is the service being introduced.

Stage	State	Action	Destination	Value
1	AB	C	ABC	$40\star$
	AC	B	ABC	$60\star$
	BC	A	ABC	$25\star$
2	A	B	AB	$\text{Max}(70, 40) = 70$
		C	AC	$\text{Max}(50, 60) = 60\star$
	B	A	AB	$\text{Max}(30, 40) = 40\star$
		C	BC	$\text{Max}(60, 25) = 60$
	C	A	AC	$\text{Max}(40, 60) = 60\star$
		B	BC	$\text{Max}(90, 25) = 90$
3	None	A	A	$\text{Max}(50, 60) = 60\star$
		B	B	$\text{Max}(100, 40) = 100$
		C	C	$\text{Max}(65, 60) = 65$

So the company should introduce A, then C, then B, for a maximum cost in one year of £6000.

8 (i) The stage is the number of months remaining before the end of June.

The state is the number of pianos in storage at the beginning of the month.

The action is the number of pianos made in the month.

The destination is the number of pianos stored at the end of the month.

(ii)

Stage	State	Action	Destination	Value
1 (June)	1	0	0	200 + 100 = 300★
	0	1	0	200★
2 (May)	1	3	1	200 + 100 + 400 + 300 = 1000
		2	0	200 + 100 + 200 = 500★
	0	4	1	200 + 400 + 300 = 900
		3	0	200 + 400 + 200 = 800★
3 (April)	2	4	1	200 + 200 + 400 + 500 = 1300★
		3	0	200 + 200 + 400 + 800 = 1600
	1	4	0	200 + 100 + 400 + 800 = 1500★
4 (March)	2	4	2	200 + 200 + 400 + 1300 = 2100★
		3	1	200 + 200 + 400 + 1500 = 2300
	1	4	1	200 + 100 + 400 + 1500 = 2200 ★
5 (February)	0	4	2	200 + 400 + 2100 = 2700★
		3	1	200 + 400 + 2200 = 2800

So the piano maker should make the following numbers of pianos each month for a total cost of £2700:

Month	February	March	April	May	June
Pianos	4	4	4	2	1

9

Stage	State	Action	Destination	Value
1	E	EH	H	18★
	F	FH	H	35★
	G	GH	H	20★
2	B	BE	E	18 + 18 = 36
		BF	F	15 + 35 = 50★
		BG	G	12 + 20 = 32
	C	CE	E	6 + 18 = 24
		CF	F	5 + 35 = 40★
		CG	G	−1 + 20 = 19
	D	DE	E	−4 + 18 = 14
		DF	F	−5 + 35 = 30
		DG	G	15 + 20 = 35★
3	A	AB	B	18 + 50 = 68★
		AC	C	11 + 40 = 51
		AD	D	25 + 35 = 60

The company should advertise on the internet in the first year, followed by the television in the second year to have a maximum profit.

10 Stage will be which biscuits are left to be made. Make plain first, then chocolate, then jam.

State – how many units are available.

Action – how many biscuits are made in this stage.

Destination – how many units remain.

Value – running total of the profit.

Stage	State	Action	Destination	Value
1 (jam)	0	0	0	0★
	1	1	0	8★
	2	2	0	13★
	3	3	0	20★
	4	4	0	27★
2 (chocolate)	0	0	0	0 + 0 = 0★
	1	0	1	0 + 8 = 8
		1	0	10 + 0 = 10★
	2	0	2	0 + 13 = 13
		1	1	10 + 8 = 18★
		2	0	15 + 0 = 15
	3	0	3	0 + 20 = 20
		1	2	10 + 13 = 23★
		2	1	15 + 8 = 23★
		3	0	20 + 0 = 20
	4	0	4	0 + 27 = 27
		1	3	10 + 20 = 30★
		2	2	15 + 13 = 28
		3	1	20 + 8 = 28
		4	0	25 + 0 = 25
3 (plain)	4	0	4	0 + 30 = 30
		1	3	17 + 23 = 40★
		2	2	19 + 18 = 37
		3	1	22 + 10 = 32
		4	0	23 + 0 = 23

So the manufacturer should make the following biscuits:

Biscuit	Plain	Chocolate	Jam
Number to make	1	1	2

OR

Biscuit	Plain	Chocolate	Jam
Number to make	1	2	1

Chapter 11

Opening activity (page 177)

The expected gain is £1 so yes.

Activity 11.2 (page 179)

This activity is answered in Example 11.1.

Discussion point (page 182)

Using utilities usually gives the same outcome as without. If there are large amounts at stake you may prefer to have more information to make your decision.

Exercise 11.1 (page 183)

1 (i) 0

(ii) $-£\frac{1}{37}$ or -2.70p (3 s.f.)

2 (i) $-£\frac{21}{36} \approx -58$p

(ii) £22

(iii) At least $\sqrt[3]{8 \times 12^4} - 2 \approx £52.95$

3 (i) $\frac{125}{216}, \frac{75}{216}, \frac{15}{216}$

(ii) $-£\frac{17}{216} \approx -7.9$p

4 (i)

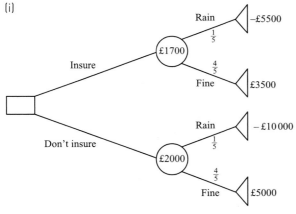

(ii) Insure, fine = £3500

Insure, rain = $-£5500$

So, insure = £500

Don't insure, fine = £5000

Don't insure, rain = $-£10\,000$

So, don't insure = £0

No, would have taken out the insurance.

5 (i)

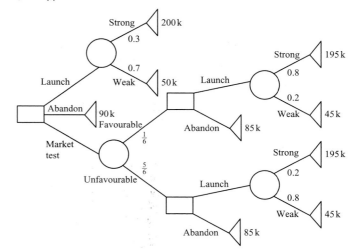

Don't test and launch = £95 000

Don't test and sell = £90 000

So don't test = £95 000

Test, favourable, launch = £165 000

Test, favourable, sell = £85 000

So test, favourable = £165 000

Test, unfavourable, launch = £75 000

Test, unfavourable, sell = £85 000

So test, unfavourable = £85 000

So test = £98 333

(ii) Test, launch if favourable and sell if not, EMV = £98 333.

(iii) £8333

6 (i)

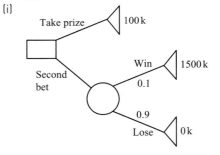

Don't take 2nd bet = £100 000

Take 2nd bet, win = £1 500 000

Take 2nd bet, lose = £0

So take 2nd bet = £150 000

So the optimal decision is to take the 2nd bet.

(ii) Utility of not taking the bet is $\sqrt{100\,000} \approx 316.2$.

Utility of taking bet is
$0.1 \times \sqrt{1\,500\,000} \approx 122.5$.

So don't take the bet.

7 (i)

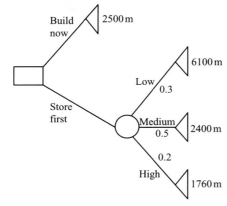

Expected cost of store first = £3382 m, so build now at a cost advantage of £882 m.

(ii) Defer at a cost advantage of £(2500 − 2080) m
= £420 m

(iii)

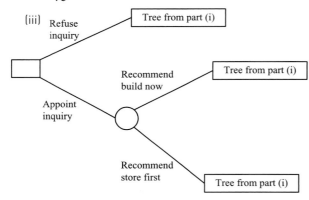

8 (i)

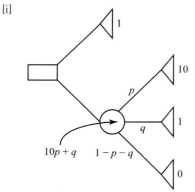

(ii) 0.05

(iii) (iv)

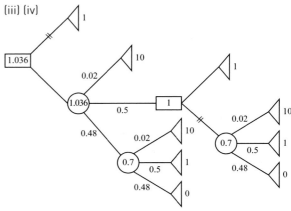

Go again, then accept the £1 if it is offered again.

9 (i) Require $100p + 20(1 − p) = 50$, giving $p = \dfrac{3}{8}$.

(ii) (a)

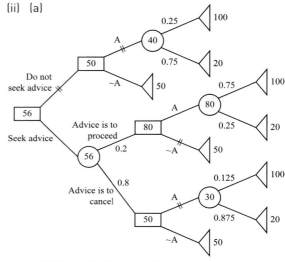

(b) Value of advice = 6
(c) Assuming the pay-off is not more than 80, require $X = 16 + 0.8X$, giving $X = 80$.

10 (i) £1150, £900, £1050, £1030

(ii)

(Invest in equities)
0.6 — 1150
1050
0.4 — 900

1050

(Invest in bonds)
0.8 — 1050
1046
0.2 — 1030

(iii) Require p such that $0.6 \times 1150^p + 0.4 \times 900^p = 0.8 \times 1050^p + 0.2 \times 1030^p$

Letting $f(p) = 0.6 \times 1150^p + 0.4 \times 900^p - 0.8 \times 1050^p - 0.2 \times 1030^p$,

$f(0.5) = 0.0053$
$f(0.45) = -0.0003$